A-Level Year 2
Statistics & Mechanics
Exam Board: Edexcel

We had no problem deciding that alpacas are better than llamas — it's obvious.
But Statistics and Mechanics? We just can't pick a favourite.

So we've given them equal billing in this brilliant Student Book. Every Year 2
topic is totally explained in our crystal-clear style, and there are masses of practice
questions to help you hone your skills — plus a practice exam at the end.

Better still, we've included step-by-step answers to every question. So even if
you love llamas, there's no excuse for any woolly reasoning in the exams.

CGP

How to get your free Online Edition

Go to **cgpbooks.co.uk/extras** and enter this code...

2579 2372 9941 7077

This code will only work once. If someone has used this book before you,
they may have already claimed the Online Edition.

Contents

About this Book

In this book you'll find...

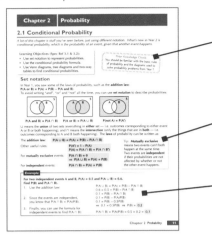

Prior Knowledge Checks and Learning Objectives
This tells you what you need to know before starting a section, and what will be covered. It also directs you to the relevant specification point(s) for Edexcel.

Tips and Hints
To help get your head around the tricky bits.

Explanations and Examples
Clear explanations for every topic, and plenty of step-by-step worked examples.

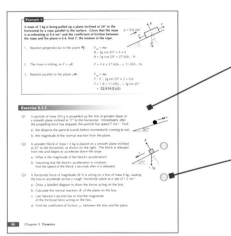

Exercises (with worked answers)
Lots of practice for every topic, with fully worked answers at the back of the book.

Modelling and Problem Solving
Examples and questions that involve modelling or problem solving are indicated with stamps.

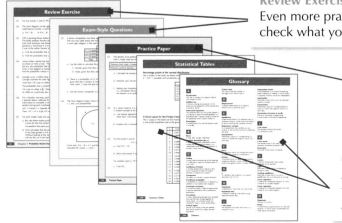

Review Exercises and Exam-Style Questions
Even more practice at the end of each Chapter to help you check what you've learned, and practice for the exam.

Practice Paper
A full set of exam-style questions testing content from the whole book.

Glossary, Statistical Tables and Formulas
All the definitions you need to know for the exam, and the relevant formulas and tables you'll get in the exam.

About this Course

This book covers the Statistics & Mechanics content in A-level Maths that's not in AS

The Edexcel **A-level** Mathematics course has **three** exam papers:

Paper 1 — Pure Mathematics 1
Paper 2 — Pure Mathematics 2

- 2 hours each
- 100 marks each
- 33.33% of your A-level each

Both of these papers test the same material.

Start off with the material covered in the **Pure Mathematics — Year 1/AS Student Book**, then move on to the rest of the content in the **Pure Mathematics — Year 2 Student Book**.

This paper tests the material in **this book** and the **Statistics & Mechanics — Year 1/AS Student Book**.

There may be some questions in Paper 3 that also use the Pure maths covered in the **Pure Mathematics — Year 1/AS Student Book** and the **Pure Mathematics — Year 2 Student Book**.

Paper 3 — Statistics and Mechanics

- 2 hours
- 100 marks — split into Sections A: Statistics (50 marks) and B: Mechanics (50 marks)
- 33.33% of your A-level

Formulas and Tables

With each exam paper you'll have a **formula booklet** which contains **formulas** and **statistical tables** that you might need to use.

The relevant ones for the material in this book are on p.188-189.

Tip: Although you don't have to learn these formulas off by heart, it's important that you practise using them, and also know which formulas are **not** given to you.

Large Data Set

You'll also be working with a **large data set** throughout your course. This will only be used in Paper 3.

You can find practice on using the data set in Chapter 1 of this book — and there's more practice and information about it in the **Statistics & Mechanics — Year 1/AS Student Book**.

Published by CGP

Editors:
Sarah George, Samuel Mann, Alison Palin, Rosa Roberts, Ben Train, Ruth Wilbourne, Dawn Wright.

Contributors:
Andy Ballard, Katharine Brown, Mick Coe, Aleksander Goodier, Rosemary Rogers,
Andy Smith, Janet West.

ISBN: 978 1 78908 364 4

Cover design concept by emc design ltd.

With thanks to Glenn Rogers for the proofreading.
With thanks to Emily Smith for the copyright research.

Printed by Elanders Ltd, Newcastle upon Tyne.
Clipart from Corel®

1.1 Regression

Correlation and linear regression were covered in Year 1. This first topic is a recap of what you should already know — Year 2 material starts on page 3.

Learning Objectives (Spec Ref 2.2):
- Know the different types of correlation.
- Know the difference between explanatory and response variables.
- Interpret a regression line in context.
- Be aware of the problems involved with extrapolation.
- Find the equation of a regression line by coding data and using logs.

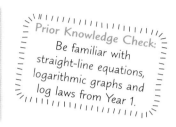

Prior Knowledge Check:
Be familiar with straight-line equations, logarithmic graphs and log laws from Year 1.

Correlation and linear regression

Correlation measures how closely two variables are **linked** — i.e. whether points on a scatter diagram lie close to a **straight line**. The three graphs below show different types of correlation:

positive correlation   **negative correlation**   **no correlation**

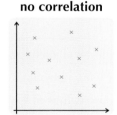

Tip: If two variables are correlated, you can draw a **line of best fit** that lies close to most of the points.

You have to be **careful** when writing about **correlation** — changes in one variable might **not cause** changes in the other. An apparent link could be due to a third factor, or it could just be coincidence.

For example, sales of umbrellas and number of traffic incidents might be positively correlated, but higher umbrella sales **don't cause** an increase in traffic incidents — they're both affected by another factor (amount of rainfall).

Explanatory and response variables
- The **explanatory variable** (or **independent variable**) is the variable you can directly control, or the one that you think is **affecting** the other. It is always drawn along the **horizontal axis**.
- The **response variable** (or **dependent variable**) is the variable you think is **being affected**. It is always drawn up the **vertical axis**.

Regression lines
Linear regression is a method for finding the equation of a line of best fit on a scatter diagram. The formula on the right shows the form of the **regression line of y on x**. The '...**of y on x**' part means that x is the explanatory variable, and y is the response variable.

$$y = a + bx$$
where a = y-intercept
and b = gradient

If **b** is **positive** then the variables x and y are **positively** correlated, and if **b** is **negative** they are **negatively** correlated. You can use your calculator's statistical functions to find the values of a and b.

A nutritionist records the amount of exercise done per week, x (in hours), and body fat, y (as a percentage of total weight), for a group of men. He calculates the regression line of y on x to be: $y = 24.6 - 0.925x$

Interpret this regression line in context.

1. When $x = 0$, $y = 24.6$, so the regression line suggests that if a man did no exercise each week, you would expect his body fat to be around 24.6%.

2. The coefficient of x is -0.925, which is negative, so there is negative correlation. This suggests that for every additional hour of exercise that a man does, you would expect his body fat to decrease by around 0.925%.

Tip: Body fat is affected by exercise so body fat is the response variable.

Interpolation and extrapolation

You can use a regression line to predict values of your **response variable**. There are two forms of this — **interpolation** and **extrapolation**.

This scatter diagram shows the data used to calculate the regression line in the example above — percentage body fat plotted against hours of exercise.

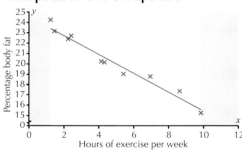

Tip: You can only use a regression line to predict a value of the response variable — **not** the explanatory variable.

In this example, the values of x were between 1.5 and 10.

- **Interpolation** is when you use values of x **within** the range of your data (the yellow part of the graph) to predict corresponding values of y. This is okay — the predicted value should be **reliable**.

- **Extrapolation** is when you use values of x **outside** the range of your original data (the grey part of the graph) to predict corresponding values of y. These predictions can be **unreliable** — you need to be very **cautious** as you don't have evidence that the relationship is true for all values of x. For example, this regression line predicts that a man who does 27 hours of exercise per week will have a negative amount of body fat, which is clearly impossible.

Exercise 1.1.1

Q1 The data below shows the number of shots, x, and the number of goals scored, y, by a football team over a number of matches.

Number of shots, x	15	18	19	7	18	12	12	21	16	13
Number of goals, y	2	3	3	0	2	1	2	3	2	2

a) Identify the explanatory variable and the response variable.

The regression line of y on x is found to be: $y = -1.1 + 0.2x$

b) Describe the type of correlation shown by the regression line.

c) In the next match the team has 5 shots. Use the regression line to estimate the number of goals scored by the team.

d) Explain why this estimate is unreliable.

Linear regression with coded data

Coded data has been transformed by some mathematical function (e.g. subtracting a constant or taking logs) to make the data **easier** to work with. You could be given a regression line for coded data, and be asked to transform it into a regression line for the original data.

Example 1

A company collects data on the age (*g*) and salary (*s*) of its senior managers.

The data is coded in the following way: $x = g - 50$ $y = \dfrac{s - 50\,000}{1000}$

If the regression line of *y* on *x* is given by $y = 1.24x + 5.44$, find the regression line of *s* on *g*.

1. Substitute the expressions defining *x* and *y* into the equation of the regression line for *y* on *x*. This gives you an equation involving just *s* and *g*.

$$\dfrac{s - 50\,000}{1000} = 1.24(g - 50) + 5.44$$

2. Rearrange this so it is in the form $s = a + bg$, where a and b are constants. This is the regression line of *s* on *g*.

$$s - 50\,000 = 1240g - 62\,000 + 5440$$
$$s = 1240g - 6560$$

Example 2

The annual heating bill (*h*, in £) for 8 office buildings is shown below, along with the total floor area (*f*, in m²) of each building.

f	600	1000	1500	1800	2400	3400	4400	4900
h	1500	2600	3100	3400	3900	5500	5900	6100

These results were coded in the following way:

$$u = \dfrac{f - 2500}{100} \qquad v = \dfrac{h - 4000}{100}$$

Tip: The numbers that have been subtracted in the coding are the means of the variables — $\bar{f} = 2500$ and $\bar{h} = 4000$.

The regression line of *v* on *u* is found to be: $v = 1.036u$

a) **Find the equation of the regression line of *h* on *f*.**

1. Substitute the expressions defining *u* and *v* into your regression equation.

$$v = 1.036u$$
$$\dfrac{h - 4000}{100} = 1.036 \times \dfrac{f - 2500}{100}$$

2. Then rearrange into the form $h = a + bf$.

$$h - 4000 = 1.036f - (1.036 \times 2500)$$
So $h = 1410 + 1.036f$

Tip: The coefficient of *f* is positive, so there is positive correlation.

b) **Predict the annual heating bill for an office building with a total floor area of 2900 m², and comment on the validity of this prediction.**

1. Substitute $f = 2900$ into the regression line:

$$h = 1410 + 1.036(2900)$$
$$= 1410 + 3004.4 = £4414.40$$

2. Comment on the validity:

$f = 2900$ is within the range of the observed data, so the prediction is interpolation and should be reliable.

If your variables x and y are linked by a **non-linear** equation in the form of either $y = ax^n$ or $y = kb^x$, you can turn it into a linear equation by **taking logs** of both sides (look back at your Year 1 notes for a reminder of how to do this).

$$y = ax^n \Rightarrow \log y = \log ax^n$$
$$\Rightarrow \log y = \log a + \log x^n$$
$$\Rightarrow \boxed{\log y = n\log x + \log a}$$

$$y = kb^x \Rightarrow \log y = \log kb^x$$
$$\Rightarrow \log y = \log k + \log b^x$$
$$\Rightarrow \boxed{\log y = x\log b + \log k}$$

Example 3

A meteorologist records the maximum temperature (t °C) and total sunshine (s hours) each day for five days in Heathrow. The relationship can be modelled by the equation $t = as^b$.

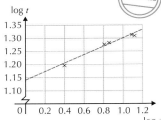

Sunshine (s hours)	12.3	13.1	6.4	2.5	7.2
Temperature (t °C)	20.5	20.4	18.9	15.7	19.2

She plots the graph of $\log t$ against $\log s$ and draws the line of best fit, as shown. Given that the line has a gradient of 0.16 and crosses the vertical axis at 1.14, estimate the values of a and b to 3 s.f.

1. Rearrange $t = as^b$ into linear form by taking logs. $\log t = b\log s + \log a$

2. This equation is in the form $y = bx + a$ — with y replaced by $\log t$ and x replaced by $\log s$. So b is the gradient and $\log a$ is the y-intercept.

    Gradient = $b = 0.16$
    Intercept = $\log a = 1.14 \Rightarrow$ $a = 13.8$ (3 s.f.)

Exercise 1.1.2

Q1   A set of bivariate data (x, y) has been coded using $p = x - 7$ and $q = y - 50$. The regression line of q on p is given by $q = 40 + 2p$. Find the equation of the regression line of y on x.

Q2   The time (t, in hours) that seedlings could survive in water containing different concentrations of salt (s, in mg per litre) was recorded. The results were coded such that $x = \frac{s}{10}$ and $y = t - 29$. The coded data is in the table below.

x	1	2	3	5	7	10
y	19	11	9	−1	−14	−24

   a) Given that the regression line of y on x is $y = 22.4 - 4.8x$, find the equation of the regression line of t on s.

   b) Use this to estimate the value of t when $s = 9$, and comment on the validity of this estimate.

Q3   The relationship between two variables is modelled by the equation $y = ab^x$. The data is transformed by taking logs and a linear graph is plotted. The line has a gradient of 0.032 and crosses the vertical axis at 0.315. Find the values of a and b.

Q4   The equation $p = at^b$ is used to model the relationship between the variables t and p. The data is transformed by taking logs and the graph of $\log p$ against $\log t$ is drawn. If the line has a gradient of 0.1596 and crosses the vertical axis at 1.1723, find the values of a and b to 3 s.f.

1.2 The Product Moment Correlation Coefficient

In this topic you'll learn about the product moment correlation coefficient (PMCC) and carry out hypothesis tests to check if variables are linked.

Learning Objectives (Spec Ref 5.1):

- Calculate the product moment correlation coefficient (PMCC) on a calculator from a set of data.
- Interpret different values of the PMCC.
- Be able to carry out hypothesis tests on the PMCC.

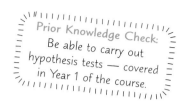
Prior Knowledge Check:
Be able to carry out hypothesis tests — covered in Year 1 of the course.

Finding the PMCC

The **product moment correlation coefficient** (r) measures the **strength** of the linear correlation between two variables. It tells you how close to a straight line the points on a scatter diagram lie. To calculate the PMCC you need to use the **statistical functions** on your calculator — some calculators use the letter r for PMCC.

The PMCC is always between +1 and –1.

- If all your points lie **exactly on a straight line** with a **positive** gradient (perfect positive correlation), $r = +1$.
- If all your points lie **exactly on a straight line** with a **negative** gradient (perfect negative correlation), $r = -1$.
- If $r = 0$ (or more likely, pretty close to 0), that would mean the variables **aren't correlated**.

Tip: The closer r is to +1 or –1, the stronger the correlation. Values of r close to zero mean there is only a weak correlation.

These graphs give you an idea of what different values of r look like.

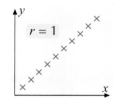
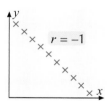
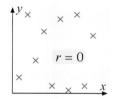

Example

MODELLING

The data below shows the score (x) of 10 students in a reading test, and the time in seconds (y) it took them to run 40 metres.

Illustrate the data with a scatter diagram, and find the product moment correlation coefficient (r) between the variables x and y.

x	3.5	5.5	6.1	4.2	2.7	1.9	5.5	3.8	5.1	3.7
y	9.8	4.7	8.4	8.4	5.8	8.4	7.6	8.2	8.9	5.4

1. First, plot the points on the scatter diagram.

2. The points look pretty randomly scattered — so you'd expect a correlation coefficient fairly close to zero. Go into the statistical functions on your calculator and input the data.

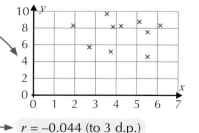

$r = -0.044$ (to 3 d.p.)

Q1 Interpret the following values of the product moment correlation coefficient (r):

 a) $r = 0.852$ b) $r = -0.0551$ c) $r = -0.483$

Q2 The table below shows the heights and weights of 8 teenage boys.

Height in cm, x	180	171	182	184	166	180	173	167
Weight in kg, y	70	67	66	59	61	75	65	56

Find and interpret the value of the product moment correlation coefficient (r) for x and y.

Q3 The table shows data for variables p and q.

p	13	9	15	10	8	11	12	14
q	5	7	2	4	3	8	1	2

Find and interpret the value of the product moment correlation coefficient (r) for p and q.

Q4 A nurse at a health centre did a memory test on some patients of different ages. Her results are shown below.

Age in years, a	57	65	94	88	71	62	79	82	52
Test score, s	8.9	4.8	5.4	2.8	7.1	7.5	3.1	6.2	8.4

Calculate the correlation coefficient r and interpret your result.

PMCC hypothesis testing

To test whether your value of r is likely to mean that the two variables are actually correlated, you need to do a hypothesis test. The method is very similar to the hypothesis testing you did in Year 1.

- A **test statistic** is a statistic calculated from the sample data — here it's r.

- A **parameter** describes a characteristic of a population. The parameter here is ρ, the PMCC of the population.

> **Tip:** ρ is the Greek letter rho.

- The **null hypothesis** (H_0) is a statement about the value of the population parameter, ρ.

- The null hypothesis here is always that ρ is **zero** — i.e. that there's **no correlation** between the two variables.

$$H_0: \rho = 0$$

The **alternative hypothesis** (H_1) is what you're going to conclude if you **reject** the null hypothesis — there are two kinds of alternative hypothesis:

- A **one-tailed** alternative hypothesis specifies whether the parameter you're investigating is **greater than** or **less than** the value you used in H_0.

- A **two-tailed** alternative hypothesis says that the parameter you're investigating is **not equal** to the value in H_0.

> For a **one-tailed** test: $H_1: \rho > 0$ or $\rho < 0$
> For a **two-tailed** test: $H_1: \rho \neq 0$

The **significance level** of a test (α) determines **how unlikely** your data needs to be under the null hypothesis (H_0) before you reject H_0. Significance levels can be given as a **decimal** or **percentage**.

You're usually told what significance level to use, but the most common values are $\alpha = 0.1$ (or 10%), $\alpha = 0.05$ (or 5%) and $\alpha = 0.01$ (or 1%).

On page 188 there's a table of critical values (you'll find these values in your formula booklet in the exam). For a given sample size and significance level you can find the **critical value** — the point at which your test statistic r would be **significant**.

The examples below show how to use the table of critical values to test for significance.

Example 1

A teacher thinks that test scores are related to the number of hours spent revising. She samples 10 students and finds that the PMCC is 0.76. Carry out a hypothesis test at the 5% significance level to investigate whether the evidence suggests that test scores and hours spent revising are positively correlated.

1. Write down the **test statistic** for the sample.
$r = 0.76$

2. The **null hypothesis** is that there is no correlation.
$H_0: \rho = 0$

3. This is a one-tailed test, so write a suitable **alternative hypothesis**.
$H_1: \rho > 0$

4. Write down the **significance level** of the test.
$\alpha = 0.05$

5. Test for **significance** — using $\alpha = 0.05$ and sample size 10.

Using the table, the **critical value** is **0.5494**.

So you would reject H_0 if $r \geq 0.5494$

Significance Level				Sample Size
(0.05)	0.025	0.01	0.005	
0.9000	0.9500	0.9800	0.9900	4
–	–	–	–	–
0.5822	0.6664	0.7498	0.7977	9
(0.5494)	0.6319	0.7155	0.7646	(10)
0.5214	0.6021	0.6851	0.7348	11

Tip: For an alternative hypothesis of $\rho < 0$, you'd make the critical value from the table negative (i.e. –0.5494).

$0.76 > 0.5494$, so the result is significant

6. Write your **conclusion** — you will either reject the null hypothesis H_0 or have insufficient evidence to do so.

There is evidence at the 5% level of significance to reject H_0 and to support the alternative hypothesis that test scores and hours spent revising are positively correlated.

Finding the critical region is another way to do a hypothesis test.

- The **critical region** is the set of **all** values of the test statistic that would cause you to **reject H_0**.

- First, find all the values that would make you reject H_0, then work out your test statistic and check if it's in the critical region.

Example 2

A student records the mean wind-speed (w, knots) and the maximum temperature (t, °C) each day for seven days in Hurn. He thinks that there is correlation between the two variables.

a) **Find the critical region for a test of the student's claim at the 5% level.**

1. This is a two-tailed test — the student thinks there is correlation, i.e. the PMCC is not zero. So write the **null** and **alternative hypotheses**.
$H_0: \rho = 0$ and $H_1: \rho \neq 0$

2. Write down the **significance level**. $\alpha = 0.05$, so $\frac{\alpha}{2} = \frac{0.05}{2} = 0.025$

3. Test for **significance** with sample size 7 and significance 0.025.

Using the table, the **critical value** is **0.7545**.

You would reject H_0 if $r \geq 0.7545$ or $r \leq -0.7545$.

Significance Level			Sample Size
(0.025)	0.01	0.005	
0.9500	0.9800	0.9900	4
–	–	–	–
0.8114	0.8822	0.9172	6
(0.7545)	0.8329	0.8745	(7)
0.7067	0.7887	0.8343	8

Tip: For two-tailed tests, the critical region is in two parts — one part near $r = -1$ and the other near $r = +1$, so you have to halve the overall significance level before looking up the critical value.

4. So the **critical region** is $r \geq 0.7545$ or $r \leq -0.7545$

b) **Calculate the PMCC of the recordings in the table below and say whether the evidence is significant enough to reject the student's claim.**

Temperature, t	24.3	21.6	21.5	19.9	18.2	20.6	21.1
Wind-speed, w	5	4	9	8	10	8	7

1. Go into the statistical functions on your calculator and input the data. ⟶ $r = -0.7282$ (to 4 d.p.)

2. Write your **conclusion**. $r = -0.7282$ is outside the critical region so there is insufficient evidence to reject H_0, the hypothesis that wind-speed and temperature aren't correlated, at the 5% level of significance.

Exercise 1.2.2

MODELLING

Q1 The ages and weights of 12 baby elephants are measured. The PMCC is $r = 0.5749$. Test the hypothesis that the PMCC for the population, ρ, is greater than zero, at the 2.5% significance level.

Q2 The lengths and widths (in cm) of 8 leaves from a tree were measured. Here are the results:

Length, l	4.6	7.2	5.1	8.3	2.4	6.4	5.7	3.3
Width, w	3.1	5.2	3.6	5.6	1.7	4.7	4.0	2.5

a) Find the product moment correlation coefficient, r.

b) Test the hypothesis that the PMCC for the population, ρ, is greater than zero, at the 2.5% significance level.

Q3 A doctor checked the kidney function (k, percentage efficiency) of some of her patients to see if it was related to their weight (w, kg). She thinks kidney function and weight are correlated. The table below shows the results from a sample of her patients.

Weight in kg, w	66	74	96	83	79	54	64	71	88
Kidney function, k	81	93	69	88	84	92	84	96	66

a) Find the critical region for a test of the doctor's claim at the 5% significance level.

b) Find the product moment correlation coefficient, r.

c) Say whether these results provide sufficient evidence to back the doctor's claim.

Review Exercise

Q1 The table below shows the number of hours spent designing the cover of a book, h, and the number of books sold in the first year, b.

Number of hours, h	5	10	8	12	4	7	15	2	9
Sales in the first year, b	5000	6500	3500	7000	1200	5200	7800	3000	4100

a) Identify the explanatory variable and the response variable.

b) The regression line of b on h is found to be $b = 1374.7 + 429.5h$.
   Describe the type of correlation shown by the regression line.

c) Interpret the value of the gradient of the regression line.

d) Use your regression line to predict the first year sales of a book which had 6 hours spent on its cover. Is your estimate reliable?

Q2 The number of fans at a venue's concerts, n, and the average cost of a ticket, c, are recorded. The data is coded as follows: $x = c - 150$, $y = \dfrac{n}{2000}$.

The regression line of y on x is $y = 1.8x + 50$. Find the regression line of n on c.

Q3 The relationship between two variables is modelled by the equation $y = kb^x$. The data is transformed by taking logs and a linear graph is plotted. The line has a gradient of 0.0963 and crosses the vertical axis at 0.3873. Find the values of k and b.

Q4 A student calculates the product moment correlation coefficient, r, for two variables. She concludes that the variables show weak positive correlation. Explain which one of the values of r below is most likely to be the value the student calculated.

$$r = 0.313, \quad r = -0.152, \quad r = 0.742$$

Q5 Find the value of the product moment correlation coefficient, r, for x and y, shown in the table below. Interpret your value of r.

x	0.6	0.4	1.2	0.8	1.1	0.5	1.2	0.7
y	62	65	52	62	50	52	51	60

Q6 The amounts spent on food and petrol in 15 households are recorded. The PMCC is $r = 0.5152$. Test the hypothesis that the PMCC for the population, ρ, is greater than zero, at the 2.5% significance level.

Q7 The ages of 12 paintings in years and their values in £ are recorded. The PMCC for the data is calculated to be $r = 0.7126$. Is there evidence at the 1% significance level to support the hypothesis that there is some correlation between a painting's age and its value?

Q1   The amount of time, t minutes, and amount of money, £p,
      that 10 customers spent in a supermarket are recorded in the table below.

Time, t minutes	12	21	26	29	30	38	39	46	48	59
Money, £p	6.51	8.94	19.02	26.55	29.13	37.39	36.80	51.17	58.62	74.23

   a) Calculate the product moment correlation coefficient between t and p.

      [1 mark]

   b) Interpret your answer to part a).

      [2 marks]

   The regression line of p on t is $p = 1.53t - 18.32$.

   c) Use this information to predict the amount of money a different
      customer who spent 24 minutes in the supermarket would spend.

      [1 mark]

Q2   Data are coded using $X = x$ and $Y = \log y$.
      The equation of the regression line of Y on X for the coded data is $Y = 0.64 - 0.1X$.
      Show that $y = pq^x$, where p and q are constants to be found.

      [4 marks]

Q3   A biologist studies the spread of a certain disease in a colony of bats over one year.
      They find the number of infected bats, b, can be modelled by the equation $b = kd^m$,
      where d is the number of days since the study began and k and m are constants.
      The graph of $\log b$ against $\log d$ has a gradient of 0.71 and crosses the vertical axis at 0.56.

   a) Find the values of k and m.

      [3 marks]

   b) Use the model to predict the number of infected bats in the colony after 100 days.

      [2 marks]

Q4   8 students take part in a race. The heights, h m, and the times taken to complete
      the race, t seconds, of each student are recorded in the table below.

Height, h metres	1.76	1.71	1.52	1.47	1.68	1.67	1.57	1.54
Time taken, t seconds	19.9	19.4	23.2	22.0	19.1	20.6	22.3	22.9

   a) Calculate the product moment correlation coefficient for the data in the table.

      [1 mark]

   b) Stating your hypotheses clearly, test at a 5% significance level whether there is a correlation
      between height and the time taken to complete the race for these 8 students.

      [3 marks]

2.1 Conditional Probability

A lot of this chapter is stuff you've seen before, just using different notation. What's new in Year 2 is conditional probability, which is the probability of an event, given that another event happens.

Learning Objectives (Spec Ref 3.1 & 3.2):
- Use set notation to represent probabilities.
- Use the conditional probability formula.
- Use Venn diagrams, tree diagrams and two-way tables to find conditional probabilities.

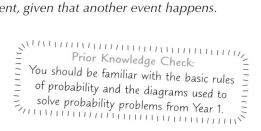
Prior Knowledge Check:
You should be familiar with the basic rules of probability and the diagrams used to solve probability problems from Year 1.

Set notation

In Year 1, you saw some of the laws of probability, such as the **addition law**:
$P(A \text{ or } B) = P(A) + P(B) - P(A \text{ and } B)$.
To avoid writing "and", "or" and "not" all the time, you can use **set notation** to describe probabilities:

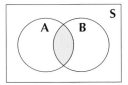

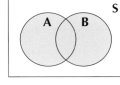

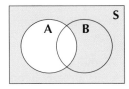

$P(A \text{ and } B) = P(A \cap B)$ $P(A \text{ or } B) = P(A \cup B)$ $P(\text{not } A) = P(A')$

$\cup$ means the **union** of two sets (everything in **either** set — i.e. outcomes corresponding to either event A or B or both happening), and $\cap$ means the **intersection** (only the things that are in **both** — i.e. outcomes corresponding to A and B both happening). The **laws** of probability can be written as:

The **addition law**: $P(A \cup B) = P(A) + P(B) - P(A \cap B)$

Other useful rules: $P(A') = 1 - P(A)$
$P(A) = P(A \cap B) + P(A \cap B')$

For **mutually exclusive** events: $P(A \cap B) = 0$
$\Rightarrow P(A \cup B) = P(A) + P(B)$

For **independent** events: $P(A \cap B) = P(A) \times P(B)$

Tip: **Mutually exclusive** means two events can't both happen at the same time. Two events are **independent** if their probabilities are not affected by whether or not the other event happens.

Example

For two independent events A and B, $P(A) = 0.5$ and $P(A \cup B) = 0.6$.
Find $P(B)$ and $P(A \cap B)$.

1. Use the addition law:

$P(A \cup B) = P(A) + P(B) - P(A \cap B)$
$0.6 = 0.5 + P(B) - P(A \cap B)$
$0.1 = P(B) - P(A \cap B)$

2. Since the events are independent, you know that $P(A \cap B) = P(A)P(B)$.

$0.1 = P(B) - P(A)P(B)$
$0.1 = P(B) - 0.5P(B)$
$\Rightarrow 0.1 = 0.5P(B) \Rightarrow P(B) = \boxed{0.2}$

3. Finally, you can use the formula for independent events to find $P(A \cap B)$:

$P(A \cap B) = P(A)P(B) = 0.5 \times 0.2 = \boxed{0.1}$

Conditional probability

A probability is **conditional** if it **depends** on what has already happened.
The probability that an event B happens, **given** that an event A has already
happened, is called the **conditional probability** of 'B given A', written **P(B|A)**.

For example, if you picked two cards from a deck **without replacement**, the probability of the
second card being a heart would be **conditional** on whether or not the first card was a heart.

You can work out the probability of **B given A**, using this formula:

$$P(B\,|\,A) = \frac{P(A \cap B)}{P(A)}$$

> **Tip:** The probability
> of A given B is:
> $$P(A|B) = \frac{P(A \cap B)}{P(B)}$$

Here's an explanation of where this formula comes from...

Event A has happened and for B|A to happen, B will also happen.

- If you know that A has already happened,
  then the only remaining possible outcomes
  must be the ones corresponding to A.

- And the only remaining possible outcomes
  corresponding to B also happening
  must be the ones in A ∩ B.

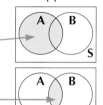

Using the **probability formula**
(and assuming event **A** has **already happened**):

$$P(B\,|\,A) = \frac{\textbf{number of possible outcomes corresponding to B}}{\textbf{total number of possible outcomes}} = \frac{\textbf{number of outcomes in A} \cap \textbf{B}}{\textbf{number of outcomes in A}}$$

So if $n(A \cap B)$ = number of outcomes in A ∩ B, and $n(A)$ = number of outcomes in A:

$$P(B|A) = \frac{n(A \cap B)}{n(A)}$$

Now, if you divide the top and bottom of the fraction by $n(S)$ (the total number of
outcomes in S), its value doesn't change, but you can write it in a different way:

$$P(B\,|\,A) = \frac{n(A \cap B)}{n(A)} = \frac{n(A \cap B)\big/n(S)}{n(A)\big/n(S)} = \frac{P(A \cap B)}{P(A)}$$

the formula
in the box
above

And if you rearrange this formula for conditional probability,
you get a formula that's known as the **product law**. For events A and B:

$$\textbf{P(A} \cap \textbf{B) = P(A)P(B\,|\,A)}$$

So to find the probability that A **and** B **both** happen, you multiply the
probability of A by the probability of B given that A has happened.

Or you can write this the other way around, by swapping A and B:

$$\textbf{P(A} \cap \textbf{B) = P(B)P(A\,|\,B)}$$

> **Tip:** The product law
> is given in this form in
> your formula booklet.
> You're also given
> another version of the
> formula for P(A|B)
> — see Example 3c)
> on page 18 to find out
> how it's used.

Example 1

For events A and B: P(A) = 0.6, P(B) = 0.5, P(A ∩ B) = 0.3, P(B′ | A) = 0.5.

a) Find P(A | B).

Using the formula for conditional probability: $P(A|B) = \dfrac{P(A \cap B)}{P(B)} = \dfrac{0.3}{0.5} = \boxed{0.6}$

b) Find P(A ∩ B′).
Using the product law: $P(A \cap B') = P(A)P(B'|A) = 0.6 \times 0.5 = \boxed{0.3}$

Tip: Just replace B with B′ in the product law.

Example 2

The Venn diagram represents two events, C and D. The numbers of equally likely outcomes corresponding to the events are shown.

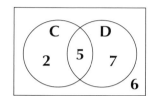

a) Find P(C | D).

Here you're given the numbers of **outcomes** rather than probabilities — so it's easier to use the formula in the middle of the orange box on the previous page.

$P(C|D) = \dfrac{\text{number of outcomes corresponding to C}}{\text{total number of possible outcomes}}$

Once event **D has happened**, the outcomes where C can happen are those in C ∩ D — so there are **5** ways that C can occur. Since D has happened, the total number of possible outcomes is the total number of outcomes in D: 5 + 7= **12**.

$= \dfrac{\text{number of outcomes in } C \cap D}{\text{number of outcomes in } D}$

$= \dfrac{5}{12}$

Tip: You could also find the probabilities of P(C ∩ D) and P(D) and use the usual formula.

b) Find P(D | C′).

Once event **C hasn't happened**, there are **7** possible outcomes corresponding to event **D** happening and **13** possible remaining outcomes in **total**.

$P(D|C') = \dfrac{\text{number of outcomes corresponding to D}}{\text{total number of possible outcomes}}$

$= \dfrac{\text{number of outcomes in } D \cap C'}{\text{number of outcomes in } C'}$

$= \dfrac{7}{13}$

Example 3

Vikram either walks or runs to the bus stop. The probability that he walks is 0.4. The probability that he catches the bus is 0.54. If he walks to the bus stop, the probability that he catches the bus is 0.3.

a) Draw a Venn diagram representing the events W, 'Vikram walks to the bus stop', and C, 'Vikram catches the bus'.

1. First write down the probabilities you know. The probability that Vikram catches the bus, given that he walks to the bus stop, is 0.3.

    P(W) = 0.4, P(C) = 0.54 and P(C|W) = 0.3

2. To draw the Venn diagram, you need to find the intersection C ∩ W. And you can do that using the **product law**.

    P(C ∩ W) = P(C|W)P(W) = 0.3 × 0.4 = 0.12

3. Now you can draw the Venn diagram:

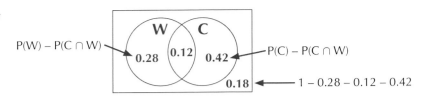

$P(W) - P(C \cap W)$ $P(C) - P(C \cap W)$

$1 - 0.28 - 0.12 - 0.42$

b) Find the probability that Vikram catches the bus, given that he runs to the bus stop.

1. He either walks or runs to the bus stop, so P(runs) = P(W'). So use the conditional probability formula to find P(C|W').

$$P(C|W') = \frac{P(C \cap W')}{P(W')}$$

2. Write down the probabilities you know.

$P(C \cap W') = 0.42$ $P(W') = 1 - 0.4 = 0.6$

3. Then put them into the formula.

So $P(C|W') = \dfrac{P(C \cap W')}{P(W')} = \dfrac{0.42}{0.6} = 0.7$

Exercise 2.1.1

Q1 Given that P(A) = 0.3, P(B) = 0.5 and P(A ∪ B) = 0.7, find:

a) P(A') b) P(A ∩ B) c) P(A ∩ B')

Q2 The events X and Y are independent, where P(X) = 0.8 and P(Y) = 0.15. Find the probability that neither X nor Y occurs.

Q2 Hint: You can use P(A∪B) + P(A'∩B') = 1 — you can see this from the Venn diagram below:

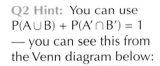

Q3 If P(G) = 0.7, P(H) = 0.63 and P(G ∩ H) = 0.24, find:

a) P(G|H) b) P(H|G)

Q4 P(A) = 0.68, P(B') = 0.44, P(C) = 0.44, P(A ∩ B) = 0.34, P(A ∩ C) = 0.16 and P(B ∩ C') = 0.49. Find:

a) P(B|A) b) P(A|C) c) P(C'|B)

Q5 Events J and K are such that P(J) = 0.4, P(J|K) = 0.64 and P(K|J) = 0.2.

a) Find P(J ∪ K). b) Find P(J' ∩ K').

Q6 In a group of eleven footballers, five are over 6 feet tall.
Two of the three players who can play in goal are over 6 feet tall.
One of the players is selected at random.

a) If the player is over 6 feet tall, what is the probability that they can play in goal?

b) If the player can play in goal, what is the probability that they are over 6 feet tall?

Q7 Given that P(X) = 0.44, P(Y') = 0.72, P(Z) = 0.61, P(X|Y) = 0.75, P(Z|X) = 0.25, P(Y ∩ Z') = 0.2 and $P(X \cap Y \mid Z) = \frac{7}{61}$, find:

a) P(Y) b) P(X ∩ Y) c) P(X ∩ Z)

d) P(Y|Z') e) P(X ∩ Y ∩ Z)

Q8 The Venn diagram shows the numbers of students studying
    Maths, English and Art, from a group of 100 students.
    One of the students is selected at random.

    a) If the student is studying Art, what is the probability
       that they are also studying Maths?

    b) If the student is studying English and Maths, what is
       the probability that they are also studying Art?

    c) If the student is not studying Maths, what is
       the probability that they are studying English?

    d) Find P(A|E′).   e) Find P(M|A ∩ E).

Q9 In a youth group with 30 members, 15 members swim, 12 play tennis and 11 play football.
    6 members play both tennis and football, 4 members swim and play football, and 3 members
    play tennis, play football and swim. The number of members who do not swim, do not play
    football and do not play tennis is double the number of members who only play football.

    a) Draw a Venn diagram to show this information.

    A member is selected at random.

    b) Find the probability that they swim, given that they play tennis.

Using conditional probability

Independent events

If A and B are **independent**, then P(B) is the same, whether A happens or not.
So the probability of B, given that A happens, is just the probability of B.
This means you have the following results:

- **P(B | A) = P(B | A′) = P(B)**. Similarly, **P(A | B) = P(A | B′) = P(A)**.

- The **conditional probability** formula becomes: $P(B\,|\,A) = P(B) = \dfrac{P(A \cap B)}{P(A)}$

- The **product law** becomes: **P(A ∩ B)** = P(A)P(B|A) = **P(A)P(B)**
  (this is the formula for independent events that you've already met).

To show that events A and B are independent, you just need
to show that **one** of the following statements is true:

- P(B|A) = P(B) [or P(A|B) = P(A)]

- P(A) × P(B) = P(A ∩ B)

Example 1

For events A and B, **P(A) = 0.25, P(B | A) = 0.8 and P(A′ ∩ B) = 0.4.**

a) Find: (i) P(A ∩ B),   (ii) P(A′),   (iii) P(B′ | A),
          (iv) P(B | A′),   (v)   P(B),   (vi)   P(A | B).

     (i)   Use the product law.   **P(A ∩ B)** = P(A)P(B|A) = 0.25 × 0.8 = 0.2

     (ii) Use P(A) + P(A′) = 1.   **P(A′)** = 1 − P(A) = 1 − 0.25 = 0.75

Now at this stage, things are starting to get a bit trickier. It'll help a lot if you draw a **Venn diagram** showing what you know so far.

- You know from the question that:
  P(A) = 0.25, P(B|A) = 0.8 and P(A' ∩ B) = 0.4
- And you've found: P(A ∩ B) = 0.2 and P(A') = 0.75

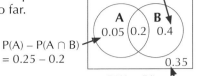

P(A) − P(A ∩ B)
= 0.25 − 0.2

P(A' ∩ B') =
1 − 0.05 − 0.2 − 0.4

Now you have the information you need to answer (iii)-(vi):

(iii)　1.　Use the conditional probability formula.

　　　　2.　Plug in the probabilities you know —
　　　　　　from the Venn diagram, P(B' ∩ A) = 0.05.

$$\mathbf{P(B' \,|\, A)} = \frac{P(B' \cap A)}{P(A)}$$
$$= \frac{0.05}{0.25}$$
$$= \boxed{0.2}$$

Tip: You could find 1 − P(B|A) instead.

(iv)　Use the conditional probability formula again.　$\mathbf{P(B \,|\, A')} = \dfrac{P(B \cap A')}{P(A')} = \dfrac{0.4}{0.75} = \dfrac{40}{75} = \boxed{\dfrac{8}{15}}$

(v)　Use the Venn diagram to find P(B).　$\mathbf{P(B)} = P(B \cap A) + P(B \cap A') = 0.2 + 0.4 = \boxed{0.6}$

(vi)　Back to the conditional probability formula.　$\mathbf{P(A \,|\, B)} = \dfrac{P(A \cap B)}{P(B)} = \dfrac{0.2}{0.6} = \boxed{\dfrac{1}{3}}$

b) Say whether or not A and B are independent.

There are different ways you can do this. Either:

- Compare the values of P(B|A) and P(B).

Or:

- Compare the values of P(A) × P(B) and P(A ∩ B).

P(B|A) = 0.8 ≠ P(B) = 0.6,
so A and B are　not independent .

P(A) × P(B) = 0.25 × 0.6 = 0.15
≠ P(A ∩ B) = 0.2,
so A and B are　not independent .

Tree diagrams

You may not have realised it when you saw them in Year 1,
but **tree diagrams** are actually all about conditional probability.
You can label the branches of a tree diagram using **set notation** like this:

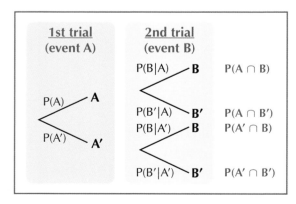

Tip: If the events are independent, then the probabilities for the second trial are just P(B) and P(B') — it doesn't matter whether or not A has happened.

Tree diagrams are really useful for seeing how the **result** of one event **affects** the probability of the other event happening.

Example 2

Horace is either late for school or on time for school, and
when he gets to school he is either shouted at or not shouted at.
The probability that he's late for school is 0.4.
If he's late, the probability that he's shouted at is 0.7.
If he's on time, the probability that he's shouted at is 0.2.

Given that Horace is shouted at, what is the probability that he was late?

1. Be careful with questions like this — the question tells you the probability
    of S conditional on L (and L'). But you need to think of the situation the
    'other way round' — with L conditional on S. So don't just rush in.

2. Define the events in this situation.

    Let L = 'Horace is late' and
    S = 'Horace is shouted at'.

3. You want to find P(L|S), so use the
    conditional probability formula.

    $$P(L|S) = \frac{P(L \cap S)}{P(S)}$$

4. You need to find P(L ∩ S) and P(S) — and
    the easiest way is by drawing a tree diagram
    using the information in the question.

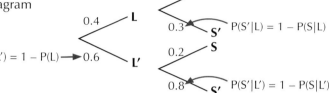

    Tip: In general, if B depends
    on A, then A depends on B.
    Here, S depends on L,
    so L depends on S.

    P(L') = 1 − P(L) ➔ 0.6

5. Use the tree diagram to find
    the information you need.

    P(L ∩ S) = P(L)P(S|L) = 0.4 × 0.7 = 0.28

    P(S) = P(L ∩ S) + P(L' ∩ S) = 0.28 + P(L')(S|L')
    = 0.28 + 0.6 × 0.2
    = 0.4

6. Then plug these probabilities
    into the formula to find
    P(Horace was late, given he is shouted at).

    So $P(L|S) = \frac{P(L \cap S)}{P(S)} = \frac{0.28}{0.4} = \boxed{0.7}$

Example 3

For events M and N: P(M) = 0.2, P(N | M) = 0.4 and P(N' | M') = 0.7.

a) Draw a tree diagram representing events M and N.

1. Draw the tree diagram and write on as much as you
    know so far. You need **two** sets of branches — one for
    event M and one for event N.

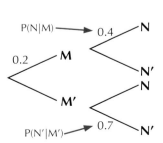

2. Since you're told the probability of M, but not that of N,
    show **M** on the **first** set and N on the second set.

3. Each pair of branches will show either **M** and its
    complement **M'**, or **N** and its complement **N'**.

4. You can find the probabilities of the remaining branches by doing 1 − the probability on the other branch.

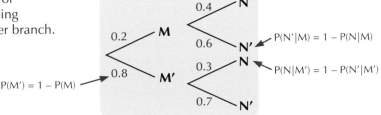

$P(N'|M) = 1 - P(N|M)$

$P(N|M') = 1 - P(N'|M')$

$P(M') = 1 - P(M)$

b) Find P(N).

There are 2 'paths' giving N, so find the probability of each, then add them together.

$P(N) = P(M \cap N) + P(M' \cap N)$
$= P(M)P(N|M) + P(M')P(N|M')$
$= 0.2 \times 0.4 + 0.8 \times 0.3$
$= \boxed{0.32}$

c) Find P(M′|N′) using the formula $P(A|B) = \dfrac{P(B|A)\,P(A)}{P(B|A)\,P(A) + P(B|A')\,P(A')}$.

1. Write the formula in terms of M and N:

$P(M'|N') = \dfrac{P(N'|M')\,P(M')}{P(N'|M')\,P(M') + P(N'|M)\,P(M)}$

2. Write down the probabilities you need from the tree diagram.

$P(N'|M') = 0.7,\ P(M') = 0.8,$
$P(N'|M) = 0.6,\ P(M) = 0.2$

3. Substitute these into the formula.

$P(M'|N') = \dfrac{0.7 \times 0.8}{(0.7 \times 0.8) + (0.6 \times 0.2)}$

$= \dfrac{0.56}{0.56 + 0.12}$

$= \dfrac{0.56}{0.68} = \dfrac{56}{68} = \boxed{\dfrac{14}{17}}$

Tip: This formula looks horrible, but it's given in your formula booklet. It's actually not as bad as it looks — the top is just $P(A \cap B)$ from the product law, and the bottom is $P(B)$ split into two parts (like in part b)).

Two-way tables

Probabilities can also be shown in **two-way tables**, like this:

	A	A′	Total
B	$P(A \cap B)$	$P(A' \cap B)$	$P(B)$
B′	$P(A \cap B')$	$P(A' \cap B')$	$P(B')$
Total	$P(A)$	$P(A')$	1

Tip: You might also see tables with numbers of objects or equally-likely outcomes instead of probabilities (like in the example on the next page).

Two-way tables can make finding conditional probabilities quite easy — if you're trying to find a probability "given A", simply look in the A column (or row) of the table. **Dividing** the **relevant entry** by the **total** for that row or column will give you the conditional probability.

Example 4

22 children are at a Halloween party. The two-way table below shows the costumes that they are wearing:

	Werewolf	Zombie	Ghost	Total
Boys	4	3	3	10
Girls	2	4	6	12
Total	6	7	9	22

A child is picked at random.

a) Given that the child is a girl, what is the probability that they're dressed as a zombie?

You're told that the child is a girl, so look at the Girls row of the table — there are 12 girls in total, and the Zombie entry in this row is 4.

$$P(\text{Zombie}|\text{Girl}) = \frac{4}{12} = \frac{1}{3}$$

b) Two girls dressed as ghosts go home.
Draw an updated two-way table showing the probabilities of selecting a child from each category.

To find the probabilities, divide every entry by the new total of 20. Don't forget to change the Ghost ∩ Girls entry to 6 – 2 = 4 and update the Girl, Ghost and overall totals before dividing.

$3 \div 20 = 0.15$

	Werewolf	Zombie	Ghost	Total
Boys	0.2	0.15	0.15	0.5
Girls	0.1	0.2	0.2	0.5
Total	0.3	0.35	0.35	1

$2 \div 20 = 0.1$

$7 \div 20 = 0.35$

$20 \div 20 = 1$

c) Another child is picked at random.
Given that the child is dressed as a werewolf, what is the probability that they're a boy?
Here you're told that the child is dressed as a werewolf, so look in the Werewolf column — the Boys entry is 0.2, and the total is 0.3.

$$P(\text{Boy}|\text{Werewolf}) = \frac{0.2}{0.3} = \frac{2}{3}$$

Tip: It doesn't matter whether the table gives the numbers or the probabilities — you can always find the conditional probability by dividing the entry by the total.

Exercise 2.1.2

Q1 Events A and B have the following probabilities:
$P(A) = 0.75$, $P(B|A') = 0.4$, $P(A \cap B') = 0.45$
Are A and B independent?

Q1 Hint: It might help to draw a suitable diagram, even if the question doesn't ask for it.

Q2 Joe records the ages of people going to a cinema
on a Sunday evening. He obtains the following data:
• 26 of the 40 people were under 20 years old.

• 18 people went to see a comedy film.

• Of the people who watched an action film, 6 of them were 20 years old or above.

a) Copy the two-way table below and fill it in using Joe's data.

	Action film	Comedy film	Total
Under 20			
20 and over			
Total			

b) One of the cinema-goers is picked at random.
Given that they saw a comedy film, what is the probability that they are under 20?

Q3 The Venn diagram below shows the probabilities for events R, S and T:

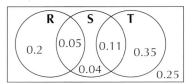

a) Which events are: (i) mutually exclusive? (ii) independent?
b) Find: (i) P(R|S) (ii) P(R|S ∩ T')

Q4 X, Y and Z are independent events, with P(X) = 0.84, P(Y) = 0.68 and P(Z) = 0.48.
Find the following probabilities: a) P(X ∩ Y) b) P(Y' ∩ Z') c) P(Y|Z) d) P(Z'|Y') e) P(Y|X')

Q5 Amena sometimes goes to the park, depending on the weather.
If it's a sunny day, the probability that she goes to the park is 0.6.
If it isn't sunny, she goes to the park with probability 0.2.
The probability that it is sunny is 0.45.

a) Draw a Venn diagram to show the event that it is sunny (S)
and the event that she goes to the park (P).

b) What is the probability that it's sunny, given that she goes to the park?

Q6 A group of people were asked about their mobile phones. 62% of them own
a smartphone and 53.9% of them have a contract costing over £25 a month.
Of the people with a smartphone, 29% have a contract costing £25 a month or less.

Use a tree diagram to find the probability that a person from the group owns a
smartphone, given that their contract costs over £25 a month.

Q7 A bag contains red, white and blue counters. There are 10 red counters, 15 white counters
and 11 blue counters. One counter is drawn at random. It is not replaced. A second
counter is then drawn. Draw a tree diagram to represent this situation, and use it to find
the probability that the second counter is blue, given that the first counter is not red.

2.2 Modelling with Probability

Doing calculations based on probabilities is all very well and good, but in real-life situations, the hardest part is often finding the probabilities in the first place. You usually need to make a few assumptions, which will affect the accuracy of your model.

Learning Objective (Spec Ref 3.3):
- Evaluate assumptions made when modelling the probability of events.

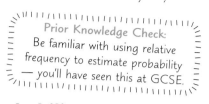

Prior Knowledge Check:
Be familiar with using relative frequency to estimate probability — you'll have seen this at GCSE.

Modelling assumptions and probability

In most models, the probability of an event is based on some **assumptions**. For example, when flipping a coin, you assume that each side is **equally likely** to come up, so the probability is 0.5 for both. However, it's possible that the coin is **biased**, giving the two outcomes **different probabilities**.

Evaluating and **criticising** the assumptions being made is an important part of the modelling process. Some common issues to think about are:

- Have you assumed that two (or more) events are **equally likely**? Is this true? Could the probabilities be **biased** in some way?

- Is the probability based on **past data**? Is the data **appropriate**? How **reliable** is the data? How was the data **sampled**?

- Is the experiment itself **truly random**? Is there anything about the way that the experiment is being **carried out** that could affect the outcome?

Example

Sanaa wants to know the probability that it will rain tomorrow. She looks up the weather data for the previous 30 days, and finds that it has rained on 12 of them. She concludes that the probability that it will rain is $\frac{12}{30}$ = 0.4. Give a reason why this model might be inaccurate.

There are lots of answers you could give. For example:

- She has only taken data from the past 30 days, which might not be a large enough sample to give an accurate estimate, or might not take seasonal variations into account.

- She has assumed that the probability that it rains on one day is not affected by whether or not it rained the day before (i.e. that they are independent events), but this might not be true.

Exercise 2.2.1

For each model, give an assumption that has been made and explain how it may lead to inaccuracy.

Q1 Raj throws a cuboid in the air. He says, "The probability that it lands on any given face is $\frac{1}{6}$."

Q2 Harriet shows 10 playing cards to a volunteer. The volunteer chooses one, replaces it and chooses another. Harriet says, "The probability of a particular card being chosen twice is 0.01."

Q3 In a class of primary school children, 56% walked to school one day. Their teacher says, "The probability that a child from any primary school walks to school on a given day is 0.56."

Review Exercise

Q1   For two events, C and D, P(C) = 0.4, P(D) = 0.24, P(C ∩ D) = 0.15. Find P(C|D) and P(D|C).

Q2   The Venn diagram on the right shows the number of outcomes
      matching two events, A and B. Find:

      a) P(A ∩ B)   b) P(A ∪ B')   c) P(A|B)   d) P(B|A')

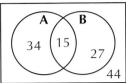

Q3   Cliff is planting flower bulbs in his garden.
      The bulbs produce flowers that are either red or yellow, and either short or tall.
      Each bulb produces one flower. If Cliff chooses a bulb at random, the probability it
      produces a red flower is 0.35 and the probability that it produces a tall flower is 0.46.
      If one of the yellow flowers is chosen at random, the probability that it is short is 0.4.

      a) Find the probability that a randomly chosen bulb produces a short yellow flower.

      b) Find the probability that a flower is short, given that it is red.

Q4   Asmaa either catches the bus to school or rides her bike to school. She either arrives
      at school on time or late. The probability that she catches the bus is 0.6. If she catches
      the bus, the probability that she's late is 0.1. The probability that she arrives on time is 0.92.
      Draw a tree diagram to represent this information, and hence
      find the probability Asmaa is late, given that she rides her bike.

Q5   Georgie owns a coffee kiosk at a railway station. The kiosk is open seven days a week.
      Georgie analyses her sales figures from the last ten weeks. The probability that she sold
      more than 150 cups of coffee on a random day, given it was a weekend, is $\frac{3}{10}$.
      The probability that a random day was not a weekend and she did not sell more than
      150 cups of coffee is $\frac{1}{2}$. Show that the probability that Georgie sold more than 150 cups
      of coffee on a particular day is independent of whether or not it was a weekend.

Q6   On a Monday morning, each student in a particular group has either a French lesson or
      a Spanish lesson, followed by one of biology, chemistry or physics. Use the following
      information to complete a two-way table showing the probabilities of a randomly chosen
      student having each combination of lessons.
      Let F = French, S = Spanish, B = biology, C = chemistry and H = physics.
      Then: P(F ∩ H) = 0.08, P(F) = 0.37, P(B) = 0.25, P(S|B) = $\frac{2}{5}$, P(F|C) = $\frac{1}{3}$

Q7   For each model, state one assumption that's been made and explain why it may not be valid.

      a) Baz sets three maths puzzles, numbered 1-3, on his website and offers
          a prize for the first correct answer he receives for each puzzle.
          He predicts that each puzzle has a probability of $\frac{1}{3}$ of being the first to be solved.

      b) Ariel calculates that the probability that she will see her neighbour's cat
          in her back garden is 0.8 on sunny days and 0.1 on rainy days.
          Without looking at the weather forecast, she predicts that the probability she
          will see the cat in her back garden tomorrow is 0.5 × 0.8 + 0.5 × 0.1 = 0.45.

Exam-Style Questions

Q1　A dance competition has three age categories, 11-13 years, 14-16 years and 17-18 years. The two-way table shows the number of male and female competitors in each age category in this year's contest.

	Male	Female	Total
11-13 years	10	15	25
14-16 years	14	16	30
17-18 years	8	12	20
Total	32	43	75

a) Use the table to calculate the probability that a randomly selected competitor is:

　(i)　Female, given that they are 11-13 years old.

　(ii)　Male, given that they are under 17 years old.

[2 marks]

b) There is a probability of 0.2 that a girl will be 11 years old given that she is chosen at random from the 11-13 age group. How many 11-year-old girls are there in the competition?

[2 marks]

c) Are the events 'competitor is male' and 'competitor is 17-18 years old' independent?

[2 marks]

Q2　The Venn diagram below shows three events, A, B and C. *x*, *y* and *z* are probabilities.

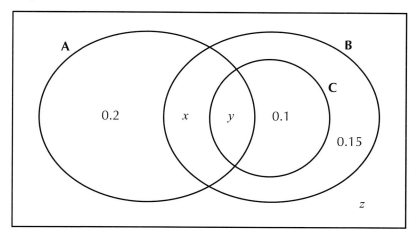

Given that $P(A \cup B) = 0.7$, and that $P(B|A \cap C') = 0.2$, calculate the values x, y and z.

[5 marks]

3.1 The Normal Distribution

In this section you'll be introduced to the normal distribution and use it to find different probabilities. Many variables can be modelled by normal distributions, which can be very useful in real-life situations.

Learning Objectives (Spec Ref 4.2):
- Know the shape and properties of the normal distribution.
- Find probabilities for normal distributions.
- Find the range of values within which a normally distributed random variable will fall with a given probability.
- Find the mean and standard deviation of a normal distribution given some probabilities for the distribution.
- Apply the normal distribution to real-life situations.

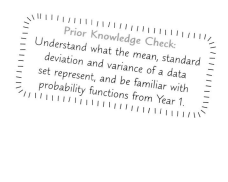
Prior Knowledge Check:
Understand what the mean, standard deviation and variance of a data set represent, and be familiar with probability functions from Year 1.

The normal distribution

The shape of a normal distribution

In real-life situations, the distribution of a set of data often follows a **particular pattern** — with most of the data values falling **somewhere in the middle**, and only a small proportion taking much higher or lower values.

- For example, this histogram shows the distribution of the weights of some hedgehogs.

- Most of the weights lie close to the mean weight — with similar numbers distributed symmetrically above and below.

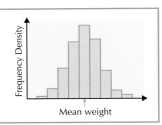

A variable like this can often be **modelled** by a **normal distribution**. A normal distribution is **continuous**, so can easily model continuous variables — such as height, weight, length, etc.

If X is a **continuous random variable** that follows a **normal** distribution, you can describe the probability distribution of X using just two measures — its **mean**, μ, and **variance**, σ^2.

Whatever the values of μ and σ^2, the **graph** of a normal distribution always looks like the **curve** below.

- The curve is 'bell-shaped'.
- There's a **peak** at the **mean**, μ.
- It's **symmetrical** about the mean — so values the same distance above and below the mean are equally likely.

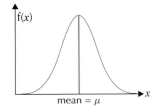

Tip: The vertical axis is labelled f(x) because the equation of the curve is a function of x.

You can see that the shape of the normal curve **approximately fits** the shape of the histogram for hedgehog weights above. The peak at the mean reflects the fact that values close to the mean are most likely.

As the distribution is symmetrical (i.e. not skewed), this means that **mean = median = mode**.

The width and height of the curve depend on the **variance** of the normal distribution. The three graphs below all show normal distributions with the **same mean** (μ), but **different variances** (σ^2).

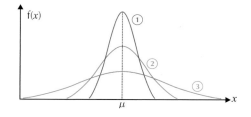

- The **larger** the variance, the **wider** the curve, so **graph 3** has the **largest** variance and **graph 1** has the **smallest** variance.

- The **total area** under the curve is always the **same**, so a wider curve needs to have a lower height.

The area under a normal curve

The **area** under a normal curve shows **probabilities**.

- The **total area** under the curve represents the **total probability** of the random variable taking one of its possible values. And since the total probability is 1, the **total area under the curve** must also be **1**.

- The **probability** of the variable taking a value **between two limits** is the **area under the curve** between those limits.

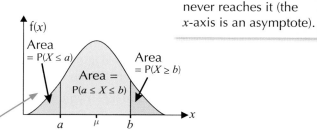

> **Tip:** As x gets further away from the mean, $f(x)$ gets closer to 0 but never reaches it (the x-axis is an asymptote).

- Values of the **cumulative distribution function** (cdf) are the **areas** under the curve to the **left of x** (the **probability** that $X \le x$) for different values of x.

- Since X is a **continuous** random variable, $P(X = x) = 0$, which means that $P(X \le x)$ and $P(X < x)$ are the **same thing**. So you can **interchange** the $\le$ and $<$ signs.

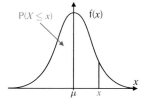

> **Tip:** For any continuous random variable X, $P(X = a) = 0$ for any value of a. That's because the area under a graph at a single point is zero.

There are some **facts** about the **area** under the curve that apply to **all** normal distributions.

- There are **points of inflection** (where the curve changes between concave and convex — these are covered in the Pure part of the course) at $x = \mu + \sigma$ and $x = \mu - \sigma$.

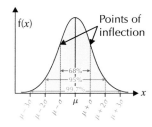

- **68%** of the total **area** lies within ±1 standard deviation (±σ) of the mean.

- **95%** of the total **area** lies within ±2 standard deviations (±2σ) of the mean.

- **99.7%** of the total **area** lies within ±3 standard deviations (±3σ) of the mean.

> **Tip:** Remember, σ is the square root of the variance — so it's a measure of dispersion (how spread out values are from the mean).

So **68%** of **observations** are within ±σ of the mean, **95%** of **observations** are within ±2σ of the mean and **99.7%** of **observations** are within ±3σ of the mean.

You can use these facts to check if a normal distribution is **suitable** for the situation you're modelling — see page 44.

Describing a normal distribution

If a continuous random variable X is **normally** distributed with mean μ and variance σ^2, it is written like this: ⟶ $X \sim N(\mu, \sigma^2)$

'**N**' stands for '**normal**' and '**~**' is short for '**is distributed**'.

- So going back to the hedgehog weights on page 24, you could define a random variable, $W \sim N(\mu, \sigma^2)$, where W represents hedgehog weight.

- Here, μ would represent the mean weight of the hedgehogs and σ would represent the standard deviation of hedgehog weights.

Calculating probabilities

Before calculating any probabilities, **draw a sketch** to show the probability you want to find. This is useful as it shows the area you're looking for and also helps check that your answer seems **sensible**.

You can use a **calculator** to find probabilities for **any** normal distribution. The method can **vary** depending on the model of your calculator, but you usually enter the **distribution** mode and choose the **normal cdf** function. Then input the required *x*-value(s), **mean** and **standard deviation**.

If you're given only **one** *x*-value (i.e. if you need to find P($X \geq x$) or P($X \leq x$) for some x) you might need to choose your own **lower** or **upper bound** — just pick a really **large negative** or **positive** number (see Example 1 below).

Tip: Make sure you know how to calculate normal probabilities on your calculator. If your calculator can only do the standard normal distribution (see p.28) you'll have to read p.29 first, then look at Example 1.

Example 1

a) If $X \sim N(100, 16)$, find P($X \leq 105$) to 4 s.f.

   1. Draw a sketch showing the area you need to find. ⟶

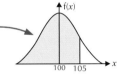

   2. You just input the upper bound $x = 105$, a lower bound (e.g. –9999), $\mu = 100$, and $\sigma = \sqrt{16} = 4$ into the normal cdf function on your calculator.

$$P(X \leq 105) = 0.894350...$$
$$= \boxed{0.8944} \ (4 \text{ s.f.})$$

b) If $X \sim N(13, 5.76)$, find P($X > 17$) to 4 s.f.

   1. X is a continuous random variable, so P($X > 17$) is just the same as P($X \geq 17$). Draw a sketch showing the area you need to find. ⟶

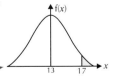

   2. Here, input the lower bound $x = 17$, an upper bound (e.g. 9999), $\mu = 13$ and $\sigma = \sqrt{5.76} = 2.4$ into the normal cdf function.

$$P(X > 17) = P(X \geq 17)$$
$$= 0.047790...$$
$$= \boxed{0.04779} \ (4 \text{ s.f.})$$

Tip: Almost all the possible values of x are within 3 standard deviations of the mean (see p.25), so choosing –9999 or 9999 means that the area you're calculating will cover the whole region you want.

Sometimes you might need to use the following trick to find the probability that X takes a value **greater than** (or greater than or equal to) x.

Using the fact that the **total area** under the curve is **1**, we get this definition:

$$P(X > x) = 1 - P(X \leq x)$$

Example 2

a) If $X \sim N(102, 144)$, find $P(X > 78)$ to 4 s.f.

1. Draw a sketch showing the area you need to find.

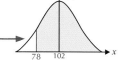

2. The total area under the curve is 1, so $P(X > 78) = 1 - P(X \leq 78)$. You might find it useful to add this to the sketch.

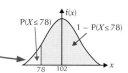

Tip: You might be able to do this straight away by using 78 as a lower bound and choosing a large upper bound. However, this method can be useful when the μ and σ^2 are unknown (see p.32).

3. Input the upper bound $x = 78$, a lower bound, $\mu = 102$ and $\sigma = \sqrt{144} = 12$ into the normal cdf function on your calculator.

$P(X \leq 78) = 0.022750...$
So $P(X > 78) = 1 - P(X \leq 78)$
$= 1 - 0.022750...$
$= \boxed{0.9772}$ (4 s.f.)

b) If $X \sim N(102, 144)$, find $P(84 \leq X \leq 106)$ to 4 s.f.

1. Draw a sketch showing the area you need to find.

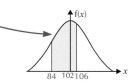

2. For this example you can either split up the probability or calculate it directly.

Method 1 — Split up

- You need to find the area to the left of $x = 106$ and subtract the area to the left of $x = 84$.

- So, $P(84 \leq X \leq 106) = P(X \leq 106) - P(X < 84)$
$= 0.630558... - 0.066807...$
$= \boxed{0.5638}$ (4 s.f.)

Using a calculator

Method 2 — Direct

- Use 84 as the lower bound and 106 as the upper bound in the normal cdf function on your calculator.

- This gives $P(84 \leq X \leq 106) = 0.563751... = \boxed{0.5638}$ (4 s.f.)

Tip: The direct method is much quicker here but for some questions you might need to split the probability up — see page 30.

Exercise 3.1.1

Q1 If $X \sim N(40, 25)$, find: a) $P(X < 50)$ b) $P(X \leq 43)$

Q2 If $X \sim N(24, 6)$, find: a) $P(X \geq 28)$ b) $P(X > 25)$

Q3 If $X \sim N(120, 40)$, find: a) $P(X > 107)$ b) $P(X > 115)$

Q4 If $X \sim N(17, 3^2)$, find: a) $P(X \leq 15)$ b) $P(X < 12)$

Q5 If $X \sim N(50, 5^2)$, find: a) $P(52 < X < 63)$ b) $P(57 \leq X < 66)$

Q4-5 Hint: You'll often see the variance written as a number squared.

Q6 If $X \sim N(0.6, 0.04)$, find:

a) $P(0.45 \le X \le 0.55)$ b) $P(0.53 < X < 0.58)$ c) $P(0.65 < X \le 0.7)$

Q7 If $X \sim N(260, 15^2)$, find:

a) $P(240 < X \le 280)$ b) $P(232 < X < 288)$ c) $P(255 \le X < 264)$

The standard normal distribution, Z

The **standard normal distribution**, Z, is a normal
distribution that has mean $\mu = 0$ and variance $\sigma^2 = 1$. ⟶ $\boxed{Z \sim N(0, 1)}$

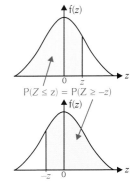

- The curve is **symmetrical** about the mean 0.

- $P(Z \le 0) = P(Z \ge 0) = \frac{1}{2}$, so you'd expect $P(Z \le z)$ to be $< \frac{1}{2}$
  for **negative values** of z and $> \frac{1}{2}$ for **positive values** of z.

- Because of the symmetry of the curve, $\mathbf{P(Z \le z) = P(Z \ge -z)}$.

- The **facts** about the area under the curve on
  p.25 still apply but with $\mu = 0$ and $\sigma = 1$
  — e.g. points of inflection are at $z = 1$ and $z = -1$.

- Values of the **cumulative distribution function** (cdf)
  are usually written $\Phi(z)$ — i.e. $\Phi(z) = P(Z \le z)$.

- Since $P(Z = z) = 0$, you can **interchange**
  the $\le$ and $<$ signs — i.e. $\Phi(z) = P(Z < z)$ as well.

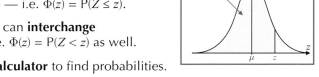

Tip: Φ is
the Greek
letter 'phi'.

As before, you can use a **calculator** to find probabilities.

Examples

Given that $Z \sim N(0, 1)$, find the following probabilities to 4 s.f.

a) $P(Z \le 0.64)$

1. Draw a sketch of the area you need to find.

2. Input $z = 0.64$, a lower bound, $\mu = 0$ and
   $\sigma = 1$ into the normal cdf function.

   So $\Phi(0.64) = P(Z \le 0.64) = 0.738913...$
   $= \boxed{0.7389}$ (4 s.f.)

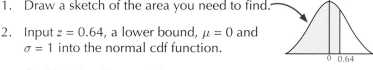

Tip: Remember to
use a lower bound
(e.g. -9999) for
'less than' probabilities
and an upper bound
(e.g. 9999) for 'greater
than' probabilities.

b) $P(Z > -0.42)$

1. Draw a sketch of the area you need to find.

2. Z is a continuous random variable, so
   $P(Z > -0.42)$ is just the same as $P(Z \ge -0.42)$.
   Your calculator still works for negative z-values.

   $P(Z > -0.42) = 0.662757... = \boxed{0.6628}$ (4 s.f.)

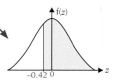

Tip: You could use
symmetry here —
i.e. $P(Z > -0.42)$
$= P(Z < 0.42)$
$= \Phi(0.42)$.

c) P(0.12 < Z ≤ 0.82)

1. Draw a sketch of the area you need to find.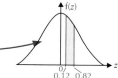

2. Use 0.12 as the lower bound and 0.82 as the upper bound with $\mu = 0$ and $\sigma = 1$.

$P(0.12 < Z \le 0.82) = 0.246133...$
$= \boxed{0.2461}$ (4 s.f.)

Tip: You could split this up like on p.27:
$\Phi(0.82) - \Phi(0.12)$
$= 0.793... - 0.547...$
$= 0.2461$ (4 s.f.)

Exercise 3.1.2

Q1 Use a calculator to find the following probabilities to 4 s.f.

a) $P(Z \le 1.87)$ b) $P(Z < 0.99)$ c) $P(Z > 2.48)$ d) $P(Z \ge 0.14)$

e) $P(Z > -0.24)$ f) $P(Z > -1.21)$ g) $P(Z < -0.62)$ h) $P(Z \le -2.06)$

Q2 Use a calculator to find the following probabilities to 4 s.f.

a) $P(1.34 < Z < 2.18)$ b) $P(0.76 \le Z < 1.92)$ c) $P(-1.45 \le Z \le 0.17)$

d) $P(-2.14 < Z < 1.65)$ e) $P(-1.66 < Z \le 1.66)$ f) $P(-0.34 \le Z < 0.34)$

g) $P(-3.25 \le Z \le -2.48)$ h) $P(-1.11 < Z < -0.17)$ i) $P(-0.27 \le Z \le -0.05)$

Converting to the Z distribution

Any continuous random variable, X, where $X \sim N(\mu, \sigma^2)$, can be **transformed** to the **standard normal variable**, Z, by **subtracting the mean (μ)**, and then **dividing by the standard deviation (σ)**.

Tip: This method comes in handy when the mean and/or standard deviation are unknown (see page 32), or if your calculator only works out standard normal probabilities.

$$\text{If } X \sim N(\mu, \sigma^2), \text{ then } \frac{X - \mu}{\sigma} = Z, \text{ where } Z \sim N(0, 1)$$

Examples

a) If $X \sim N(5, 16)$, find $P(X < 7)$ by transforming X to the standard normal variable Z.

1. Start by transforming X to Z. You know $\mu = 5$, $\sigma = \sqrt{16} = 4$.

$P(X < 7) = P\left(Z < \frac{7-5}{4}\right) = P(Z < 0.5)$

2. Draw a sketch showing the area you need to find.

Tip: Remember to take the square root of the variance to get the standard deviation.

3. Use a calculator to find the probability. $P(Z < 0.5) = \boxed{0.6915}$ (4 d.p.)

b) If $X \sim N(5, 16)$, find $P(5 < X < 11)$.

1. Start by transforming X to Z. $P(5 < X < 11) = P\left(\frac{5-5}{4} < Z < \frac{11-5}{4}\right)$
$= P(0 < Z < 1.5)$

2. Draw a sketch showing the area you need to find.

3. You need to find the area to
    the left of $z = 1.5$, then subtract
    the area to the left of $z = 0$.

$P(0 < Z < 1.5)$
$= P(Z < 1.5) - P(Z \le 0)$
$= 0.93319... - 0.5$
$= \boxed{0.4332}$ (4 d.p.)

Tip: You can check your
answers using $X \sim N(5, 16)$
and finding $P(5 < X < 11)$
on your calculator.

Exercise 3.1.3

Q1   If $X \sim N(106, 100)$, transform X to the standard normal variable to find:

   a) $P(X \le 100)$ b) $P(X > 122)$ c) $P(X \ge 112)$

Q2   If $X \sim N(11, 2^2)$, transform X to the standard normal variable to find:

   a) $P(X \ge 9)$ b) $P(10 \le X \le 12)$ c) $P(7 < X < 11)$

Q3   If $X \sim N(260, 15^2)$, transform X to the standard normal variable to find:

   a) $P(240 < X < 280)$ b) $P(232 < X < 288)$ c) $P(259 < X \le 269)$

Finding x-values

You might be given a **probability**, p, and be asked to find a specific **range
of x-values** where the probability of X falling in this range is equal to p.

For any probability involving **less than** or **less than or equal to**
(e.g. find x where $P(X \le x) = p$) these questions can be done **directly**
on your calculator. To do this, choose the **inverse normal** function on
your calculator. Then input the **probability**, **mean** and **standard deviation**.

Tip: The inverse
normal function
on your calculator
might be labelled
'InvNorm' or 'InvN'.

Example 1

$X \sim N(85, 25)$. If $P(X < a) = 0.9192$, find the value of a to 2 s.f.

1. Draw a sketch of the area you need to find.

2. Input probability $= 0.9192$, $\mu = 85$ and $\sigma = \sqrt{25} = 5$
    into the inverse normal function on your calculator.

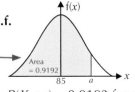

$P(X < x) = 0.9192$ for $x = \boxed{92}$ (2 s.f.)

More complicated problems involving two x-values
need splitting up (see page 27) using this formula:

$$P(a \le x \le b) = P(x \le b) - P(x < a)$$

Example 2

$X \sim N(24, 9)$. If $P(x < X < 24) = 0.2$, find the value of x to 3 s.f.

1. Draw a sketch of the area you need to find.

2. Split up the probability. $P(x < X < 24) = P(X < 24) - P(X < x) = 0.2$
    So $P(X < x) = P(X < 24) - 0.2$

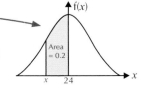

3. Use the information given in the question.	Mean = 24, so $P(X < 24) = 0.5$ and $P(x < X < 24) = 0.2$. So $P(X < x) = 0.5 - 0.2 = 0.3$
4. Use a calculator to find the value of x.	$P(X < x) = 0.3$ for $x = 22.426798...$, so $x = $ 22.4 (3 s.f.)

For the **standard normal distribution**, there's a **table of percentage points** for certain 'nice' probabilities (such as 0.5, 0.1, 0.05 etc.).

Tip: The table of percentage points is on page 188.

- The **percentage points** table gives the value of z for some probabilities, p, where $p = \mathbf{P(Z > z)}$.

- So, as on the previous page, you **start** off with the **probability** that Z is **greater** than a value of z, but now you can look up the value of z in the table.

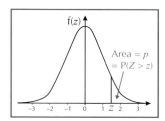

- The area under the curve is 1, so $P(Z > z) = 1 - P(Z \le z) = 1 - \Phi(z)$.

- However, depending on the **value of p**, you might not be able to find what you want from the percentage points table. In which case you would have to use your calculator.

Tip: If you need a value that gives one of the percentages for a non-standard normal distribution, convert to Z, then use the percentage points table.

- You can still work out 'greater than' probabilities on your **calculator**, like in the example below.

Example 3

$Z \sim N(0, 1)$. **If $P(Z > z) = 0.15$, find the value of z.**

1. Draw a sketch of the area you need to find.

2. For this example you can either use the percentage points table or a calculator.

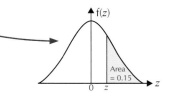

Method 1 — Percentage points table

- Try looking up $p = 0.15$ in the **percentage points** table (see p.188).

- From the table, if $p = 0.15$, then $z = 1.0364$.

- So if $P(Z > z) = 0.15$, then $z = 1.0364$

Method 2 — Calculator

- The area under the curve is 1, so subtract 0.15 from 1 to get the area to the **left** of z: $1 - 0.15 = 0.85$

- Draw another sketch showing the new area.

- Use a calculator to find the value of z. $\Phi(z) = 0.85$ for $z = 1.036433... = 1.0364$ (4 d.p.)

Tip: Rearrange $P(Z > z) = 1 - \Phi(z)$ to give $\Phi(z) = 1 - P(Z > z)$.

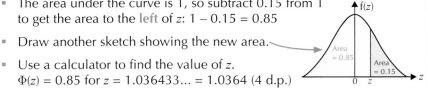

3. Both methods give the answer: $P(Z > z) = 0.15$ for $z = $ 1.0364 (4 d.p.)

Q1 If $X \sim N(12, 0.64)$, find the value of x such that:

    a) $P(X < x) = 0.8944$ b) $P(X \leq x) = 0.0304$

    c) $P(X \geq x) = 0.2660$ d) $P(X > x) = 0.7917$

Q2 For the standard normal distribution, find the value of z to 2 d.p.
that gives each of the following probabilities:

    a) $P(Z < z) = 0.004$ b) $P(Z > z) = 0.0951$

    c) $P(-z < Z < z) = 0.9426$ d) $P(z < Z < -1.25) = 0.0949$

Q2c) Hint: Draw a graph of the area given, then use its symmetry to find the values of z.

Q3 If $X \sim N(48, 5^2)$, find the value of x such that:

    a) $P(53 < X < x) = 0.05$ b) $P(x < X < 49) = 0.4312$

Q4 Use the percentage points table to find the value of z such that:

    a) $P(Z > z) = 0.005$ b) $P(Z > z) = 0.2$

    c) $P(Z < z) = 0.7$ d) $P(Z < z) = 0.999$

Q5 If $X \sim N(25, 4^2)$, use the percentage points table to find the value of x such that:

    a) $P(X > x) = 0.4$ b) $P(X < x) = 0.975$

Finding the mean and standard deviation of a normal distribution

On page 29 you saw how any normally distributed variable, $X \sim N(\mu, \sigma^2)$, can be **transformed** to the standard normal variable, Z, by using $Z = \dfrac{X - \mu}{\sigma}$.

So far you've used this relationship to find probabilities when the mean and standard deviation have been **known**. But you can use it to find the **mean** and **standard deviation** when they're **unknown** and you know some **probabilities** for the distribution.

Example 1

If the random variable $X \sim N(\mu, 4)$ and $P(X < 23) = 0.9015$, find μ.

1. Start by transforming the probability you're given for X into a probability for Z. The mean is unknown, so just leave it as μ for now.

    $P(X < 23) = P\left(Z < \dfrac{23 - \mu}{2}\right)$
    $= 0.9015$

2. Draw a sketch to show the information.

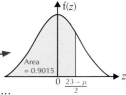

3. Now, if you use a calculator to find z for which $\Phi(z) = 0.9015$, you can form an equation in μ.

    $\Phi(z) = 0.9015$ for $z = 1.2901...$
    So $\dfrac{23 - \mu}{2} = 1.2901...$

4. Now **solve** this equation for μ.

    $\dfrac{23 - \mu}{2} = 1.2901... \Rightarrow 23 - \mu = 2.5802...$
    $\Rightarrow \mu = \boxed{20.42}$ (2 d.p.)

Example 2

If the random variable $X \sim N(\mu, 4^2)$ and $P(X > 19.84) = 0.025$, find μ.

1. Transform the probability you're given for X into a probability for Z.

   $$P(X > 19.84) = P\left(Z > \frac{19.84 - \mu}{4}\right) = 0.025$$

2. Draw a sketch to show the information.

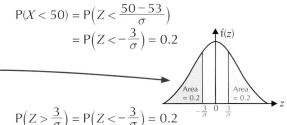

3. Your calculator finds the z-value for $P(Z \leq z)$, so work out $P(Z \leq z)$.

   $$P(Z \leq z) = 1 - P(Z > z)$$
   $$= 1 - 0.025 = 0.975$$

4. Use your calculator to find z for which $\Phi(z) = 0.975$ and form an equation in μ.

   $\Phi(z) = 0.975$ for $z = 1.9600$ (4 d.p.)

   So $\dfrac{19.84 - \mu}{4} = 1.9600$

5. Now solve this equation for μ.

   $$\frac{19.84 - \mu}{4} = 1.9600 \Rightarrow 19.84 - \mu = 7.84 \Rightarrow \boxed{\mu = 12}$$

In the first two examples you found the mean, but you can find the **standard deviation** (s.d.) in exactly the same way.

Example 3

If the random variable $X \sim N(53, \sigma^2)$ and $P(X < 50) = 0.2$, find σ.

1. Start by transforming the probability you're given for X into a probability for Z. The s.d. is unknown, so just leave it as σ for now.

   $$P(X < 50) = P\left(Z < \frac{50 - 53}{\sigma}\right)$$
   $$= P\left(Z < -\frac{3}{\sigma}\right) = 0.2$$

2. Draw a sketch to show the information.

3. Z is symmetrical about the mean 0, so you can use this to find $P\left(Z > \frac{3}{\sigma}\right)$.

   $$P\left(Z > \frac{3}{\sigma}\right) = P\left(Z < -\frac{3}{\sigma}\right) = 0.2$$

4. Look up the z-value in the percentage points table (p.188) to form an equation in σ.

   For $P\left(Z > \frac{3}{\sigma}\right)$, $z = 0.8416 \Rightarrow \frac{3}{\sigma} = 0.8416$

5. Now solve the equation for σ.

   $$\sigma = 3 \div 0.8416 \Rightarrow \boxed{\sigma = 3.56} \text{ (3 s.f.)}$$

When you're asked to find the mean **and** the standard deviation, the method is a little bit **more complicated**.

You start off as usual, but instead of getting one equation in one unknown to solve, you end up with **two equations** in **two unknowns**, μ and σ. In other words, you have **simultaneous equations**, which you **solve** to find μ and σ.

Tip: You can solve simultaneous equations by adding or subtracting them to get rid of one unknown.

Example 4

The random variable $X \sim N(\mu, \sigma^2)$.
If $P(X < 9) = 0.5596$ and $P(X > 14) = 0.0322$, find μ and σ.

1. Transform the first probability for X into a probability for Z.

   $$P(X < 9) = P\left(Z < \frac{9 - \mu}{\sigma}\right) = 0.5596$$

2. Draw a sketch to show the information.

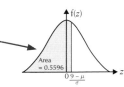

3. Now, if you use a calculator
    to find z for which $\Phi(z) = 0.5596$,
    you can form an equation in μ and σ.

    $\Phi(z) = 0.5596$ for $z = 0.14995...$

    So $\dfrac{9 - \mu}{\sigma} = 0.14995...$ $\Rightarrow$ $9 - \mu = 0.14995...\sigma$

4. Now do the same thing for the second
    probability for X. First, transform to Z.

    $P(X > 14) = P\left(Z > \dfrac{14 - \mu}{\sigma}\right) = 0.0322$

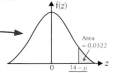

5. Draw a sketch to show the information.

6. Use the graph to work out $P\left(Z \le \dfrac{14 - \mu}{\sigma}\right)$.

    $P\left(Z \le \dfrac{14 - \mu}{\sigma}\right) = 1 - P\left(Z > \dfrac{14 - \mu}{\sigma}\right)$
    $= 1 - 0.0322 = 0.9678$

7. Now, by using a calculator
    to find z for which $\Phi(z) = 0.9678$,
    you can form an equation in μ and σ.

    $\Phi(z) = 0.9678$ for $z = 1.8494...$

    So $\dfrac{14 - \mu}{\sigma} = 1.8494...$ $\Rightarrow$ $14 - \mu = 1.8494...\sigma$

8. Set up the two simultaneous equations,
    giving each a number you can refer to.

    $9 - \mu = 0.14995...\sigma$ ❶

    $14 - \mu = 1.8494...\sigma$ ❷

    Tip: Remember to
    use the unrounded
    z-values here.

9. Each equation has one 'μ', so you can
    subtract them to get rid of μ, which will
    leave you with an equation in σ to solve.

    ❷ − ❶: $14 - 9 - \mu - (-\mu) = 1.8494...\sigma - 0.14995...\sigma$
    $\Rightarrow$ $5 = 1.6994...\sigma$
    $\Rightarrow$ $\sigma = 2.9421... = $ 2.94 (3 s.f.)

10. Finally, find μ by substituting $\sigma = 2.94...$
    back into one of the equations.

    Using equation ❶: $9 - \mu = 0.14995...\sigma$
    $\Rightarrow$ $\mu = 9 - 0.14995... \times 2.9421...$
    $= 8.5588... = $ 8.56 (3 s.f.)

Exercise 3.1.5

Q1 For each of the following, use the information to find μ.

a) $X \sim N(\mu, 6^2)$ and $P(X < 23) = 0.9332$

b) $X \sim N(\mu, 8^2)$ and $P(X < 57) = 0.9970$

c) $X \sim N(\mu, 100^2)$ and $P(X > 528) = 0.1292$

d) $X \sim N(\mu, 0.4^2)$ and $P(X < 11.06) = 0.0322$

e) $X \sim N(\mu, 0.02^2)$ and $P(X > 1.52) = 0.9938$

Q2 $X \sim N(\mu, 3.5^2)$. If the middle 95% of the distribution
    lies between 6.45 and 20.17, find the value of μ.

Q3 For each of the following, use the information to find σ.

    a) $X \sim N(48, \sigma^2)$ and $P(X < 53) = 0.8944$

    b) $X \sim N(510, \sigma^2)$ and $P(X < 528) = 0.7734$

    c) $X \sim N(17, \sigma^2)$ and $P(X > 24) = 0.0367$

    d) $X \sim N(0.98, \sigma^2)$ and $P(X < 0.95) = 0.3085$

    e) $X \sim N(5.6, \sigma^2)$ and $P(X > 4.85) = 0.8365$

Q4 $X \sim N(68, \sigma^2)$. If the middle 70% of the distribution lies between 61 and 75, find σ.

Q5 For each of the following, find μ and σ.

    a) $X \sim N(\mu, \sigma^2)$, $P(X < 30) = 0.9192$ and $P(X < 36) = 0.9953$

    b) $X \sim N(\mu, \sigma^2)$, $P(X < 4) = 0.9332$ and $P(X < 4.3) = 0.9987$

    c) $X \sim N(\mu, \sigma^2)$, $P(X < 20) = 0.7881$ and $P(X < 14) = 0.0548$

    d) $X \sim N(\mu, \sigma^2)$, $P(X < 696) = 0.9713$ and $P(X < 592) = 0.2420$

    e) $X \sim N(\mu, \sigma^2)$, $P(X > 33) = 0.1056$ and $P(X > 21) = 0.9599$

    f) $X \sim N(\mu, \sigma^2)$, $P(X > 66) = 0.3632$ and $P(X < 48) = 0.3446$

The normal distribution in real-life situations

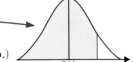

Now it's time to use everything you've learnt about normal distributions to answer questions in real-life contexts. These are the kind of questions that usually come up in exams.

You always start by **defining** a **normally-distributed random variable** to represent the information you're given. Then you use the methods on pages 24-30 to find out what you need to know.

Example 1

A machine which fills boxes of cereal is set so that the mass of cereal going into the boxes follows a normal distribution with mean 766 g and standard deviation 8 g.

a) Find the probability that a randomly selected box of cereal contains less than 780 g of cereal.

    1. Define a random variable to represent the mass of cereal in a box.
        If X represents the mass of cereal in g, then $X \sim N(766, 64)$. 8^2

    2. Write out the probability for X the question is asking for.
        Probability of box containing less than 780 g $= P(X < 780)$

    3. Draw a sketch showing the area you need to find.

    4. Use a calculator to find the probability. $P(X < 780) = $ **0.9599** (4 d.p.)

b) The machine fills 2138 boxes of cereal in an hour.
Find the number of boxes that you would expect to contain less than 780 g.

    Multiply the total number of boxes by the probability calculated in a).
    $2138 \times P(X < 780)$
    $= 2138 \times 0.9599 \approx$ **2052 boxes**

c) **Find the probability that a randomly selected box of cereal contains between 780 g and 790 g of cereal.**

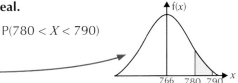

1.   Again, write out the probability for X the question is asking for.

   $P(780 < X < 790)$

2.   Draw a sketch to help you picture this area.

3.   Find the probability using a calculator.

   $P(780 < X < 790) = 0.038709...$
   $= \boxed{0.0387}$ (4 d.p.)

Example 2

The times taken by 666 people to complete an assault course are normally distributed with a mean of 600 seconds and a variance of 105 seconds.

a) **Find the probability that a randomly selected person took more than 620 seconds.**

1.   Start by defining a random variable to represent the time taken.

   If X represents the time taken in seconds, then $X \sim N(600, 105)$.

2.   Write out the probability for X.

   $P(X > 620)$

3.   Draw a sketch to show the information.

4.   Find the probability using a calculator.

   $P(X > 620) = 0.025480... = \boxed{0.0255}$ (4 d.p.)

b) **Find the number of people you would expect to complete the assault course in over 620 seconds.**

Multiply the total number of people by the probability calculated in a).

   $666 \times P(X > 620) = 666 \times 0.025480...$
   $= \boxed{17 \text{ people}}$ (to the nearest whole number)

Real-life normal distribution questions also ask you to **find values**, when you're **given probabilities** (see page 30).

Example 3

The forces needed to snap lengths of a certain type of elastic are normally distributed with $\mu = 13$ N and $\sigma = 1.8$ N.

Tip: Use a sensible letter for the variable — it doesn't have to be X.

a) **The probability that a randomly selected length of elastic is snapped by a force of less than a N is 0.7580. Find the value of a.**

1.   Start by defining a random variable to represent the force needed.

   If F represents the force needed in N, then $F \sim N(13, 1.8^2)$.

2.   Write out the probability for F.

   $P(F < a) = 0.7580$

3.   Next, transform F to Z.

   $P(F < a) = P\left(Z < \dfrac{a-13}{1.8}\right)$
   $= 0.7580$

4.   Draw a sketch to show the information.

   Area $= 0.7580$

   $0 \quad \frac{a-13}{1.8}$

5. Use a calculator to find z for which $\Phi(z) = 0.7580$.

$\Phi(z) = 0.7580$ for $z = 0.6998...$,

so $\dfrac{a-13}{1.8} = 0.6998...$

6. Now, just solve for a.

$\dfrac{a-13}{1.8} = 0.6998... \Rightarrow a - 13 = 1.26$
$\Rightarrow a = \boxed{14.26}$

b) Find the range of values that includes the middle 80% of forces needed to snap the length of elastic.

1. It's difficult to know where to start with this one. So it's a good idea to sketch the distribution of F, to show the range you need to find.

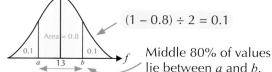

$(1 - 0.8) \div 2 = 0.1$

Middle 80% of values lie between a and b.

2. Now you can write two probability statements — one for a and one for b.

$P(F < a) = 0.1$ and $P(F > b) = 0.1$

3. Next, transform F to Z.

$P(F < a) = P\left(Z < \dfrac{a-13}{1.8}\right) = 0.1$ and
$P(F > b) = P\left(Z > \dfrac{b-13}{1.8}\right) = 0.1$

4. Draw another sketch to show this information.

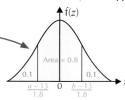

Tip: Using Z is useful because the range is symmetrical about $z = 0$. So $\dfrac{a-13}{1.8} = -\dfrac{b-13}{1.8}$.

5. Now, use the percentage points table to find b (or a).

$p = 0.1$ for $z = 1.2816$.
So $\dfrac{b-13}{1.8} = 1.2816 \Rightarrow b = 15.31$ (2 d.p.)

6. Use symmetry to find a (or b).

$\dfrac{a-13}{1.8} = -1.2816 \Rightarrow a = 10.69$ (2 d.p.)

7. Write down the range of values.

The range of values is $\boxed{10.69 \text{ N to } 15.31 \text{ N}}$.

Exercise 3.1.6

Q1 The lengths of time taken by a group of 56 blood donors to replace their donated red blood cells are modelled by a normal distribution with a mean of 36 days and a standard deviation of 6 days.

a) It takes Edward 28 days to replace his red blood cells. Find the probability that a randomly selected donor from the group takes less time than Edward to replace their red blood cells.

b) Find the number of blood donors in the group that this model would predict to take less time than Edward to replace their blood cells.

c) 7.14% of the group take longer than Bella to replace their red blood cells. How long does it take Bella?

Q2   The personal best times taken by athletes at a sports club to run 400 m are known to follow a normal distribution with a mean of 51 seconds and a standard deviation of 2.1 seconds.

  a) Gary's personal best time is 49.3 seconds. What percentage of the athletes have a slower personal best time than Gary?

  b) The athletes with personal bests in the top 20% of times are selected for a special training programme. What time do they have to beat to be selected for the programme?

Q3   The volume of vinegar contained in bottles is modelled by a normal distribution with a standard deviation of 5 ml. It is found that 71.9% of bottles contain less than 506 ml of vinegar.

  a) Find the mean volume of vinegar contained in the bottles.

  b) The label on each bottle says it contains 500 ml of vinegar. Find the probability that a random bottle contains less than 500 ml.

  c) A shop's store room has 1303 bottles of vinegar. Find the number of bottles that this model would predict to contain at least 500 ml.

> **Q3 Hint:** See p.32 for a reminder of how to find the mean of a normal distribution.

Q4   A particular type of toy car uses two identical batteries. The lifetimes of individual batteries can be modelled by a normal distribution with a mean of 300 hours and a standard deviation of 50 hours.

  a) Find the probability that a battery lasts less than 200 hours.

  b) Find the probability that a battery lasts at least 380 hours.

  c) Stating any assumptions you make, find the probability that both of the batteries in a car last at least 380 hours.

  d) The probability that a randomly selected battery lasts more than 160 hours, but less than h hours, is 0.9746. Find the value of h.

> **Q4 Hint:** See p.11 for a reminder of finding probabilities of multiple events.

Q5   The heights of a population of 17-year-old boys are assumed to follow a normal distribution with a mean of 175 cm. 80% of this population of 17-year-old boys are taller than 170 cm.

  a) Find the standard deviation of the heights of the 17-year-old boys in this population.

  b) One 17-year-old boy is selected from the population at random. Find the probability that his height is within 4 cm of the mean height.

Q6   The masses of the eggs laid by the hens on farmer Elizabeth's farm are assumed to follow a normal distribution with mean 60 g and standard deviation 3 g.

  a) The probability that a randomly selected egg has a mass of at least $60 - m$ grams is 0.9525. Find the value of m to the nearest gram.

  b) Farmer Elizabeth keeps the lightest 10% of eggs for herself and uses them to make sponge cakes. Find the maximum mass of an egg that could end up in one of farmer Elizabeth's sponge cakes.

Q7   In a particularly wet village, it rains almost continuously. The daily rainfall, in cm, is modelled by a normal distribution. The daily rainfall is less than 4 cm on only 10.2% of days, and it's greater than 7 cm on 64.8% of days.

  Find the mean and standard deviation of the daily rainfall.

3.2 Normal Approximation to a Binomial Distribution

Under certain conditions you can use a normal distribution $N(\mu, \sigma^2)$ to approximate the binomial distribution that you saw in Year 1 — this can simplify calculations and is usually pretty accurate.

Learning Objectives (Spec Ref 4.1 & 4.2):

- Apply a continuity correction when using a normal distribution to approximate a discrete random variable.
- Use a normal approximation to a binomial random variable.

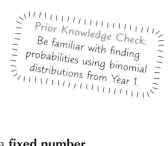

Prior Knowledge Check:
Be familiar with finding probabilities using binomial distributions from Year 1.

Continuity corrections

The **binomial distribution** is **discrete** and occurs in situations with a **fixed number** (n) of **independent** trials, where the outcome of each trial can be either a **success** or **failure**. If the probability of success is p and X is the number of successes, then:

$$X \sim B(n, p)$$

The normal distribution can be used to **approximate** the binomial distribution under particular circumstances.

But using the normal distribution (which is continuous) to approximate a discrete distribution is slightly awkward.

- The binomial distribution is **discrete**, so if the random variable X follows this distribution, you can work out $P(X = 0)$, $P(X = 1)$, etc.

- But a normally distributed variable is **continuous**, and so if $Y \sim N(\mu, \sigma^2)$, $P(Y = 0) = P(Y = 1) = 0$, etc. (see page 25).

To allow for this, you have to use a **continuity correction**.

- You assume that the discrete value $X = 1$ is '**spread out**' over the interval $0.5 < Y < 1.5$.

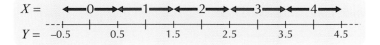

- Then to **approximate** the discrete probability **P(X = 1)**, you find the continuous probability **P(0.5 < Y < 1.5)**.

- Similarly, the discrete value $X = 2$ is **spread out** over the interval $1.5 < Y < 2.5$, so $P(X = 2)$ is **approximated** by $P(1.5 < Y < 2.5)$, and so on.

The **interval** you need to use with the normal distribution depends on the discrete **probability** you're trying to find.

The general idea is always the same, though — each **discrete value b** covers the **continuous interval** from $b - \frac{1}{2}$ up to $b + \frac{1}{2}$.

Discrete	Normal	
$P(X = b)$	$P(b - \frac{1}{2} < Y < b + \frac{1}{2})$	
$P(X \leq b)$	$P(Y < b + \frac{1}{2})$	...to include b
$P(X < b)$	$P(Y < b - \frac{1}{2})$	...to exclude b
$P(X \geq b)$	$P(Y > b - \frac{1}{2})$	...to include b
$P(X > b)$	$P(Y > b + \frac{1}{2})$	...to exclude b

Q1 A discrete random variable X has possible values 0, 1, 2, 3...
X is to be approximated by the normal variable Y.
Write the interval for Y that you would use to approximate:

a) $P(X = 5)$ b) $P(12 \leq X \leq 15)$ c) $P(X \leq 10)$

Q2 The random variable X follows a binomial distribution.
The normal random variable Y is to be used to approximate probabilities for X.
Write down the probability for Y that would approximate:

a) $P(X = 50)$ b) $P(X < 300)$ c) $P(X \geq 99)$

Q3 An unfair coin is to be tossed 1000 times and the number of heads (X) recorded.
A random variable Y following a normal distribution is to be used to approximate
the probabilities below. Write down the probability for Y that would approximate:

a) the probability of getting exactly 200 heads

b) the probability of getting at least 650 heads

c) the probability of getting less than 300 heads

d) the probability of getting exactly 499, 500 or 501 heads

e) the probability of getting between 250 and 750 heads (inclusive)

f) the probability of getting at least 100 heads but less than 900 heads

Normal approximation to a binomial distribution

Certain **binomial** distributions can be approximated by a
normal distribution (as long as you use a **continuity correction**).

For the normal approximation to a binomial distribution to
work well, you need the following conditions to be true:

> Suppose the random variable X follows
> a **binomial distribution**, i.e. $X \sim B(n, p)$.
>
> If (i) $p \approx \frac{1}{2}$,
> and (ii) n is large,
>
> then X can be approximated by the normal
> random variable $Y \sim N(np, np(1 - p))$

Tip: Remember...
the symbol '$\approx$' means
'approximately equal to'.

Tip: This can also be
written $Y \sim N(np, npq)$,
where $q = 1 - p$.

This means that as long as p isn't too far from $\frac{1}{2}$ and n is quite **large**, then you don't need to
use $B(n, p)$ to work out probabilities for X. (And if n is large, $B(n, p)$ can be quite tricky to use.)

Instead you can get a **good approximation** to the probabilities for X using a normal distribution.

In fact, even if p isn't all that close to 0.5, this approximation
usually works well as long as np and $n(1 - p)$ are both **bigger than 5**.

Example 1

The random variable $X \sim B(80, 0.4)$ is to be approximated using the normally distributed random variable $Y \sim N(\mu, \sigma^2)$.

a) Verify that a normal approximation is appropriate, and specify the distribution of Y.

1. Firstly, verify that a normal approximation is appropriate.

n is fairly large, and $p \approx \frac{1}{2}$, so a normal approximation is appropriate.

2. Work out the mean and variance.

$\mu = np = 80 \times 0.4 = 32$
$\sigma^2 = np(1 - p) = 80 \times 0.4 \times 0.6 = 19.2$

3. Write out the approximation.

$Y \sim N(32, 19.2)$

b) Apply a continuity correction to the probability $P(32 < X \leq 35)$.

1. You're looking for the probability for Y that corresponds to this probability for X, so first work out what the probability for X means.

$P(32 < X \leq 35)$
$= P(X = 33) + P(X = 34) + P(X = 35)$

2. Use a continuity correction to write the probability for Y.

$P(32.5 < Y < 35.5)$

c) Find an approximate value for $P(32 < X \leq 35)$.

The probabilities can be found directly from your calculator.

$P(32.5 < Y < 35.5) = 0.2424$ (4 d.p.)

d) Find an approximate value for $P(X < 45)$.

Write the probability for Y using a continuity correction and use a calculator to work it out.

$P(Y < 44.5) = 0.9978$ (4 d.p.)

Example 2

The random variable $X \sim B(90, 0.47)$.
Use a normal approximation to find $P(X \geq 35)$.

1. $n = 90$ is large and $p = 0.47$ is close to 0.5, so approximate X with $Y \sim N(\mu, \sigma^2)$. To do so, work out the mean and variance.

$\mu = 90 \times 0.47 = 42.3$
$\sigma^2 = 90 \times 0.47 \times (1 - 0.47) = 22.419$

2. Write the probability for Y using a continuity correction and use a calculator to work it out.

$P(Y > 34.5) = 0.9503$ (4 d.p.)

This is one of the reasons why the normal distribution is so amazingly useful — because it can be used to approximate other distributions. It means you can use it in all sorts of real-life situations.

Example 3

Each piglet born on a farm is equally likely to be male or female.

a) **250 piglets are born. Use a suitable approximation to find the probability that there will be more males born than females.**

1. First define the random variable, and state how it is distributed.

   If X represents the number of males born, then $X \sim B(250, 0.5)$.

2. Since n is large and p is 0.5, X can be approximated by a normal random variable $Y \sim N(\mu, \sigma^2)$. Work out the mean and variance of X to find the values of μ and σ^2.

   $\mu = np = 250 \times 0.5 = 125$, and
   $\sigma^2 = np(1 - p) = 250 \times 0.5 \times 0.5 = 62.5$
   So $Y \sim N(125, 62.5)$.

3. Apply a continuity correction to the normal variable Y.

   $P(X > 125) \approx P(Y > 125.5)$

4. Use your calculator to find the probability.

   $P(Y > 125.5) = \boxed{0.4748}$ (4 d.p.)

b) **Use your approximation to find the probability that exactly 110 male piglets will be born.**

1. Apply a continuity correction to the normal variable Y.

   $P(X = 110)$
   $\approx P(109.5 < Y < 110.5)$

2. Use your calculator to find the probability.

   $P(109.5 < Y < 110.5)$
   $= \boxed{0.0084}$ (4 d.p.)

> **Tip:** Using B(250, 0.5) instead gives 0.4748 (4 d.p.) and 0.0084 (4 d.p.) for a) and b) respectively. So these are very good approximations.

Example 4

a) **Only 23% of robin chicks survive to adulthood. If 80 robin chicks are randomly selected, use a suitable approximation to find the probability that at least 30% of them survive.**

1. Start by defining the random variable, and stating how it is distributed.

   If X represents the number of survivors, then $X \sim B(80, 0.23)$.

2. Here, p isn't particularly close to 0.5, but n is quite large, so calculate np and $n(1 - p)$.

   $np = 80 \times 0.23 = 18.4$ and
   $n(1 - p) = 80 \times (1 - 0.23) = 61.6$

3. Both np and $n(1 - p)$ are much greater than 5 (see p.40), so X can be approximated by a continuous random variable $Y \sim N(\mu, \sigma^2)$. Work out the values of μ and σ^2.

   $\mu = np = 18.4$, and
   $\sigma^2 = np(1 - p)$
   $= 80 \times 0.23 \times 0.77$
   $= 14.168$
   So $Y \sim N(18.4, 14.168)$.

   > **Tip:** This is the area you're trying to find:
   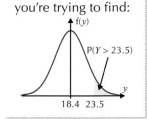

4. Work out the probability for X you're looking for and apply a continuity correction to the normal variable Y.

   30% of 80 = 24
   $\Rightarrow P(X \geq 24)$
   $\Rightarrow P(Y > 23.5)$

5. Use your calculator to find the probability.

   $P(Y > 23.5) = \boxed{0.0877}$ (4 d.p.)

b) **If the survival rate was 18%, use a suitable approximation to find the probability that more than three-quarters of the 80 chicks would die.**

1. The distribution of X has changed, so you should check that a normal approximation is still reasonable.

    If X is the number of survivors, then $X \sim B(80, 0.18)$.
    $np = 80 \times 0.18 = 14.4$ and
    $n(1 - p) = 80 \times (1 - 0.18) = 65.6$.

2. Again, even though p is now quite far from 0.5, these values are both much greater than 5, so a normal approximation should be reasonable.

    $np = 14.4$ and
    $np(1 - p) = 80 \times 0.18 \times (1 - 0.18)$
    $\qquad\qquad = 11.808$
    So approximate X with the random variable $Y \sim N(14.4, 11.808)$.

3. Work out the probability for X you're looking for and apply a continuity correction to the normal variable Y.

    Three-quarters of $80 = 60$, $80 - 60 = 20$, so you need to find $P(X < 20) \Rightarrow P(Y < 19.5)$

4. Use your calculator to find the probability.

    $P(Y < 19.5) = \boxed{0.9311}$ (4 d.p.)

Exercise 3.2.2

Q1 Which of the binomial distributions described below would a normal approximation be suitable for? Give reasons for your answers.

a) $X \sim B(600, 0.51)$

b) $X \sim B(100, 0.98)$

c) $X \sim B(100, 0.85)$

d) $X \sim B(6, 0.5)$

Q2 The normal random variable $Y \sim N(\mu, \sigma^2)$ is to be used to approximate these binomial distributions. Find μ and σ^2 in each case.

a) $X \sim B(350, 0.45)$

b) $X \sim B(250, 0.35)$

c) $X \sim B(70, 0.501)$

Q3 The random variable $X \sim B(200, 0.6)$.
Use the normal approximation to the binomial distribution to find:

a) $P(X < 105)$

b) $P(X = 122)$

c) $P(110 < X < 130)$

Q4 The random variable X is such that $X \sim B(80, 0.8)$.

a) Calculate $P(X = 70)$ using a normal approximation.

b) Calculate $P(X = 70)$ using the binomial distribution.
Give your answer correct to four decimal places.

Q5 It is estimated that 5% of people are carriers of a certain disease. A health authority tests a sample of 1000 people to see if they carry the disease. If more than 75 people test positive they will offer a vaccination to the whole population.

a) Explain why the normal distribution would be a suitable approximation for the number of people in the sample (X) carrying the disease.

b) Estimate the probability that the whole population will be offered a vaccination.

3.3 Choosing Probability Distributions

This section shows you how to choose a suitable probability distribution for a given context and explain why it is suitable for that context.

Learning Objectives (Spec Ref 4.3):
- Choose a suitable probability distribution for a given context.
- Explain why a probability distribution is or isn't suitable for a given context.

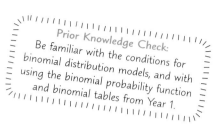

Prior Knowledge Check:
Be familiar with the conditions for binomial distribution models, and with using the binomial probability function and binomial tables from Year 1.

Choosing probability distributions

An exam question might ask you to choose a suitable probability distribution or explain why one is appropriate. This can get quite confusing — so here's a handy summary of it all.

Normal distribution: $X \sim N(\mu, \sigma^2)$

Conditions:
- The values are **continuous** and are **symmetrically distributed**, with a **peak** in the **middle** — this peak represents the **mean** of the values.
- The values **'tail off'** either side of the mean — i.e. values become **less likely** as you move **further away** from the mean.

Then the situation can be modelled by a **normal distribution**, $N(\mu, \sigma^2)$.

For the continuous random variable $X \sim N(\mu, \sigma^2)$:
- X is a **continuous** random variable with **mean** μ and **standard deviation** σ. The mean of X (μ) will correspond to the mean of the values.
- The graph of X has **points of inflection** at $x = \mu - \sigma$ and $x = \mu + \sigma$.
- **68%** of the area under the graph of X is between $x = \mu + \sigma$ and $x = \mu - \sigma$. This means that 68% of the values should fall between $x = \mu \pm \sigma$. Similarly **95%** of the values should fall between $x = \mu \pm 2\sigma$ and **nearly all** of the values (99.7%) should fall between $x = \mu \pm 3\sigma$.
- You can estimate the **probability** that a value will fall within a range by using the normal distribution functions on your **calculator**.

Binomial distribution: $X \sim B(n, p)$

Conditions:
- The values represent the **number of 'successes'** in a **fixed number** (n) of trials, where each trial involves either **'success'** or **'failure'**.
- Trials are **independent**, and the probability of 'success' (p) is **constant**.

Then the situation can be modelled by a **binomial distribution**, $B(n, p)$.

For the discrete random variable $X \sim B(n, p)$:
- $P(X = x) = \binom{n}{x} \times p^x \times (1 - p)^{n - x}$
- Probabilities can be found using **binomial tables** (for certain values of n and p) or the binomial distribution functions on your **calculator**.
- If n is large and $p \approx \frac{1}{2}$, then the values can also be approximately modelled using a **normal distribution**, $N(np, np(1 - p))$. In this case, you will need to use a **continuity correction**.

The conditions for the normal distribution are useful when you're given a diagram and asked to find μ and σ.

Example 1

The times taken by runners to finish a 10 km race are normally distributed. Use the diagram to estimate the mean and standard deviation of the times.

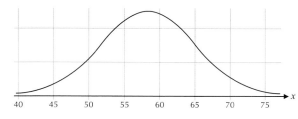

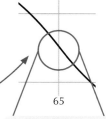

65

The line changes from concave to convex at approximately $x = 65$.

1. The mean is in the middle, so $\mu \approx 58$.

2. For a normal distribution there is a point of inflection at $x = \mu + \sigma$.

3. Use the diagram to find the point of inflection. This is where the line changes from concave to convex — i.e. at $x = 65$.

4. Use your values for x and μ to find σ. $65 \approx 58 + \sigma \implies \sigma \approx 7$

You might be asked to explain why a distribution is or isn't suitable, so try to spot the conditions from the previous page.

Example 2

A restaurant has several vegetarian meal options on its menu. The probability of any person ordering a vegetarian meal is 0.15. One lunch time, 20 people order a meal.

a) Suggest a suitable model to describe the number of people ordering a vegetarian meal and give the values of any parameters.

There are a fixed number of trials (20 meals), with probability of success (i.e. vegetarian meal) 0.15. Use this information to define the random variable, and state how it is distributed.

If X is the number of people ordering a vegetarian meal, then $X \sim B(20, 0.15)$.

b) Explain why it wouldn't be suitable to use a normal approximation here.

$n = 20$ is not particularly large and $p = 0.15$ is quite far away from 0.5.

Or $np = 20 \times 0.15 = 3$, which is less than 5.

c) Find the probability that at least 5 people order a vegetarian meal.

Use the binomial tables for $n = 20$ and $p = 0.15$ to find the probability you're looking for. The binomial tables show probabilities for $P(X \leq x)$ so you'll need to do a bit of rearranging.

$$P(X \geq 5) = 1 - P(X < 5) = 1 - P(X \leq 4)$$
$$= 1 - 0.8298$$
$$= 0.1702$$

Example 3

The heights of 1000 sunflowers are measured and the mean height is calculated
to be 9.8 ft. The distribution of the sunflowers' heights is symmetrical
about the mean, with the shortest sunflower measuring 5.8 ft and the tallest
measuring 13.7 ft. The standard deviation of the sunflowers' heights is 1.3 ft.

a) **Explain why the distribution of the sunflowers' heights
   might reasonably be modelled using a normal distribution.**

   - The data collected is **continuous** and the distribution of the heights is **symmetrical**
     about the **mean**. This is also true for a normally distributed random variable X.

   - **Almost all** the data is within **3 standard deviations** of the mean:
     $9.8 - (3 \times 1.3) = \mathbf{5.9}$ and $9.8 + (3 \times 1.3) = \mathbf{13.7}$

   - So the random variable $X \sim N(\mathbf{9.8, 1.3^2})$ seems a reasonable model.

b) **Sunflowers that measure 7.5 ft or taller are harvested.
   Estimate the number of sunflowers that will be harvested.**

   1. Use a calculator to find the probability
      of a sunflower measuring 7.5 ft or taller. $P(X \geq 7.5) = 0.961572...$

   2. Multiply the total number of $1000 \times 0.961572...$
      sunflowers by this probability. $= \boxed{962}$ (to the nearest whole number)

Exercise 3.3.1

Q1 The speeds of 100 randomly selected cars on a stretch of road are
recorded by a speed camera. The table below shows the results.

Speed s, mph	$s < 35$	$35 \leq s < 40$	$40 \leq s < 45$	$45 \leq s < 50$	$50 \leq s < 55$	$55 \leq s < 60$	$s \geq 60$
Frequency	0	3	28	40	27	2	0

a) Explain why it would be reasonable to use a normal distribution to model the cars' speeds.

b) The distribution of cars' speeds on a different stretch of road is shown
   in the diagram below. Estimate the standard deviation of the speeds.

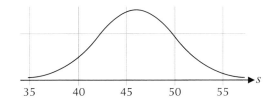

Q2 A tennis player successfully completes a first serve 65% of the time.
The number of successful first serves by the player during a match (X) can be modelled
using a binomial distribution $B(n, p)$, where n is the number of first serves attempted.

a) Assuming that, during a typical match, the player attempts over 100 first serves,
   explain why X can be approximated using a normal distribution.

b) If the player attempts 105 first serves during a match, use the normal approximation
   to find the probability that she completes more than 80 first serves successfully.

3.4 Hypothesis Tests of the Mean of a Population

In Chapter 1 you saw the general theory of hypothesis testing. In this section we'll go through testing the mean of a population. There's not much to learn — it's mostly just applying what you already know.

Learning Objectives (Spec Ref 5.1 & 5.3):
- Conduct a hypothesis test about the population mean of a normal distribution when the variance is known.

Hypothesis tests of a population mean

You'll be carrying out hypothesis tests of the **mean** of a normal distribution, based on a **random sample** of n **observations** from the population.

In the tests you need to carry out, the population will be **normally distributed** with **known variance** (i.e. $X \sim N(\mu, \sigma^2)$). Here's how the hypothesis test works:

- The population parameter you're testing will always be μ, the mean of the population.
- The null hypothesis will be: $H_0: \mu = a$ for some constant a.
- The alternative hypothesis, H_1, will either be

    $H_1: \mu < a$ or $H_1: \mu > a$ (one-tailed test) or $H_1: \mu \neq a$ (two-tailed test)

- State the significance level, α — you'll usually be given this.
- To find the value of the test statistic:
    — Calculate the **sample mean**, $\bar{x}$.

    — If $X \sim N(\mu, \sigma^2)$, then $\bar{X} \sim N\left(\mu, \dfrac{\sigma^2}{n}\right) \Rightarrow Z = \dfrac{\bar{X} - \mu}{\sigma/\sqrt{n}} \sim N(0, 1)$ **Tip:** $\bar{X}$ is a random variable representing the mean of any sample. $\bar{x}$ is the mean for a particular sample.

    — Then the value of your **test statistic** will be: $z = \dfrac{\bar{x} - \mu}{\sigma/\sqrt{n}}$

- Use a calculator to test for significance, either by:
    — finding the **probability** of your test statistic taking a value **at least as extreme** as your observed value (this probability is the ***p*-value**) and comparing it to the significance level α.
    — finding the **critical value(s)** of the test statistic and seeing if your observed value lies in the **critical region**.

Example 1

The times, X, in minutes, taken by the athletes in a running club to complete a certain run follow a normal distribution $X \sim N(12, 4)$. The coach increases the number of training sessions per week, and a random sample of 20 times run since the increase has a mean of 11.2 minutes. Assuming that the variance has remained unchanged, test at the 5% level whether there is evidence that the mean time has decreased.

1. Define μ for the model.   Let μ = mean time (in minutes) since the increase in training sessions

2. Write out the hypotheses. $H_0: \mu = 12$, $H_1: \mu < 12$ ◀——— So this is a one-tailed test.

3. The significance level is 5%, so $\alpha = 0.05$.
Now find the value of your test statistic.

$\overline{x} = 11.2$, so $z = \dfrac{\overline{x} - \mu}{\sigma / \sqrt{n}} = \dfrac{11.2 - 12}{2/\sqrt{20}} = -1.7888...$

4. All that's left is to test for significance.
Here are the two methods...

Tip: $\sigma^2 = 4$, so $\sigma = 2$.

Method 1 — Finding the p-value

- Work out the p-value — this is the probability of the test statistic (Z) being **at least as extreme** as the observed value of $z = -1.7888...$

- This is a **one-tailed test** and values more likely to occur under H_1 are at the **lower end** of the distribution. So 'at least as extreme as the observed value' means '$-1.7888...$ or lower'.

- The p-value is $P(Z \leq -1.7888...) = 0.0368 < 0.05$
  $\alpha = 0.05$

- So the result is **significant**.

Tip: Under H_0,
$X \sim N(12, 4)$,
so $\overline{X} \sim N(12, \frac{4}{20})$
$\overline{X} \sim N(12, 0.2)$.
So under H_0,
$Z = \dfrac{\overline{X} - 12}{\sqrt{0.2}} \sim N(0, 1)$

Method 2 — Finding the critical region

- This is a **one-tailed test** and the critical region will be at the **lower end** of the distribution.
So the critical value is z such that $P(Z < z) = 0.05$.

- Using the percentage points table, the critical value is $z = -1.645$, meaning the critical region is $Z < -1.645$.

$P(Z < -1.645) = 0.05$

$P(Z = z)$

-1.645 0 z

Tip:
From the percentage points table,
$P(Z \leq 1.645) = 0.95$,
so using the symmetry of the normal distribution,
$P(Z < -1.645) = 0.05$.

- Since $z = -1.788... < -1.645$, the observed value of the test statistic lies in the critical region.

- So the result is **significant**.

5. All you need to do now is write your conclusion.

There is evidence at the 5% level of significance to **reject H_0** and to suggest that the mean time has decreased.

Example 2

The volume (in ml) of a cleaning fluid dispensed in each operation of a machine is normally distributed with mean μ and standard deviation 3. Out of a random sample of 20 measured volumes, the mean volume dispensed was 30.9 ml.

Does this data provide evidence at the 1% level of significance that the machine is dispensing a mean volume that is different from 30 ml?

1. Define μ for the model.

Let μ = mean volume (in ml) dispensed in all possible operations of the machine (i.e. μ is the mean volume of the 'population').

2. Write out the hypotheses.

H_0: $\mu = 30$ and H_1: $\mu \neq 30$

3. The significance level is 1%, so $\alpha = 0.01$.
   Now find the value of your test statistic.

   $\bar{x} = 30.9$, so $z = \dfrac{\bar{x} - \mu}{\sigma/\sqrt{n}} = \dfrac{30.9 - 30}{3/\sqrt{20}} = 1.3416...$

4. This is a **two-tailed** test, so you need to check whether the p-value (the probability of the test statistic being at least as extreme as the observed value) is less than $\frac{\alpha}{2} = 0.005$.

   $P(Z \geq 1.3416...) = 0.0899 > \frac{\alpha}{2}$.

   This means this result is not significant at this level.

5. Write your conclusion.

   This data does not provide evidence at the 1% level to support the claim that the machine is dispensing a mean volume different from 30 ml.

Exercise 3.4.1

MODELLING

Q1 The weight of plums (in grams) from a tree was known to follow the distribution N(42, 16).
    It is suggested that the weight of plums has increased.
    A random sample of 25 plums gives a mean weight of 43.5 grams.
    Assuming the variance has remained unchanged, test this claim at:

    a) the 5% significance level   b) the 1% significance level

Q2 Bree plays cards with her friends, and the amount of money she wins each week
    is normally distributed with a mean, μ, of £24 and standard deviation, σ, of £2.
    A new friend has joined the game and Bree thinks this will change the amount she wins.
    In a random sample of 12 weeks the sample mean, $\bar{x}$, was found to be £22.50.
    Test Bree's claim at the 1% level of significance.

Q3 The marks obtained in a language test by students in a school have followed a normal distribution
    with mean 70 and variance 64. A teacher suspects that this year the mean score is lower.
    A sample of 40 students is taken and the mean score is 67.7.
    Assuming the variance remains unchanged, test the teacher's claim at the 5% level of significance.

Q4 The weights (in grams) of pigeons in a city centre in previous years were normally distributed
    with mean 300 and standard deviation 45. The council claims that this year the city's pigeons
    are, on average, heavier. A random sample of 25 pigeons gives a mean of 314 g.

    a) State the null hypothesis and the alternative hypothesis.

    b) State whether it is a one- or two-tailed test.

    c) Assuming the variance remains unchanged,
       use a 1% level of significance to test the hypothesis.

Q5 The number of hours that Kyle used to spend studying each week followed a normal distribution
    with mean 32 and standard deviation 5. Kyle believes that the mean amount of time he spends
    studying each week has increased. In a random sample of 20 weeks over the past year,
    the mean number of hours he spent studying was recorded as 34. Test Kyle's belief at
    the 5% and 1% level of significance. Comment on your answers.

Review Exercise

Q1 If $X \sim N(50, 16)$ find: a) $P(X < 42)$ b) $P(X > 56)$ c) $P(47 < X < 57)$

Q2 Find the probability that:

    a) $Z < 0.84$ b) $Z \leq -0.01$ c) $-0.99 < Z \leq -0.74$ d) $-0.55 \leq Z < 0.35$

Q3 If $X \sim N(21, 6.25)$, transform X to the standard normal variable to find:

    a) $P(X \leq 18)$ b) $P(X > 20)$ c) $P(19 < X < 22)$ d) $P(23 \leq X \leq 25)$

Q4 If $X \sim N(64, 6^2)$ find, to the nearest whole number, the value of x such that:

    a) $P(X \leq x) = 0.5$ b) $P(X > x) = 0.9332$ c) $P(x \leq X < 75) = 0.6581$

Q5 $X \sim N(80, 15)$.

    a) If $P(X < a) = 0.99$, find a.   b) If $P(|X - 80| < b) = 0.8$, find b.

Q6 Find the value of z if:

    a) $P(Z > z) = 0.0359$ b) $P(Z > z) = 0.01$ c) $P(z \leq Z \leq 0.5) = 0.2902$

Q7 $X \sim N(\mu, 8^2)$ and $P(X > 221) = 0.3085$. Find μ.

Q8 The random variable $X \sim N(\mu, \sigma^2)$.
If $P(X < 15.2) = 0.9783$ and $P(X > 14.8) = 0.1056$, then find μ and σ.

Q9 The masses of items made by a factory are normally distributed with $\mu = 55$ g
and $\sigma = 4.4$ g. Find the probability that a randomly chosen item has a mass of:

    a) less than 55 g   b) less than 50 g   c) more than 60 g

Q10 The random variable X follows a binomial distribution: $X \sim B(100, 0.45)$.
Using a normal approximation and continuity corrections, find:

    a) $P(X = 50)$ b) $P(X > 50)$ c) $P(X \leq 45)$ d) $P(40 < X \leq 47)$

Q11 The probability that an applicant is accepted into a particular university is 0.28.
The university randomly samples 120 applicants to see if they are accepted or not.
X is the number of applicants that are successful from the sample:

    a) Calculate $P(X = 34)$ using a binomial distribution and a normal approximation.

    b) Comment on the accuracy of the normal approximation.

Q12 Carry out the following test of the mean, μ, of a normal distribution with variance $\sigma^2 = 9$.
A random sample of 16 observations from the distribution was taken and the sample mean ($\bar{x}$)
calculated. Test $H_0: \mu = 45$ against $H_1: \mu < 45$, at the 5% significance level, using $\bar{x} = 42$.

Q1   The variable X is normally distributed with $\mu = 30$ and $\sigma = 4$.

   a) Define a suitable distribution to model X.

[1 mark]

   b) Find the value of a, given that $P(30 - a < X < 30 + a) = 0.4$.

[3 marks]

Q2   The mass of some clementines at a greengrocer's is normally distributed
      with a mean of μ g and a standard deviation of 5.5 g. The probability
      that a clementine picked at random weighs less than 80 g is 0.8623.

   a) Find the value of μ to the nearest gram.

[3 marks]

   b) The probability that a clementine weighs less than w g is the same
       as the probability that it weighs more than 80 g. State the value of w.

[1 mark]

Q3   A garden centre grows rose plants. 40% of the rose plants have red flowers when in bloom.
      A sample of 200 rose plants is selected at random.

   a) Define a suitable distribution to model the number
       of rose plants that have red flowers in this sample.

[1 mark]

   b) Use a normal approximation to find the probability that at
       least 90 of the rose plants in the sample have red flowers.

[3 marks]

   c) Justify the use of a normal approximation in this case.

[1 mark]

Q4   The lengths (in cm) of the brown trout living in a particular lake
      are normally distributed with mean 46.0 and a standard deviation of 9.6.

   a) Find the probability that a brown trout picked at random
       from the lake will be between 40 cm and 50 cm long.

[1 mark]

After fishing restrictions are introduced, an angler claims that the mean length of the
brown trout in the lake has increased. In a random sample of 32 brown trout caught
one year after the restrictions were introduced, the mean length was 51.7 cm.

   b) Assuming the variance remains unchanged, test the angler's claim
       at the 1% significance level. Clearly state your hypotheses.

[5 marks]

4.1 Projectiles

A projectile is an object which has been projected (e.g. thrown or fired) through the air. For projectile questions, you'll have to split the projectile's velocity into its horizontal and vertical components.

Learning Objectives (Spec Ref 7.1, 7.3 & 7.5):
- Resolve a body's velocity into its horizontal and vertical components.
- Perform calculations involving projectile motion, including the use of **i-j** vectors.
- Model projectile motion under gravity, and understand the modelling assumptions.
- Derive general equations that describe the path of a projectile.

Prior Knowledge Check:
*You should be familiar with **i-j** vectors from the Pure part of this course.*

The two components of velocity

When you project a body through the air with **initial speed u**, at an **angle of θ** to the horizontal, it will move along a **curved path**:

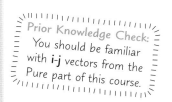

You can use **trigonometry** to resolve the body's initial velocity into its **horizontal** and **vertical components**:

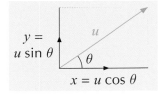

- Horizontal component (x): $\cos\theta = \dfrac{\text{adjacent}}{\text{hypotenuse}} = \dfrac{x}{u}$, so $x = u\cos\theta$

- Vertical component (y): $\sin\theta = \dfrac{\text{opposite}}{\text{hypotenuse}} = \dfrac{y}{u}$, so $y = u\sin\theta$

You can split the projectile's velocity at any point along its path into horizontal and vertical components — as long as you know its speed and direction at that particular point.

Example 1

A ball is thrown with initial speed 9 ms⁻¹ at an angle of 40° above the horizontal. Find the horizontal and vertical components of the ball's initial velocity.

1. Resolve horizontally: Horizontal component = 9 cos 40° = 6.89 ms⁻¹ (3 s.f.)

2. Resolve vertically: Vertical component = 9 sin 40° = 5.79 ms⁻¹ (3 s.f.)

Given the horizontal and vertical components of a projectile's velocity, you can find its **speed** using **Pythagoras' theorem**.

You can find its **direction of motion** using **trigonometry**.

Example 2

At a particular point on its trajectory, a particle has velocity v, with horizontal component 12 ms⁻¹ and vertical component –5 ms⁻¹. Find the particle's speed, *v*, and direction of motion at this point.

1. Draw a diagram to show the particle's motion.

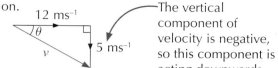

The vertical component of velocity is negative, so this component is acting downwards.

> **Tip:** A projectile's trajectory is just the path that it moves along.

2. Use Pythagoras' theorem to find the speed: $v = \sqrt{12^2 + (-5)^2} = 13$ ms⁻¹

3. Use trigonometry to find the direction: $\theta = \tan^{-1}\left(\frac{5}{12}\right) = 22.6°$ (3 s.f.) below the horizontal

---

Exercise 4.1.1

Q1 Each diagram below shows the speed of a projectile and the angle its velocity makes with the horizontal. In each case, find the horizontal and vertical components of the projectile's velocity.

a)
10 ms⁻¹
20°

b) 18 ms⁻¹
65°

c)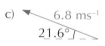
6.8 ms⁻¹
21.6°

> **Q1 Hint:** If you're not asked to give answers to a specific accuracy, rounding to 3 significant figures is fine for most situations.

d)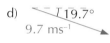
19.7°
9.7 ms⁻¹

e) 84°
24 ms⁻¹

f)
16 ms⁻¹
123°

g)
27°
7.5 ms⁻¹

h)
19 ms⁻¹
31°

i)
114°
6.6 ms⁻¹

Q2 A particle is moving with speed 8 ms⁻¹ at an angle of 35° to the horizontal. Find the horizontal and vertical components of its velocity.

Q3 A rocket is fired vertically upwards with speed 45 ms⁻¹. Find the horizontal and vertical components of its initial velocity.

Q4 A body is fired at an angle α to the horizontal with speed 22 kmh⁻¹. Find the horizontal and vertical components of its initial velocity, giving your answer in metres per second.

Q5 A ball is thrown with velocity **v**, with horizontal component 6 ms⁻¹ and vertical component 8 ms⁻¹. Find the speed and direction of projection of the ball.

Q6 A particle moves with velocity **u**. The horizontal component of **u** is 17 ms⁻¹ and the vertical component is –2.5 ms⁻¹. Find the magnitude and direction of **u**.

Q7 A particle moves with velocity **v**. The horizontal component of **v** is –2*a* ms⁻¹ and the vertical component is 3*a* ms⁻¹, where *a* > 0. Find the direction of **v**.

The constant acceleration equations

To solve problems involving projectile motion, you will need to make certain **modelling assumptions**:

- The projectile is moving only under the influence of **gravity** (i.e. there'll be **no external forces** acting on it).

- The projectile is a **particle** — i.e. its weight acts from a single point, so its dimensions don't matter.

- The projectile moves in a **two-dimensional vertical plane** — i.e. it doesn't swerve from side to side. For example, in the diagram of the projectile's path on page 52, the projectile stays flat on the page — it doesn't move towards you (out of the page) or away from you (into the page).

Tip: An external force is any force acting on a body other than the body's weight — e.g. air resistance, friction, tension etc.

Because the projectile is modelled as moving only under the influence of gravity, the only acceleration the projectile will experience will be **acceleration due to gravity (g = 9.8 ms^{-2})**. You might be asked to use different values for g (e.g. 10 ms^{-2} or 9.81 ms^{-2}), so read the question carefully. The examples and questions in this chapter use g = 9.8 ms^{-2}, unless stated otherwise.

Acceleration due to gravity acts **vertically downwards**, so will only affect the **vertical component** of the projectile's velocity. The **horizontal component** of the velocity will remain **constant** throughout the motion.

> When **modelling real situations**, consider which of these assumptions would not be **valid**. For example, a falling parachutist would encounter significant **air resistance**, so the model should allow for this.

To answer a projectiles question, split all the vector quantities you know — **velocity**, **acceleration** and **displacement** — into their **horizontal** and **vertical components**. Then you can deal with the two components **separately** using the *suvat* equations below — you have to use the components because the *suvat* equations only work for motion in a **straight line**.

The thing that connects the two components is **time** — this will be the same no matter what direction you're resolving in.

The Constant Acceleration Equations

$v = u + at$

$s = ut + \frac{1}{2}at^2$

$s = \left(\frac{u+v}{2}\right)t$

$v^2 = u^2 + 2as$

$s = vt - \frac{1}{2}at^2$

s = displacement in m

u = initial speed (or velocity) in ms^{-1}

v = final speed (or velocity) in ms^{-1}

a = acceleration in ms^{-2}

t = time that passes in s (seconds)

Tip: Always look at what information you're given, and what you've been asked to find, in order to decide which *suvat* equation to use.

Remember — these equations only work if the acceleration is **constant**.
Speed, distance and time must always be **positive**.
But velocity, acceleration and displacement can be **positive or negative**.

Example 1

A particle is projected with initial speed 18 ms⁻¹ from a point on horizontal ground, at an angle of 40° above the horizontal. Find the distance of the particle from its point of projection 1.8 seconds after it is projected.

18 ms⁻¹
40°

Consider the horizontal and vertical motion separately.

1. Resolve horizontally, taking right as positive:

   $s = s_x$, $u = 18 \cos 40°$, $a = 0$, $t = 1.8$

   > **Tip:** s_x is the particle's horizontal displacement and s_y is its vertical displacement.

   Using $s = ut + \frac{1}{2}at^2$:

   $s_x = (18 \cos 40° \times 1.8) + 0 = 24.8198...$

2. Then resolve vertically, taking up as positive:

   $s = s_y$, $u = 18 \sin 40°$, $a = -9.8$, $t = 1.8$

   Using $s = ut + \frac{1}{2}at^2$:

   $s_y = (18 \sin 40° \times 1.8) + (\frac{1}{2} \times -9.8 \times 1.8^2)$
   $= 4.9503...$

   So the particle's horizontal displacement from its starting point is 24.8198... m and its vertical displacement is 4.9503... m.

3. Use Pythagoras' theorem to find its distance from the starting point.

   4.9503... m
   24.8198... m

   > **Tip:** Distance must be positive, so ignore the negative square root.

   distance $= \sqrt{(24.8198...)^2 + (4.9503...)^2}$

   $= \boxed{25.3 \text{ m (3 s.f.)}}$

Example 2

A ball is kicked from a point on horizontal ground. The initial velocity of the ball is 23 ms⁻¹, at an angle α to the horizontal. The ball reaches a maximum vertical height above the ground of 4.8 m.

Find the value of α.

When the ball reaches its maximum height, the vertical component of its velocity will momentarily be zero.

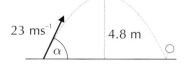
23 ms⁻¹
4.8 m
α

Resolve vertically, taking up as positive:

$s = 4.8$, $u = 23 \sin \alpha$, $v = 0$, $a = -9.8$

Using $v^2 = u^2 + 2as$:
$0 = (23 \sin \alpha)^2 + (2 \times -9.8 \times 4.8)$
$0 = 529 \sin^2 \alpha - 94.08$

$\sin^2 \alpha = 94.08 \div 529 = 0.1778...$
$\sin \alpha = 0.4217...$

$\Rightarrow \alpha = \boxed{24.9° \text{ (3 s.f.)}}$

Example 3

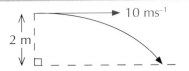

A stone is thrown horizontally with speed 10 ms⁻¹ from a height of 2 m above horizontal ground.

a) **Find the speed and direction of motion of the stone after 0.5 seconds.**

Consider the vertical and horizontal motion separately.

1. Resolve vertically, taking down as positive. The stone is thrown horizontally, so the vertical component of its initial velocity is zero.

   $u = 0, \quad v = v_y, \quad a = 9.8, \quad t = 0.5$

   Using $v = u + at$:

   $v_y = 9.8 \times 0.5 = 4.9 \text{ ms}^{-1}$

2. The horizontal component of velocity is constant, as there is no acceleration horizontally.

   $v_x = u_x = 10 \text{ ms}^{-1}$

3. You can now use Pythagoras and trigonometry to find the speed and direction of motion of the stone at this time.

   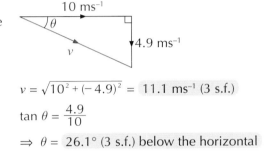

   $v = \sqrt{10^2 + (-4.9)^2} = \boxed{11.1 \text{ ms}^{-1} \text{ (3 s.f.)}}$

   $\tan \theta = \dfrac{4.9}{10}$

   $\Rightarrow \theta = \boxed{26.1° \text{ (3 s.f.) below the horizontal}}$

b) **Find the stone's horizontal displacement when it lands on the ground.**

   Tip: You may see this asked as 'find the horizontal range'.

1. First, you need to find the length of time that the stone is in the air before it lands. This is usually referred to as the 'time of flight'.

   Resolve vertically, taking down as positive:

   $s = 2, \quad u = 0, \quad a = 9.8, \quad t = t$

   Using $s = ut + \dfrac{1}{2}at^2$:

   $2 = \dfrac{1}{2} \times 9.8 \times t^2$

   $t^2 = 0.4081... \Rightarrow t = 0.6388... \text{ s}$

2. Now you know how long the stone is in the air, you can find its horizontal displacement in this time.

   Resolve horizontally, taking right as positive:

   $s = s, \quad u = 10, \quad a = 0, \quad t = 0.6388...$

   Using $s = ut + \dfrac{1}{2}at^2$:

   $s = 10 \times 0.6388... = \boxed{6.39 \text{ m (3 s.f.)}}$

Example 4

A particle is projected from a point y m above flat horizontal ground.
The initial velocity of the particle is U ms^{-1} at an angle θ to the horizontal:

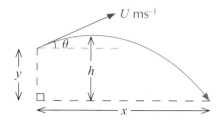

a) **Find the maximum height the particle reaches above the ground, h, in terms of y, U and θ.**

Resolve vertically, taking up as positive:

$s = h - y, \quad u = U \sin \theta, \quad v = 0, \quad a = -g$

Using $v^2 = u^2 + 2as$:

$0 = (U \sin \theta)^2 + (2 \times -g \times (h - y))$

$0 = U^2 \sin^2 \theta - 2gh + 2gy$

$2gh = U^2 \sin^2 \theta + 2gy$

$$h = \frac{U^2 \sin^2 \theta}{2g} + y$$

b) **Find the horizontal range of the particle, x, in terms of y, U and θ.**

1. Resolve vertically, taking up as positive.

$s = -y, \quad u = U \sin \theta, \quad a = -g, \quad t = t$

Using $s = ut + \frac{1}{2}at^2$:

$-y = (U \sin \theta \times t) + (\frac{1}{2} \times -g \times t^2) = (U \sin \theta)t - \frac{g}{2}t^2$

$\frac{g}{2}t^2 - (U \sin \theta)t - y = 0$

2. Use the quadratic formula to find t in terms of y:

$t = \dfrac{U \sin \theta \pm \sqrt{U^2 \sin^2 \theta - \left(4 \times \frac{g}{2} \times -y\right)}}{g}$

$t = \dfrac{U \sin \theta \pm \sqrt{U^2 \sin^2 \theta + 2gy}}{g}$

3. Since g and y are positive, $\sqrt{U^2 \sin^2 \theta + 2gy}$ is greater than $\sqrt{U^2 \sin^2 \theta}$ (i.e. $U \sin \theta$). So when the $\pm$ is a $-$, t is negative.

Time must be positive so $t = \dfrac{U \sin \theta + \sqrt{U^2 \sin^2 \theta + 2gy}}{g}$

4. Now resolve horizontally:

$s = x, \quad u = U \cos \theta, \quad a = 0, \quad t = \dfrac{U \sin \theta + \sqrt{U^2 \sin^2 \theta + 2gy}}{g}$

Using $s = ut + \frac{1}{2}at^2$:

$$x = \frac{U^2 \sin \theta \cos \theta + (\sqrt{U^2 \sin^2 \theta + 2gy})U \cos \theta}{g}$$

Tip: For projections at ground level ($y = 0$):
$t = \dfrac{2U \sin \theta}{g}$ and
$x = \dfrac{2U^2 \sin \theta \cos \theta}{g}$

The particle is used to model a ball thrown at a velocity of 30 ms⁻¹
at an angle of 25° above the horizontal, from a vertical height of 1.5 m.

c) Find the length of time the ball is at least 5 m above the ground.

1. Resolve vertically, taking up as positive. Because the ball is thrown from 1.5 m above the ground, it only has to travel 3.5 m to reach a height of 5 m above ground level.

$s = 3.5, \quad u = 30 \sin 25°, \quad a = -9.8, \quad t = t$

Using $s = ut + \frac{1}{2}at^2$:

$3.5 = (30 \sin 25° \times t) + (\frac{1}{2} \times -9.8 \times t^2)$

$4.9t^2 - (12.67...)t + 3.5 = 0$

2. Use the quadratic formula to solve for t:

$t = \dfrac{12.67... \pm \sqrt{(-12.67...)^2 - (4 \times 4.9 \times 3.5)}}{9.8}$

$\Rightarrow t = 0.314...$ or $t = 2.273...$

3. So the ball is exactly 5 m above the ground 0.314... seconds after being thrown, and again 2.273... seconds after being thrown:

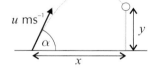

0.314... s   2.273... s

5 m   5 m

4. Subtract to find the length of time that the ball is at least 5 m above the ground:

$2.273... - 0.314... = \boxed{1.96 \text{ s (3 s.f.)}}$

Example 5

A golf ball is struck from a point A on a horizontal plane. When the ball has moved a horizontal distance x, its height above the plane is y. The ball is modelled as a particle projected with initial speed u ms⁻¹ at an angle α above the horizontal.

a) Show that $y = x \tan \alpha - \dfrac{gx^2}{2u^2 \cos^2 \alpha}$.

u ms⁻¹

α

y

x

1. Resolve horizontally, taking right as positive:

$s = x, \quad u_x = u \cos \alpha, \quad a = 0, \quad t = t$

Using $s = ut + \frac{1}{2}at^2$:

$x = u \cos \alpha \times t$

$t = \dfrac{x}{u \cos \alpha}$ — call this equation ①

2. Resolve vertically, taking up as positive:

Tip: It would be a massive pain to rearrange equation 2 to make t the subject, so you're better off doing it to equation 1.

$s = y, \quad u_y = u \sin \alpha, \quad a = -g, \quad t = t$

Using $s = ut + \frac{1}{2}at^2$:

$y = (u \sin \alpha \times t) - \frac{1}{2}gt^2$ — call this equation ②

3. t doesn't appear in the formula you're given in the question, so you know that's what you should be trying to eliminate. t is the same horizontally and vertically, so you can substitute equation ① into equation ② and eliminate t:

$$y = \left(u \sin\alpha \times \frac{x}{u\cos\alpha}\right) - \frac{1}{2}g\left(\frac{x}{u\cos\alpha}\right)^2$$

> **Tip:** This is the general equation of the path of a particle projected from a point on a horizontal plane. The path of a particle projected from a point above the horizontal (as in Example 4) could be derived in the same way.

$$= x\frac{\sin\alpha}{\cos\alpha} - \frac{1}{2}g\left(\frac{x^2}{u^2\cos^2\alpha}\right)$$

$$= x\tan\alpha - \frac{gx^2}{2u^2\cos^2\alpha} \quad \text{— as required.}$$

b) **The ball just passes over the top of a 10 m tall tree, which is 45 m from A. Given that $\alpha = 45°$, find the speed of the ball as it passes over the tree.**

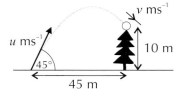

First of all, you need to find the ball's initial speed, u, then you can resolve horizontally and vertically and use the *suvat* equations as usual.

1. Using the result from part a), and substituting $x = 45$ m, $y = 10$ m and $\alpha = 45°$:

$$y = x\tan\alpha - \frac{gx^2}{2u^2\cos^2\alpha}$$

$$10 = 45\tan 45° - \frac{9.8 \times 45^2}{2u^2 \times \cos^2 45°}$$

$$10 = 45 - \frac{19\,845}{u^2}$$

$$\frac{19\,845}{u^2} = 35 \Rightarrow u = 23.811... \text{ ms}^{-1}$$

So the ball has initial speed 23.811... ms⁻¹, at an angle of 45° above the horizontal.

2. Resolve horizontally, taking right as positive:

$$v_x = u_x = (23.811...)\cos 45° = 16.837... \text{ ms}^{-1}$$

> **Tip:** Remember that the horizontal component of velocity stays constant throughout the motion — so v_x always equals u_x.

3. Resolve vertically, taking up as positive:

$$s = 10, \quad u = (23.811...)\sin 45° = 16.837...,$$
$$v = v_y, \quad a = -9.8$$

Using $v^2 = u^2 + 2as$:

$$v_y^2 = (16.837...)^2 + (2 \times -9.8 \times 10) = 87.5 \text{ m}^2\text{s}^{-2}$$

Don't bother square-rooting to find v_y — you'll need to use v_y^2 in the next step.

4. Now you can find the speed using Pythagoras' theorem:

$$\text{speed} = \sqrt{(16.837...)^2 + 87.5} = 19.3 \text{ ms}^{-1} \text{ (3 s.f.)}$$

Exercise 4.1.2

Q1

A projectile is launched from a point on horizontal ground with speed 15 ms^{-1} at an angle of 50° above the horizontal. Find:

a) the time taken for the projectile to reach its maximum height,

b) the maximum height the projectile reaches above the ground.

Q2 A stone is catapulted with speed 12 ms^{-1} at an angle of 37° above the horizontal. It hits a target 0.5 seconds after being fired. Find:

a) the stone's horizontal displacement 0.5 seconds after being fired,

b) the stone's vertical displacement 0.5 seconds after being fired,

Hint: Drawing a diagram might help.

c) the straight-line distance from the stone's point of projection to the target.

Q3 A ball is kicked from a point on a flat, horizontal field. It has initial speed 8 ms^{-1}, leaves the ground at an angle of 59° and then lands in the same field. Find:

a) the ball's time of flight,

b) the horizontal range of the ball.

Q4 Hint: When you're given a value for tan θ, it often means you can use it to get sin θ and cos θ without needing a calculator. Watch out for familiar right-angled triangles such as

Q4 A particle is projected at an angle θ above the horizontal with speed 18 ms^{-1}. Given that tan $\theta = \sqrt{3}$, find:

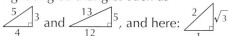

a) the particle's speed 2 seconds after projection,

b) the direction of motion of the particle at this time.

Q5

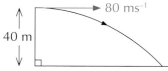

A bullet is fired horizontally at a speed of 80 ms^{-1} directly away from the edge of a vertical cliff 40 m above sea level, as shown.

a) How long after being fired does the bullet hit the sea?

b) Find the horizontal distance from the bottom of the cliff to the point that the bullet hits the sea.

c) Suggest how the model used to calculate the bullet's motion in air should be refined to calculate its motion in the water.

Q6 A gun fires a pellet horizontally at 145 ms^{-1}. The pellet hits the flat, horizontal ground after falling a vertical distance of h m from the gun. Find, in terms of h, the horizontal distance, d m, between the gun and where the pellet lands.

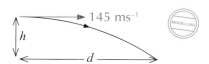

Q7 A man throws a cabbage horizontally from the top of a cliff. The cliff is 215 m high. The cabbage strikes the sea 179 m from the base of the cliff. Ignoring air resistance, calculate the speed at which the cabbage is thrown. Give your answer to 3 significant figures.

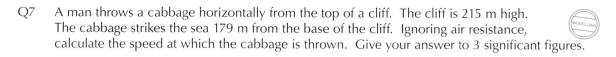

Q8 An object is fired from a point 4 m directly above flat, horizontal ground. It has initial speed 20 ms^{-1} at an angle of 45° above the horizontal.
For how long is it higher than 11 m above the ground?

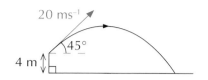

Q9

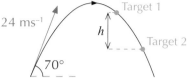

A ball is fired from a machine with speed 24 ms^{-1} at an angle of 70° above the horizontal. The ball passes through a target 3 seconds after being fired, and then passes through a second target 4 seconds after being fired. Find h, the difference in height between the two targets.

Q10 A particle is projected from a point 0.6 m above flat, horizontal ground. Its initial speed is 7.5 ms^{-1} at an angle of α above the horizontal. It reaches a maximum height of 2.8 m above the ground. Find the horizontal distance travelled by the particle in the first 1.2 s of its motion.

Q11 A ball is hit by a bat from a point on flat, horizontal ground.
The ball leaves the ground with speed V ms^{-1}, at an angle of θ above the horizontal, where $\tan \theta = \frac{3}{4}$.
The ball lands a horizontal distance of 50 m away.
Find the value of V.

Q11 Hint: You should be able to find $\sin \theta$ and $\cos \theta$ without a calculator.

Q12 A particle is fired from a point 16 m above flat, horizontal ground.
The particle's initial speed is 3 ms^{-1} at an angle of 7° below the horizontal. Find:

a) the horizontal range of the particle,

b) the speed and direction of the particle when it lands.

Q13

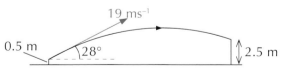

A cricket ball is hit from a point 0.5 m above flat, horizontal ground.
The ball's initial speed is 19 ms^{-1}, at an angle of 28° above the horizontal.
It is caught on its descent by a fielder when it is 2.5 m above the ground. Find:

a) the length of time that the ball is in the air,

b) the fielder's horizontal distance from where the ball was struck,

c) the speed of the ball at the point where it is caught.

Q14 A golf ball is struck by a golf club from a point on flat, horizontal ground.
It leaves the ground at an angle of 40° to the horizontal. 2 seconds after being struck,
the ball is travelling upwards at an angle of 10° to the horizontal. Find:

a) the ball's speed of projection,

b) the height of the ball above the ground 2 seconds after being struck by the golf club.

Q15 A body is projected from a point on flat, horizontal ground with speed U ms^{-1}
at an angle θ above the horizontal. Show that:

a) the body reaches a maximum height of $\dfrac{U^2 \sin^2 \theta}{2g}$ metres above the ground,

b) the body reaches its maximum height $\dfrac{U \sin \theta}{g}$ seconds after it is projected.

Q16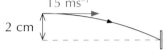

A dart is thrown horizontally towards a dartboard with speed 15 ms^{-1}.
It hits the dartboard 2 cm vertically below the level at which it was thrown.

a) Find the horizontal distance from the point the dart is released to the dartboard.

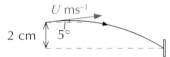

A second dart is thrown from the same point, but at an angle of 5° above the horizontal.
It hits the dartboard at the same point as the first dart.

b) Find U, the speed that the second dart is thrown at.

Q17 A projectile is moving relative to the x- and y-coordinate axes.
The projectile is fired from the origin with speed 3 ms^{-1}, at an angle α above the x-axis.
The projectile moves freely under gravity and passes through the point $(3, 1)$ m.
Show that: $1 = 3 \tan \alpha - \dfrac{g}{2 \cos^2 \alpha}$

Q18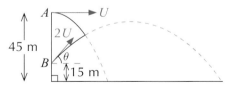

Particle A is projected horizontally from a point 45 m above ground level. At the same time,
particle B is projected at an angle θ above the horizontal, from a point 15 m above ground level,
directly below the point of projection of particle A.
The particles collide 2 seconds after they are projected.
Given that the speed of projection of B is twice the speed of projection of A, find:

a) the value of θ,

b) the speed of projection of each of the two particles.

i and j vectors

You can describe projectile motion using **vectors** expressed in terms of **i** and **j**. **i** and **j** are a pair of perpendicular vectors, each of **magnitude one unit**, directed **horizontally** and **vertically** respectively.

This isn't really all that different from any of the stuff from the last few pages — the **i**-component of the vector describes the **horizontal** motion of the projectile, and the **j**-component of the vector describes the **vertical** motion of the projectile.

When you're using **i** and **j** vectors to describe projectile motion, you can either consider horizontal and vertical motion **separately**, as before, or you can deal with both components in one go using the *suvat* equations in **vector form**:

$$\mathbf{v} = \mathbf{u} + \mathbf{a}t \qquad\qquad \mathbf{s} = \mathbf{u}t + \frac{1}{2}\mathbf{a}t^2$$

$$\mathbf{s} = \frac{1}{2}(\mathbf{u} + \mathbf{v})t \qquad\qquad \mathbf{s} = \mathbf{v}t - \frac{1}{2}\mathbf{a}t^2$$

Tip: $v^2 = u^2 + 2as$ doesn't have a vector equivalent, as you can't really square a vector.

If you're using the *suvat* equations in vector form, then acceleration due to gravity will be $\mathbf{a} = -g\mathbf{j}$ ($= -9.8\mathbf{j}$ ms^{-2}). It has no horizontal component as acceleration due to gravity always acts vertically downwards.

Example 1

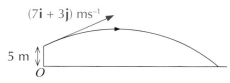

$(7\mathbf{i} + 3\mathbf{j})$ ms^{-1}

5 m

O

A particle is projected from the point 5j m, relative to a fixed origin O. The particle's initial velocity is $(7\mathbf{i} + 3\mathbf{j})$ ms^{-1}, and it moves freely under gravity.

a) Find the position vector of the particle 0.8 seconds after it is projected.

   1. Write down the *suvat* values:

        $\mathbf{s} = \mathbf{s}, \quad \mathbf{u} = (7\mathbf{i} + 3\mathbf{j}), \quad \mathbf{a} = -9.8\mathbf{j}, \quad t = 0.8$

   2. Use $\mathbf{s} = \mathbf{u}t + \frac{1}{2}\mathbf{a}t^2$ to find the particle's displacement from the point of projection 0.8 seconds after it is projected:

        $\mathbf{s} = 0.8(7\mathbf{i} + 3\mathbf{j}) - \frac{1}{2} \times (9.8\mathbf{j}) \times 0.8^2$

        $= 5.6\mathbf{i} + 2.4\mathbf{j} - 3.136\mathbf{j}$

        $= (5.6\mathbf{i} - 0.736\mathbf{j})$ m

   3. Add this to the particle's initial position vector to find its new position vector:

        $5\mathbf{j} + 5.6\mathbf{i} - 0.736\mathbf{j} = (5.6\mathbf{i} + 4.264\mathbf{j})$ m

b) Find the velocity of the particle at this time.

   Use $\mathbf{v} = \mathbf{u} + \mathbf{a}t$:

        $\mathbf{v} = (7\mathbf{i} + 3\mathbf{j}) + 0.8(-9.8\mathbf{j})$

        $= 7\mathbf{i} + 3\mathbf{j} - 7.84\mathbf{j}$

        $= (7\mathbf{i} - 4.84\mathbf{j})$ ms^{-1}

Example 2

A stone is launched from a point 1.2 metres vertically above the point O, which is on flat, horizontal ground. The stone is launched with velocity $\begin{pmatrix} 2q \\ q \end{pmatrix}$ ms⁻¹, where q is a constant. It travels freely under gravity for 4 seconds, before landing on the ground.

a) **Find the value of q and hence the initial speed of the stone.**

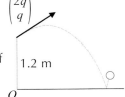

1. An initial velocity of $\begin{pmatrix} 2q \\ q \end{pmatrix}$ ms⁻¹ means that the horizontal component of velocity is $2q$ ms⁻¹ and the vertical component is q ms⁻¹. Use column vectors in the *suvat* equations just as you would use **i** and **j** vectors.

2. Resolve vertically, taking up as positive, then use $s = ut + \frac{1}{2}at^2$.

$$s = -1.2, \quad u = q, \quad a = -9.8, \quad t = 4$$

$$-1.2 = 4q + (-4.9 \times 4^2) \implies 4q = 77.2$$

$$\implies q = \boxed{19.3}$$

So the stone's initial velocity is $\begin{pmatrix} 38.6 \\ 19.3 \end{pmatrix}$ ms⁻¹.

3. Now you can find its initial speed using Pythagoras' theorem:

$$\text{speed} = \sqrt{38.6^2 + 19.3^2} = \boxed{43.2 \text{ ms⁻¹ (3 s.f.)}}$$

b) **Find the horizontal range of the stone.**

Resolve horizontally, taking right as positive, then use $s = ut + \frac{1}{2}at^2$.

$$s = s, \quad u = 38.6, \quad a = 0, \quad t = 4$$

$$s = 38.6 \times 4 = \boxed{154.4 \text{ m}}$$

c) **Find the position vector of the stone relative to O when it is at its highest point.**

1. First consider only the vertical motion to find the time taken for the stone to reach its maximum height.

Resolve vertically, taking up as positive: $\quad u = 19.3, \quad v = 0, \quad a = -9.8, \quad t = t$

Using $v = u + at$:

$$0 = 19.3 - 9.8t \implies t = 1.969... \text{ seconds}$$

2. Now find the stone's displacement from its starting point when it reaches its highest point. Consider the horizontal and vertical components of motion together using the *suvat* equations in column vector form:

$$\mathbf{s} = \mathbf{s}, \quad \mathbf{u} = \begin{pmatrix} 38.6 \\ 19.3 \end{pmatrix}, \quad \mathbf{a} = \begin{pmatrix} 0 \\ -9.8 \end{pmatrix}, \quad t = 1.969...$$

Using $\mathbf{s} = \mathbf{u}t + \frac{1}{2}\mathbf{a}t^2$:

Tip: You could just find the stone's horizontal and vertical displacements separately, then write it in vector form at the end.

$$\mathbf{s} = (1.969...) \times \begin{pmatrix} 38.6 \\ 19.3 \end{pmatrix} + \frac{1}{2} \times (1.969...^2) \times \begin{pmatrix} 0 \\ -9.8 \end{pmatrix}$$

$$\mathbf{s} = \begin{pmatrix} 76.01... \\ 38.00... \end{pmatrix} + \begin{pmatrix} 0 \\ -19.00... \end{pmatrix} = \begin{pmatrix} 76.01... \\ 19.00... \end{pmatrix} \text{ m}$$

3. Add **s** to the stone's initial position vector to find its new position vector:

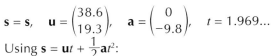

$$\begin{pmatrix} 0 \\ 1.2 \end{pmatrix} + \begin{pmatrix} 76.01... \\ 19.00... \end{pmatrix} = \begin{pmatrix} 76.01... \\ 20.20... \end{pmatrix} = \boxed{\begin{pmatrix} 76.0 \\ 20.2 \end{pmatrix} \text{ m (3 s.f.)}}$$

Not all constant acceleration problems involve gravity — you can use the *suvat* equations whenever you're told to assume that acceleration is constant.

Example 3

An ice hockey puck is modelled as a particle moving with constant acceleration, a, across a horizontal surface. It is projected across the surface at a point (0.4i + 1.6j) m from the origin at time $t = 0$ with velocity (0.5i – 1.2j) ms⁻¹. It comes to rest after 4 seconds.

MODELLING

a) **Find the acceleration of the puck.**

   1. Write down the *suvat* values as usual: $\mathbf{u} = 0.5\mathbf{i} - 1.2\mathbf{j}$, $\mathbf{v} = 0$, $\mathbf{a} = \mathbf{a}$, $t = 4$

   2. Using $\mathbf{v} = \mathbf{u} + \mathbf{a}t$: $0 = 0.5\mathbf{i} - 1.2\mathbf{j} + 4\mathbf{a}$

                                $\Rightarrow$ $\mathbf{a} = (-0.125\mathbf{i} + 0.3\mathbf{j})$ ms⁻²

b) **Find the position vector, r, at the point that the puck comes to rest.**

   1. First find the displacement, **s**: $\mathbf{s} = \mathbf{s}$, $\mathbf{u} = 0.5\mathbf{i} - 1.2\mathbf{j}$, $\mathbf{v} = 0$, $t = 4$

                               Using $\mathbf{s} = \frac{1}{2}(\mathbf{u} + \mathbf{v})t$:

                               $\mathbf{s} = \frac{1}{2}(0.5\mathbf{i} - 1.2\mathbf{j} + 0) \times 4$

                               $\mathbf{s} = (\mathbf{i} - 2.4\mathbf{j})$ m

   2. Add this displacement to the initial position vector to find **r**: $\mathbf{r} = 0.4\mathbf{i} + 1.6\mathbf{j} + \mathbf{i} - 2.4\mathbf{j} = (1.4\mathbf{i} - 0.8\mathbf{j})$ m

---

Exercise 4.1.3

Q1 A particle is projected from a point on flat, horizontal ground with velocity (12i + 16j) ms⁻¹. Find the particle's velocity:

   a) 2 seconds after projection,

   b) when it reaches its maximum height,

   c) when it hits the ground.

> **Hint:** Again, you might find it useful to draw diagrams for these questions.

Q2 A projectile is fired from a height of 5 m directly above a fixed point O, which is on flat, horizontal ground. The particle's initial velocity is $\begin{pmatrix} 17 \\ 10 \end{pmatrix}$ ms⁻¹. Find:

   a) the particle's maximum height above the ground,

   b) the speed of the particle as it hits the ground,

   c) the direction of motion of the particle when it hits the ground.

Q3 A stone is thrown with velocity (6i + 9j) ms⁻¹ from a window 2.5 m vertically above flat, horizontal ground. It is thrown towards a target on the ground, a horizontal distance of 20 m from the window. Find:

   a) the length of time that the stone is at least 6 m above the ground,

   b) the distance by which the stone falls short of the target.

Q4   A golf ball is hit off the edge of a 40 m high vertical cliff with velocity $(a\mathbf{i} + b\mathbf{j})$ ms^{-1}, where a and b are constants. It takes 5 seconds to land on the ground below, level with the foot of the cliff, a horizontal distance of 200 m away. Find:

a) the values of a and b,

b) the velocity of the golf ball when it hits the ground.

Q5

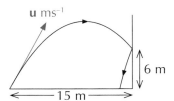

A football is kicked from a point on flat, horizontal ground towards a vertical wall, a horizontal distance of 15 m away. The ball's initial velocity is $\mathbf{u}$ ms^{-1}.
The ball hits the wall 6 m above the ground, 3 seconds after being kicked.

Find, as vectors in $\mathbf{i} + \mathbf{j}$ notation:

a) the initial velocity of the ball,

b) the velocity of the ball as it hits the wall.

The ball rebounds from the wall and lands on the ground. As a result of the impact with the wall, the horizontal component of the ball's velocity is reversed and halved in magnitude. The vertical component of its velocity is unaffected by the impact.

c) Find the horizontal distance between the wall
      and the point on the ground where the ball lands.

d) Suggest how the model you have used could be improved.

Q6   A model submarine is moving underwater at a constant depth, with an initial velocity at time $t = 0$ of $(-0.6\mathbf{i} + 3\mathbf{j})$ ms^{-1}, where the $\mathbf{i}$ direction is due east and the $\mathbf{j}$ direction due north. The toy is modelled as a particle moving with a constant acceleration of $(0.1\mathbf{i} + 0.5\mathbf{j})$ ms^{-2}.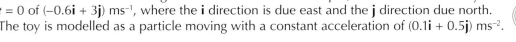

a) At what value of t will the model submarine be moving due north?

b) Find the approximate bearing on which the submarine is moving at $t = 2.5$ s.

c) Find the distance of the model submarine from its starting point after 20 seconds.

d) Suggest two adaptations that would allow the model to
      better represent the movement of an object underwater.

Q7   A particle moves across a horizontal surface with a constant, non-zero acceleration of $(p\mathbf{i} + q\mathbf{j})$ ms^{-2}, where the $\mathbf{i}$ direction is due east and the $\mathbf{j}$ direction due north. At $t = 0$, the particle is moving north-west with a speed of 5 ms^{-1}. After 10 seconds, it is moving due south with a speed of $\sqrt{2}$ ms^{-1}.

Find p and q, in simplified surd form.

4.2 Non-Uniform Acceleration in 2 Dimensions

The constant acceleration equations can only be used where acceleration in a particular direction isn't changing. In real life, the forces acting on objects change as a result of motion, so acceleration will vary.

Learning Objectives (Spec Ref 7.4):

- Differentiate and integrate vectors with respect to time.
- Find a body's position vector, velocity or acceleration at a particular time given an expression for one of the other vectors.

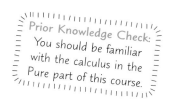
Prior Knowledge Check:
You should be familiar with the calculus in the Pure part of this course.

Using vectors

For a body moving in **two dimensions** (i.e. in a **plane**), you can describe its **position**, **velocity** and **acceleration** using the **unit vectors i** and **j**. The **i**-component describes the body's **horizontal** motion, and the **j**-component usually describes the body's **vertical** motion.

You've already seen how to use the *suvat* equations in vector form on pages 63-65, but if the body is moving with **variable acceleration**, you'll have to use **calculus** instead.

The relationships between **displacement** (or **position**), **velocity** and **acceleration** are shown below. This should be familiar from Year 1, where you used these relationships for motion in one dimension.

Tip: In two dimensions, questions will usually refer to a body's position vector. This is just the vector describing the body's displacement from the origin.

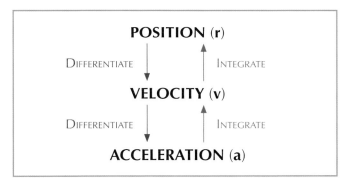

To differentiate or integrate vectors written in **i** and **j** notation, just differentiate or integrate each component **separately**:

Tip: The shorthand for $\frac{d\mathbf{r}}{dt}$ is $\dot{\mathbf{r}}$ (the single dot means differentiate r once with respect to time). The shorthand for $\frac{d^2\mathbf{r}}{dt^2}$ is $\ddot{\mathbf{r}}$ (the double dots mean differentiate r twice with respect to time).

Differentiating Vectors

If $\mathbf{r} = x\mathbf{i} + y\mathbf{j}$ is the position vector of a body, then:

the body's velocity, $\mathbf{v} = \dfrac{d\mathbf{r}}{dt} = \dfrac{dx}{dt}\mathbf{i} + \dfrac{dy}{dt}\mathbf{j}$

and the body's acceleration, $\mathbf{a} = \dfrac{d\mathbf{v}}{dt} = \dfrac{d^2\mathbf{r}}{dt^2}$

$\qquad\qquad = \dfrac{d^2x}{dt^2}\mathbf{i} + \dfrac{d^2y}{dt^2}\mathbf{j}$

Integrating Vectors

If $\mathbf{a} = p\mathbf{i} + q\mathbf{j}$ is the acceleration of a body, then:

the body's velocity, $\mathbf{v} = \int \mathbf{a}\, dt = \int (p\mathbf{i} + q\mathbf{j})\, dt$

$$= \left(\int p\, dt \right)\mathbf{i} + \left(\int q\, dt \right)\mathbf{j}$$

If $\mathbf{v} = w\mathbf{i} + z\mathbf{j}$ is the velocity of a body, then:

the body's position vector, $\mathbf{r} = \int \mathbf{v}\, dt = \int (w\mathbf{i} + z\mathbf{j})\, dt$

$$= \left(\int w\, dt \right)\mathbf{i} + \left(\int z\, dt \right)\mathbf{j}$$

Tip: When you're integrating, you'll still need to add a constant of integration, **C**, but it will be a vector with **i** and **j** components.

Example 1

A particle is moving in a plane. At time t seconds, its position in the plane is given by $\mathbf{r} = [(t^2 - 1)\mathbf{i} + (2 + 5t)\mathbf{j}]$ m relative to a fixed origin O.

Find the particle's speed and direction of motion at time $t = 7.5$ seconds.

1. Differentiate the expression for the particle's position vector to find its velocity. Remember to treat the **i** and **j** components separately:

   $\mathbf{v} = \dfrac{d\mathbf{r}}{dt} = \left[\dfrac{d}{dt}(t^2 - 1) \right]\mathbf{i} + \left[\dfrac{d}{dt}(2 + 5t) \right]\mathbf{j}$

   $\mathbf{v} = [2t\mathbf{i} + 5\mathbf{j}]$ ms^{-1}

2. Substitute $t = 7.5$ into this expression:

   $\mathbf{v} = 2(7.5)\mathbf{i} + 5\mathbf{j} = (15\mathbf{i} + 5\mathbf{j})$ m

3. Use the **i** and **j** components to draw a right-angled triangle:

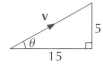

4. Now use Pythagoras' theorem to find the particle's speed, and trigonometry to find its direction of motion:

   speed $= |\mathbf{v}| = \sqrt{15^2 + 5^2} = $ 15.8 ms^{-1} (3 s.f.)

   $\theta = \tan^{-1}\left(\dfrac{5}{15} \right)$

   $=$ 18.4° (3 s.f.) from the **i**-direction

Example 2

A particle moves in a vertical plane. At time t seconds it has velocity $v = [(8 + 2t)\mathbf{i} + (t^3 - 6t)\mathbf{j}]$ ms^{-1}. When $t = 2$, the particle has position vector $(10\mathbf{i} + 3\mathbf{j})$ m with respect to a fixed origin O.

a) **Find the acceleration of the particle at time t.**

   Differentiate the expression for velocity with respect to time:

   $\mathbf{a} = \dfrac{d\mathbf{v}}{dt} = \left[\dfrac{d}{dt}(8 + 2t) \right]\mathbf{i} + \left[\dfrac{d}{dt}(t^3 - 6t) \right]\mathbf{j}$

   $\mathbf{a} = [2\mathbf{i} + (3t^2 - 6)\mathbf{j}]$ ms^{-2}

b) Show that the position vector of the particle when $t = 4$ is r = (38i + 27j) m.

1. Integrate the expression for velocity with respect to time:

$$\mathbf{r} = \int \mathbf{v}\, dt = \left(\int (8 + 2t)\,dt\right)\mathbf{i} + \left(\int (t^3 - 6t)\,dt\right)\mathbf{j}$$

$$= (8t + t^2)\mathbf{i} + \left(\frac{t^4}{4} - 3t^2\right)\mathbf{j} + \mathbf{C}$$

2. When $t = 2$, $\mathbf{r} = (10\mathbf{i} + 3\mathbf{j})$. Use these values to find **C**:

$$10\mathbf{i} + 3\mathbf{j} = (8(2) + 2^2)\mathbf{i} + \left(\frac{2^4}{4} - 3(2)^2\right)\mathbf{j} + \mathbf{C}$$

$$10\mathbf{i} + 3\mathbf{j} = 20\mathbf{i} - 8\mathbf{j} + \mathbf{C}$$

> **Tip:** Remember that **C** is a vector, so you need to collect **i** and **j** terms, and add or subtract to simplify.

$$\Rightarrow \quad \mathbf{C} = (10 - 20)\mathbf{i} + (3 - -8)\mathbf{j} = -10\mathbf{i} + 11\mathbf{j}$$

$$\Rightarrow \quad \mathbf{r} = \left[(8t + t^2 - 10)\mathbf{i} + \left(\frac{t^4}{4} - 3t^2 + 11\right)\mathbf{j}\right] m$$

3. Substitute $t = 4$ into the equation:

$$\mathbf{r} = (8(4) + 4^2 - 10)\mathbf{i} + \left(\frac{4^4}{4} - 3(4)^2 + 11\right)\mathbf{j}$$

$$= (32 + 16 - 10)\mathbf{i} + (64 - 48 + 11)\mathbf{j}$$

$$= (38\mathbf{i} + 27\mathbf{j}) \text{ m} \quad \text{— as required.}$$

c) Find the value of t for which the particle is directly above O.

1. When the particle is directly above O, the **i**-component of its position vector will be zero:

$$8t + t^2 - 10 = 0$$

2. Solve for t using the quadratic formula:

$$t = \frac{-8 \pm \sqrt{8^2 - (4 \times 1 \times -10)}}{2}$$

Ignore — t can't be negative

$$\Rightarrow t = 1.099... \quad \text{or} \quad t = -9.099...$$

3. Check that the **j**-component of **r** is greater than zero for $t = 1.099...$ This is to make sure that the particle is **above** O (rather than at it or below it).

$$\frac{(1.099...)^4}{4} - 3(1.099...)^2 + 11 = 7.741... > 0$$

So the particle is directly above O when $t = 1.10$ s (3 s.f.)

Example 3

A body is moving on a plane. At time t seconds, the body's acceleration is given by a = [(4 − 18t)i + 72tj] ms⁻², relative to a fixed origin O. When $t = 1$, the body has position vector r = 2i m, relative to O. When $t = 2$, the body is moving with velocity v = (−20i + 135j) ms⁻¹.

Find the body's position vector when it is moving parallel to i.

1. First, integrate the expression for acceleration with respect to time to find an expression for velocity:

$$\mathbf{v} = \int \mathbf{a}\, dt = \left(\int (4 - 18t)\,dt\right)\mathbf{i} + \left(\int 72t\, dt\right)\mathbf{j}$$

$$\mathbf{v} = (4t - 9t^2)\mathbf{i} + 36t^2\mathbf{j} + \mathbf{C}$$

2. When $t = 2$, $\mathbf{v} = -20\mathbf{i} + 135\mathbf{j}$.
   Use these values to find $\mathbf{C}$:

   $-20\mathbf{i} + 135\mathbf{j} = (4(2) - 9(2)^2)\mathbf{i} + 36(2)^2\mathbf{j} + \mathbf{C}$

   $-20\mathbf{i} + 135\mathbf{j} = -28\mathbf{i} + 144\mathbf{j} + \mathbf{C}$

   $\Rightarrow \quad \mathbf{C} = 8\mathbf{i} - 9\mathbf{j}$

3. So the particle's velocity at time t is:

   $\mathbf{v} = [(4t - 9t^2 + 8)\mathbf{i} + (36t^2 - 9)\mathbf{j}]$ ms^{-1}

4. Find the time when the particle is moving parallel to $\mathbf{i}$ by setting the $\mathbf{j}$-component of $\mathbf{v}$ equal to zero.

   $36t^2 - 9 = 0$ — As always, ignore the negative value of t.

   $t^2 = 9 \div 36 = 0.25 \Rightarrow t = 0.5$ seconds

5. Plug this time into the $\mathbf{i}$ component of $\mathbf{v}$ to check this component is positive.

   $4(0.5) - 9(0.5)^2 + 8 = 7.75 > 0$

   Tip: If the $\mathbf{i}$ component of velocity is zero for this value of t, then the particle will be stationary. If the $\mathbf{i}$ component is negative, the particle will move parallel to $\mathbf{i}$, but in the opposite direction.

6. So the particle is moving parallel to $\mathbf{i}$ at time $t = 0.5$ seconds.
   Now integrate the expression for velocity to find an expression for the particle's position vector:

   $\mathbf{r} = \int \mathbf{v}\, dt = \left(\int (4t - 9t^2 + 8)\, dt\right)\mathbf{i} + \left(\int (36t^2 - 9)\, dt\right)\mathbf{j}$

   $= (2t^2 - 3t^3 + 8t)\mathbf{i} + (12t^3 - 9t)\mathbf{j} + \mathbf{D}$

7. When $t = 1$, $\mathbf{r} = 2\mathbf{i}$.
   Use these values to find $\mathbf{D}$:

   $2\mathbf{i} = (2(1)^2 - 3(1)^3 + 8(1))\mathbf{i} + (12(1)^3 - 9(1))\mathbf{j} + \mathbf{D}$

   $2\mathbf{i} = 7\mathbf{i} + 3\mathbf{j} + \mathbf{D} \Rightarrow \mathbf{D} = -5\mathbf{i} - 3\mathbf{j}$

8. So the particle's position vector relative to O at time t is given by:

   $\mathbf{r} = [(2t^2 - 3t^3 + 8t - 5)\mathbf{i} + (12t^3 - 9t - 3)\mathbf{j}]$ m

9. Substitute $t = 0.5$ into this equation to find the particle's position vector when it is travelling parallel to $\mathbf{i}$.

   $\mathbf{r} = (2(0.5)^2 - 3(0.5)^3 + 8(0.5) - 5)\mathbf{i}$
   $\qquad + (12(0.5)^3 - 9(0.5) - 3)\mathbf{j}$

   $\mathbf{r} = (-0.875\mathbf{i} - 6\mathbf{j})$ m

Example 4

A boat is modelled as a particle moving across a horizontal surface with acceleration $\mathbf{a} = (e^{0.2t}\mathbf{i} + \sin t\, \mathbf{j})$ ms^{-2} at time t seconds (for $0 \le t \le 5$). At time $t = 0$, the boat is at $2\mathbf{j}$ m from the origin, moving in the positive $\mathbf{j}$ direction at a speed of 10 ms^{-1}.
Find an expression for the boat's position vector, r, at time t.

1. Integrate the expression for acceleration with respect to time to find an expression for velocity:

   $\mathbf{v} = \int \mathbf{a}\, dt = \left(\int e^{0.2t}\, dt\right)\mathbf{i} + \left(\int \sin t\, dt\right)\mathbf{j}$

   $= \left(\frac{e^{0.2t}}{0.2}\right)\mathbf{i} - (\cos t)\mathbf{j} + \mathbf{C} = 5e^{0.2t}\mathbf{i} - (\cos t)\mathbf{j} + \mathbf{C}$

   Tip: You'll be expected to know how to differentiate and integrate any of the types of expressions that were covered in the Pure part of this course — any calculus that comes up there can also come up in Mechanics.

2. When $t = 0$, $\mathbf{v} = 0\mathbf{i} + 10\mathbf{j}$.
   Use this information to find $\mathbf{C}$, and hence $\mathbf{v}$:

$$0\mathbf{i} + 10\mathbf{j} = 5e^0\,\mathbf{i} - (\cos 0)\mathbf{j} + \mathbf{C}$$
$$0\mathbf{i} + 10\mathbf{j} = 5\mathbf{i} - 1\mathbf{j} + \mathbf{C}$$
$$\Rightarrow \quad \mathbf{C} = -5\mathbf{i} + 11\mathbf{j}$$
$$\Rightarrow \quad \mathbf{v} = (5e^{0.2t} - 5)\mathbf{i} + (-\cos t + 11)\mathbf{j}$$
$$\Rightarrow \quad \mathbf{v} = 5(e^{0.2t} - 1)\mathbf{i} + (11 - \cos t)\mathbf{j}$$

3. Integrate again to find an expression for the position vector $\mathbf{r}$ at time t:

$$\mathbf{r} = \int \mathbf{v}\,dt = \left(\int 5(e^{0.2t} - 1)dt\right)\mathbf{i} + \left(\int (11 - \cos t)dt\right)\mathbf{j}$$
$$= 5\left(\frac{e^{0.2t}}{0.2} - t\right)\mathbf{i} + (11t - \sin t)\mathbf{j} + \mathbf{D}$$
$$= 5(5e^{0.2t} - t)\mathbf{i} + (11t - \sin t)\mathbf{j} + \mathbf{D}$$

4. When $t = 0$, the boat is at $\mathbf{r} = 2\mathbf{j}$.
   Use this information to find $\mathbf{D}$, and hence $\mathbf{r}$:

$$0\mathbf{i} + 2\mathbf{j} = 5(5e^0 - 0)\mathbf{i} + (0 - \sin 0)\mathbf{j} + \mathbf{D}$$
$$0\mathbf{i} + 2\mathbf{j} = 25\mathbf{i} - 0\mathbf{j} + \mathbf{D}$$
$$\Rightarrow \quad \mathbf{D} = -25\mathbf{i} + 2\mathbf{j}$$
$$\Rightarrow \quad \mathbf{r} = (5(5e^{0.2t} - t) - 25)\mathbf{i} + (11t - \sin t + 2)\mathbf{j}$$
$$\Rightarrow \quad \mathbf{r} = 5(5e^{0.2t} - t - 5)\mathbf{i} + (2 + 11t - \sin t)\mathbf{j}$$

Example 5

A particle's acceleration is connected to its velocity, $\mathbf{v} = x\mathbf{i} + y\mathbf{j}$, such that $\dfrac{dx}{dt} = \dfrac{9}{x^2}$ and $\dfrac{dy}{dt} = \dfrac{2}{y}$.
The particle is stationary at $t = 0$. Given that $x \geq 0$ and $y \geq 0$,
show that the velocity vector, $\mathbf{v}$, at time t, is given by $\mathbf{v} = 3t^{\frac{1}{3}}\mathbf{i} + 2t^{\frac{1}{2}}\mathbf{j}$.

(PROBLEM SOLVING)

The question gives each component of acceleration as a differential equation.
Solve these separately and then combine to give $\mathbf{v}$ in terms of t.

1. Solve the $\mathbf{i}$ equation first:

$$\frac{dx}{dt} = \frac{9}{x^2} \quad \Rightarrow \quad \int x^2\,dx = \int 9\,dt \quad \Rightarrow \quad \frac{x^3}{3} = 9t + C$$
$x = 0$ when $t = 0$, so $C = 0$ and $\dfrac{x^3}{3} = 9t$

2. Rearrange to get x in terms of t:

$$x = \sqrt[3]{27t} = 3\sqrt[3]{t} = 3t^{\frac{1}{3}}$$

3. Now solve the $\mathbf{j}$ equation:

$$\frac{dy}{dt} = \frac{2}{y} \quad \Rightarrow \quad \int y\,dy = \int 2\,dt \quad \Rightarrow \quad \frac{y^2}{2} = 2t + D$$
$y = 0$ when $t = 0$, so $D = 0$ and $\dfrac{y^2}{2} = 2t$

4. Rearrange to get y in terms of t:

$$y = \sqrt{4t} = 2\sqrt{t} = 2t^{\frac{1}{2}} \quad \longleftarrow \quad y \geq 0, \text{ so ignore the negative root here}$$

5. Substitute the expressions for x and y into $\mathbf{v} = x\mathbf{i} + y\mathbf{j}$:

$$\mathbf{v} = 3t^{\frac{1}{3}}\mathbf{i} + 2t^{\frac{1}{2}}\mathbf{j} \quad \text{as required}$$

Q1 A particle is moving in a plane. At time t seconds, the particle's position relative to a fixed origin O is given by $\mathbf{r} = [(t^3 - 3t)\mathbf{i} + (t^2 + 2)\mathbf{j}]$ m. Find:

   a) (i) an expression for the particle's velocity in terms of t,

   (ii) the particle's speed and direction of motion at time $t = 3$ s,

   b) (i) an expression for the particle's acceleration in terms of t,

   (ii) the magnitude of the particle's acceleration at time $t = 4$ s.

Q2 A particle is moving in a vertical plane so that at time t seconds it has velocity $\mathbf{v}$ ms^{-1}, where $\mathbf{v} = (2 + 4t^2)\mathbf{i} + (t - 3)\mathbf{j}$. Find the acceleration of the particle at time $t = 8$ s.

Q3 A car is modelled as a particle travelling in a plane. Its velocity at time t seconds is given by the expression:

$\mathbf{v} = [(\frac{1}{3}t^3 + 2t^2 - 12t)\mathbf{i} + 14\mathbf{j}]$ ms^{-1}, where $0 \le t \le 4$.

At a certain time, the car reaches its maximum velocity when the acceleration falls to zero. Find the car's velocity at this time.

Q4 A body moving in a plane has acceleration $\mathbf{a} = \begin{pmatrix} 3e^{3t} \\ 6 \\ \sqrt{t} \end{pmatrix}$ ms^{-2} at time t seconds.

At $t = 0$, the body has position vector $\mathbf{r} = \begin{pmatrix} 2 \\ -9 \end{pmatrix}$ m relative to a fixed origin O, and is travelling at $\begin{pmatrix} 4 \\ 6 \end{pmatrix}$ ms^{-1}. Find:

Q4 Hint: Column vectors are just another way of showing the horizontal and vertical components: $\begin{pmatrix} a \\ b \end{pmatrix} = a\mathbf{i} + b\mathbf{j}$.

   a) a column vector expression for the body's velocity in terms of t,

   b) the body's position vector, as a column vector, in terms of t.

Q5 An object is travelling in a plane with non-uniform acceleration. At time t seconds, the particle's position relative to a fixed origin O is given by $\mathbf{r} = [(\sin t)\mathbf{i} + (\cos t)\mathbf{j}]$ m.
$\mathbf{i}$ and $\mathbf{j}$ are the unit vectors directed due east and due north respectively.

   a) What is the first non-zero value of t for which the object is moving in an easterly direction?

   b) Describe the object's position and distance from O at this time.

Q5 Hint: Remember that you need to work in radians when differentiating and integrating trig functions.

Q6 A particle is moving in a vertical plane so that at time t seconds it has velocity $\mathbf{v}$ ms^{-1}, where $\mathbf{v} = (3 - 6t)\mathbf{i} + (t^2 + 2t)\mathbf{j}$. When $t = 2$, the particle has position vector $(-2\mathbf{i} + 7\mathbf{j})$ m with respect to a fixed origin O.

   a) Find the acceleration of the particle at time $t = 5$ s.

   b) Find the value of t for which the particle is directly above O.

Q7 A particle is moving in a plane. At time t seconds, the particle's acceleration is given by $\mathbf{a} = [(2t - 1)\mathbf{i} + (t^2 + t)\mathbf{j}]$ ms^{-2}. When $t = 3$ s, the particle has velocity $7(\mathbf{i} + 2\mathbf{j})$ ms^{-1}. Find:

   a) an expression for the particle's velocity in terms of t,

   b) the particle's speed and direction of motion at time $t = 5$ s.

Q8 The velocity of a particle at time t seconds $(t \geq 0)$ is given by $\mathbf{v} = [(t^2 - 6t)\mathbf{i} + (4t + 5)\mathbf{j}]$ ms^{-1}. The particle is moving in a plane, and at time $t = 0$ the particle passes through the origin, O. The particle passes through the point with position vector $(b\mathbf{i} + 12\mathbf{j})$ m, where b is a constant. Find the value of b.

Q9 The velocity of a particle at time t seconds $(t \geq 0)$ is given by $\mathbf{v} = [-\mathbf{i} + (8t + 2)\mathbf{j}]$ ms^{-1}. The particle's displacement at $t = 1$ s is $\mathbf{r} = (4\mathbf{i} + 12\mathbf{j})$ m.

a) Find the particle's displacement $\mathbf{r}$ at time t.

b) Show that the Cartesian equation representing the particle's path is $y = 4x^2 - 42x + 116$.

Q10 Particle A is moving in a vertical plane. At time t seconds, the particle's position relative to a fixed origin O is given by $\mathbf{r}_A = [(t^3 - t^2 - 4t + 3)\mathbf{i} + (t^3 - 2t^2 + 3t - 7)\mathbf{j}]$ m. Find:

a) the value of t for which the particle's velocity is $(-3\mathbf{i} + 2\mathbf{j})$ ms^{-1},

b) the value of t for which the direction of motion of the particle is 45° above $\mathbf{i}$.

> **Q10b) Hint:** Think about the relationship between the horizontal and vertical components of the particle's velocity when it is moving in this direction.

A second particle, B, is moving in the same plane as particle A. At time t seconds, the acceleration of B is $\mathbf{a}_B = (6t\mathbf{i} + 6t\mathbf{j})$ ms^{-2}. At time $t = 1$ second, B passes the point $(2\mathbf{i} + 3\mathbf{j})$ m relative to O, with velocity $(4\mathbf{i} - \mathbf{j})$ ms^{-1}. Find:

c) an expression for the position vector of particle B relative to O in terms of t,

d) an expression for the position vector of particle B relative to particle A in terms of t,

e) the distance between particles A and B at time $t = 4$ seconds.

Q11 A particle moves so that it traces a curve C, as defined by the parametric equations $y = \ln t$ and $x = \dfrac{1}{t^3}$. x and y represent the displacement of the particle from the origin in the $\mathbf{i}$ and $\mathbf{j}$ directions respectively, at time t seconds.

> **Q11 Hint:** To differentiate parametric equations, use $\dfrac{dy}{dx} = \dfrac{dy}{dt} \div \dfrac{dx}{dt}$.

a) Find the gradient of C, $\dfrac{dy}{dx}$, when $t = \dfrac{1}{2}$.

b) Show that the acceleration of the particle at this time is $384\mathbf{i} - 4\mathbf{j}$.

Q12 The velocity of a particle at time t seconds is given by $\mathbf{v} = [(2 \sin^2 t)\mathbf{i} + (4 \sin 2t \cos 2t)\mathbf{j}]$ ms^{-1}. At time $t = \dfrac{\pi}{4}$, the particle has position vector $\mathbf{r} = \left[\dfrac{\pi}{4}\mathbf{i} + \mathbf{j}\right]$ m, relative to the origin.

What was the particle's initial distance from the origin at time $t = 0$?

> **Q12 Hint:** Trig identities will help here.

Q13 A particle is moving with a velocity of $\mathbf{v} = [m\mathbf{i} + n\mathbf{j}]$ ms^{-1}. It has a constant acceleration of 0.1 ms^{-2} in the $\mathbf{i}$ direction, and a variable acceleration in the $\mathbf{j}$ direction, such that $\dfrac{dn}{dt} = (kn - 10)$ ms^{-2} and $\dfrac{dn}{dt} < 0$ (k is a constant).

The particle is stationary at $t = 0$, and when its acceleration is -2 ms^{-2} in the $\mathbf{j}$ direction, its velocity in the $\mathbf{j}$ direction is -4 ms^{-1}.

a) Show that $n + 5 > 0$.

b) Hence show that the velocity of the particle can be expressed as $\mathbf{v} = [0.1t\mathbf{i} + 5(e^{-2t} - 1)\mathbf{j}]$ ms^{-1}.

Review Exercise

Q1 A golf ball is hit with a golf club from a point on flat, horizontal ground. The ball lands 4 seconds after it is hit. Given that the ball leaves the club with a speed of 22 ms^{-1}, at an angle of α to the horizontal, find α.

Q2 A rifle fires a bullet horizontally at 120 ms^{-1}. The bullet hits a target a horizontal distance of 60 m from the end of the rifle. Find the vertical distance, d, between the target and the rifle.

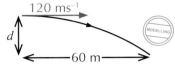

Q3 A projectile is fired from a point 0.3 m above flat, horizontal ground. The projectile's initial speed is 6.5 ms^{-1}, at an angle of 29° above the horizontal. Find:

a) the horizontal range of the projectile, b) the speed of the projectile when it lands.

Q4 A javelin is thrown from a height of 1.5 m above flat horizontal ground at an angle of 38° to the horizontal. It reaches a maximum height of 12.5 m.

a) Calculate the javelin's initial velocity in ms^{-1} to 1 d.p.

b) Calculate the horizontal distance travelled by the javelin to the nearest metre.

Q5 A body is projected from a point on flat, horizontal ground with velocity $(2\mathbf{i} + 11\mathbf{j})$ ms^{-1}. Find:

a) the velocity of the body 0.8 seconds after projection,

b) the time of flight of the body, c) the maximum height reached by the body.

Q6 A ball is projected from the top of a building of height 10 m with velocity $(20\mathbf{i} - 4\mathbf{j})$ ms^{-1}. The ball is aimed towards a target on flat, horizontal ground, 21 m from the foot of the building. The ball overshoots, and lands beyond the target. Find:

a) the time taken for the ball to land on the ground,

b) the horizontal distance by which the ball overshoots the target,

c) the speed of the ball when it is vertically above the target.

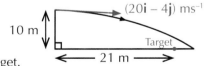

Q7 At time $t = 0$, a particle sets off from rest at the origin, O, and moves in a plane with velocity $\mathbf{v} = (4t\mathbf{i} + t^2\mathbf{j})$ ms^{-1}, where t is the time in seconds. Find:

a) the particle's acceleration at time t, b) the particle's position vector at time t.

Q8 A buggy is modelled as a particle moving across a horizontal surface with acceleration $\mathbf{a} = (e^{0.75t}\,\mathbf{i} + \cos t\,\mathbf{j})$ ms^{-2} at time t seconds (for $0 \le t \le 5$). At time $t = 0$, the buggy is moving in the positive $\mathbf{i}$ direction at a speed of 17 ms^{-1}. Find an expression for the buggy's velocity vector $\mathbf{v}$ at time t.

Q9 A body is moving in a plane with acceleration $\mathbf{a} = -10\mathbf{j}$ ms^{-2} relative to a fixed origin, O. The body's initial velocity is $(15\mathbf{i} + 12\mathbf{j})$ ms^{-1}. At time $t = 1$ second, the body passes through the point with position vector $(15\mathbf{i} + 16\mathbf{j})$ m. Given that $\mathbf{i}$ and $\mathbf{j}$ are unit vectors directed due east and due north respectively, find:

a) an expression for the body's velocity at time t seconds,

b) an expression for the body's position vector at time t seconds,

c) the body's velocity when it is due east of O.

Q1   A football is kicked along the ground with initial velocity $(7.2\mathbf{i} + 3.2\mathbf{j})$ ms^{-1} from the point O. At time $t = 2$ seconds, the ball is travelling with velocity $(2.7\mathbf{i} + 1.2\mathbf{j})$ ms^{-1}. By modelling the ball as a particle with constant acceleration, and assuming that the model is valid until the ball stops moving, find:

a) the acceleration of the ball,

[3 marks]

b) an expression for the displacement, $\mathbf{s}$, of the ball from O in terms of t,

[3 marks]

c) the maximum time and distance the ball can travel.

[4 marks]

At the point when the ball is kicked, a defender starts running so that she has position vector $\mathbf{s} = [4.05t\mathbf{i} + (xt - 1.4)\mathbf{j}]$ m relative to O at time $t > 0$.

d) Given that the defender intercepts the ball, find the value of x.

[4 marks]

Q2   A pebble falls into a lake 3.6 m deep and sinks such that the acceleration at time t seconds is proportional to the velocity at that time. The velocity on initial impact is 3.6 ms^{-1} and after 3 seconds it has velocity 0.2 ms^{-1}.

a) Show that its velocity is $v = A\mathrm{e}^{kt}$ where A and k are constants to be found.

[4 marks]

b) Find an expression for the distance travelled by the pebble.

[3 marks]

c) Explain why this model is only valid when $t < 3.43$ (3 s.f.).

[2 marks]

Q3   Particle P moves in a plane with velocity $\mathbf{v} = [(6t^2 - 3t + 2)\mathbf{i} + (4t^2 - 6)\mathbf{j}]$ ms^{-1} after t seconds.

a) Find the acceleration of P after t seconds.

[2 marks]

b) Find the distance travelled in the 3rd second.

[4 marks]

c) Find the velocity when the particle is travelling parallel to $2\mathbf{i} + \mathbf{j}$.

[4 marks]

Q4   A particle moves in a plane such that, relative to a fixed point O, it has position vector $\mathbf{s} = [7\cos t\,\mathbf{i} + 6\sin t\,\mathbf{j}]$ metres at time t seconds.

a) Find the initial position and velocity of the particle.

[3 marks]

b) Show that $6 \leq v \leq 7$, where v is the speed of the particle at time t, and state the times when the maximum speed is achieved.

[4 marks]

Exam-Style Questions

Q5   A tennis ball is hit underarm at velocity U ms^{-1}, at a horizontal distance of 12 m from the 1.07 m high net, at an angle of elevation of θ and initial height above the ground of 0.5 m.

    a) Given that the highest point of the ball is <u>2 m</u> above the ground, show that the initial vertical velocity is $\sqrt{29.4}$ ms^{-1}.

[2 marks]

    b) The ball just clears the net on the way down. By modelling the ball as a particle, find the values of θ and U.

[6 marks]

Q6   A child is playing with a yo-yo with a string of length 0.8 m.
It spins out of the child's hand horizontally at a velocity of 1.2 ms^{-1} from a height of 1.1 m.

    a) Find the time taken for the string to become taut.

[5 marks]

    b) Give one limitation of this model, and explain why it is especially important in this case.

[2 marks]

Q7   At time t seconds, $0 \leq t \leq 2\pi$, an ant moves on a plane so that its velocity $\mathbf{v}$ cms^{-1} is given by:
$$\mathbf{v} = 2t\sin t\,\mathbf{i} + 3\cos t\,\mathbf{j}$$
The ant is initially at the point with position $(5\mathbf{i} - 2\mathbf{j})$ cm with respect to its nest.

    a) Find the ant's acceleration at time $t = \frac{\pi}{2}$.

[3 marks]

    b) Show that, in the given interval, the ant will not return to its nest.

[6 marks]

Q8   A group of children are playing pooh-sticks from a bridge. A stick is thrown into the water from a point on the upstream side of the bridge with position vector $2.2\mathbf{j}$ m above the surface of the water. The stick is thrown with velocity $(4p\mathbf{i} + p\mathbf{j})$ ms^{-1} relative to the surface of the water, where $\mathbf{i}$ is the unit vector parallel to the stream's flow, and p is a constant. After t seconds, the stick passes through a point R with position vector $(2p\mathbf{i} + 1.375\mathbf{j})$ m before hitting the stream at point S.

By modelling the stick as a particle moving freely under gravity and the stream as a horizontal plane:

    a) Find the time the stick takes to reach R.

[2 marks]

    b) Find the velocity of the stick at point R.

[5 marks]

    c) Find the time taken for the stick to hit the stream.

[2 marks]

Given that the flow of the stream has velocity $-1.2\mathbf{i}$ ms^{-1} and the width of the bridge is 1 m:

    d) How long after being thrown will the stick emerge on the other side of the bridge?

[4 marks]

5.1 Resolving Forces

Dynamics can get more complicated when you have different forces acting at different angles. You'll often need to use trigonometry to resolve the forces into their horizontal and vertical components.

Learning Objectives (Spec Ref 8.2, 8.4 & 8.5):
- Resolve force vectors into horizontal and vertical components.
- Calculate the resultant force and solve problems for objects in equilibrium.

Prior Knowledge Check:
Be familiar with **i-j** vectors from Year 1 of the Pure part of the course and resultant forces from Year 1 of the Applied part of the course.

Components of forces

You've already seen resolving vectors on page 52, so some of this should be familiar.

A **component of a force** is the **magnitude** of the force in a **particular direction**. You can use trigonometry to **resolve** forces and find their components in a particular direction.

Often it's very useful to resolve forces into their **horizontal** and **vertical** components — together with the force vector, these components form a **right-angled triangle**.

You can find the horizontal and vertical components of a force, F, using **trigonometry**.

Horizontal component, F_x:

$\cos \theta = \dfrac{\text{adjacent}}{\text{hypotenuse}} = \dfrac{F_x}{F}$, so $\boldsymbol{F_x = F \cos \theta}$

Vertical component, F_y:

$\sin \theta = \dfrac{\text{opposite}}{\text{hypotenuse}} = \dfrac{F_y}{F}$, so $\boldsymbol{F_y = F \sin \theta}$

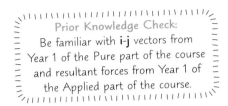

Example 1

A particle is acted on by a force of 15 N at 30° above the positive horizontal. Find the horizontal and vertical components of the force.

1. Draw a vector triangle.

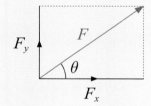

2. Use trigonometry to calculate the horizontal and vertical components:

Horizontal component = 15 cos 30°

= 13.0 N (3 s.f.) to the right

Vertical component = 15 sin 30°

= 7.5 N upwards

If you're resolving in a direction which is **perpendicular** to the line of action of a force, then the component of the force in that direction will be **zero**. For example, a force which acts horizontally has zero vertical component, and vice versa.

When you're resolving a force, you should state which direction you're taking as being positive (you can draw an arrow to show this, as in Example 2). Then any components acting in the **opposite direction** will be **negative**.

Example 2

Find the i and j components of the force shown on the right.

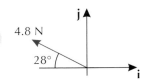

1. Resolving in the **i**-direction (→): $-4.8 \cos 28° = -4.24$ N (to 3 s.f.)

2. Resolving in the **j**-direction (↑): $4.8 \sin 28° = 2.25$ N (to 3 s.f.)

You can resolve forces in **any two perpendicular directions**, not just horizontally and vertically. For example, for an object on an **inclined plane**, you might want to resolve the forces in directions **parallel** and **perpendicular** to the plane.

Example 3

The diagram shows a particle at rest on a smooth inclined plane. A force of magnitude 4 N acts on the particle at an angle of 10° to the horizontal. Find the components of the force that act parallel and perpendicular to the plane.

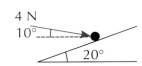

1. Use the alternate angles theorem to find the angle between the direction of the force and the slope of the plane. $20° + 10° = 30°$

2. Resolving parallel to the plane (↗): $F_{parallel} = 4 \cos 30°$
   $= 3.46$ N (to 3 s.f.)

3. Resolving perpendicular to the plane (↖): $F_{perpendicular} = -4 \sin 30°$
   $= -2$ N

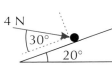

Exercise 5.1.1

Q1 Find the horizontal and vertical components of each of the forces shown:

a)
6.5 N

b)
4 N

c)
20 N
40°

d)
17 N
25°

e)
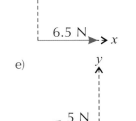
5 N
10°

f)
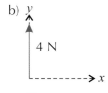
30°
3 N

g)
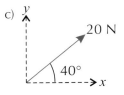
60°
13 N

h)
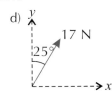
45°
11 N

Q2 Each of the following diagrams shows a force and the angle it makes with the horizontal or vertical. Write each force in the form $(a\mathbf{i} + b\mathbf{j})$ N.

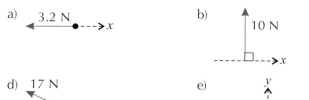
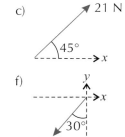

Q3 The force $(c\mathbf{i} + 7\mathbf{j})$ N acts at 25° to $\mathbf{i}$, where c is a positive constant.

a) Find the value of c.   b) Find the magnitude of this force.

Q4 A horizontal force of 17 N acts on a particle at rest on a plane inclined at 14° to the horizontal. Find the components of this force that are parallel and perpendicular to the slope.

Q5 A block lies on a horizontal surface, and is acted on by a force of 65 N at an angle of 17° below the horizontal. Find the horizontal and vertical components of the force.

Q6 A particle lies at rest on an inclined plane. A force of magnitude 20 N acts on the particle at an angle of 22° to the plane, as shown. The vertical component of the force is 10 N.

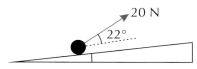

Find the angle between the plane and the horizontal.

Q7 The diagram shows a force of magnitude 10 N acting on an object on an inclined plane. The component of the force in the direction parallel to the plane is 7.1 N.

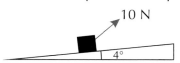

a) Find the angle between the direction of the force and the incline of the plane.

b) Find the horizontal component of the force.

Resultant forces and equilibrium

In Year 1, you learned about **resultant forces** and what it means for an object to be in **equilibrium**:

- The resultant force is the sum of all the forces acting on an object. You can calculate the resultant force by **adding the corresponding components** of the forces.

- An object is in equilibrium if the resultant force on it is **zero**.

You will often have to resolve one or more forces to find the resultant force on an object, or use the fact that it is in equilibrium to find a missing force.

Example 1

The diagram on the right shows a force of 15 N and a horizontal force of 20 N applied to a particle. Find the magnitude and direction of the resultant force on the particle.

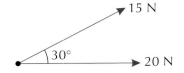

1. Resolve to find the horizontal and vertical components of the 15 N force.

   Horizontal component = 15 cos 30° = 12.99... N
   Vertical component = 15 sin 30° = 7.5 N

2. Find the horizontal and vertical components of the resultant force.

   Horizontal component = 20 + 12.99... = 32.99... N
   Vertical component = 7.5 N

3. Use Pythagoras' theorem to find the magnitude of the force.

   $R^2 = (20 + 12.99...)^2 + (7.5)^2$
   $R = \sqrt{32.99...^2 + 7.5^2}$
   = 33.8 N (to 3 s.f.)

   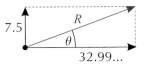

4. Use trigonometry to find its direction, θ:

   $\tan \theta = \dfrac{7.5}{32.99...}$

   $\Rightarrow \theta = \tan^{-1}\left(\dfrac{7.5}{32.99...}\right)$

   = 12.8° (3 s.f.) above the horizontal

Example 2

Three forces of magnitude 9 N, 12 N and 13 N act on a particle P in the directions shown in the diagram on the right. Find the magnitude and direction of the resultant of the three forces.

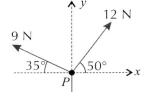

1. Resolving in the y-direction (↑):

   9 sin 35° + 12 sin 50° − 13 = 1.354...
   = 1.35 N (3 s.f.)

2. Resolving in the x-direction (→):

   12 cos 50° − 9 cos 35° = 0.3410...
   = 0.341 N (3 s.f.)

3. Use the components to form a right-angled triangle.

   The resultant is shown by the hypotenuse: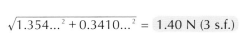

   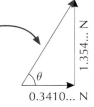

4. Use Pythagoras' theorem to find the magnitude:

   $\sqrt{1.354...^2 + 0.3410...^2}$ = 1.40 N (3 s.f.)

5. Use trigonometry to find the required direction:

   $\theta = \tan^{-1}\left(\dfrac{1.354...}{0.3410...}\right)$

   = 75.9° (3 s.f.) above the positive x-axis

Example 3

The diagram shows all the forces acting on a particle. Given that the particle is in equilibrium, find the magnitudes of the missing forces P and Q.

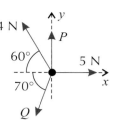

The particle is in equilibrium, so the resultant force on the particle is zero. This means that each component of the resultant force must also be zero.

1. Resolving in the x-direction ($\rightarrow$):

$$5 - Q \cos 70° - 4 \cos 60° = 0$$
$$\Rightarrow Q \cos 70° = 5 - 4 \cos 60° = 3$$
$$\Rightarrow Q = \frac{3}{\cos 70°} = \boxed{8.77 \text{ N (3 s.f.)}}$$

2. Resolving in the y-direction ($\uparrow$):

$$P + 4 \sin 60° - Q \sin 70° = 0$$
$$\Rightarrow P = \frac{3}{\cos 70°} \sin 70° - 4 \sin 60° = \boxed{4.78 \text{ N (3 s.f.)}}$$

Example 4

The diagram on the right shows the forces acting on particle P. Find the magnitude of force F, given that the resultant force on the particle acts in the negative x-direction.

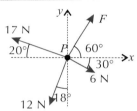

You're told that the resultant force acts in the x-direction — this means that the vertical component of the resultant must be zero.

1. Resolving in the y-direction ($\uparrow$):

$$F \sin 60° + 17 \sin 20° - 12 \cos 18° - 6 \sin 30° = 0$$

2. Rearrange and solve this equation to find the magnitude of F:

$$F = \frac{-17 \sin 20° + 12 \cos 18° + 6 \sin 30°}{\sin 60°} = \boxed{9.93 \text{ N (3 s.f.)}}$$

Exercise 5.1.2

Q1   Each of the diagrams below shows the forces acting on a particle. Find the magnitude and direction (measured from the positive x-axis) of the resultant force on each particle.

a)
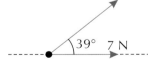

b)
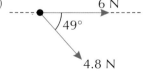

c)
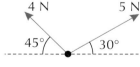

d)
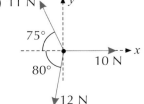

e)
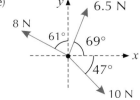

f)
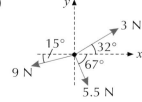

Q2   A force of magnitude 18 N acts on a particle at 60° above the positive horizontal.
     A force of magnitude 16 N also acts vertically upwards on the particle.

     a) Draw a diagram to illustrate the forces acting on the particle.

     b) Find the magnitude and direction of the resultant of the two forces.

Q3   The diagram below shows all the forces acting on a particle in equilibrium.

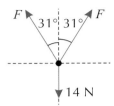

     Find the magnitude of the force F.

Q4   The diagrams below show all the forces acting on a particle in equilibrium.
     Find the magnitude of the missing forces acting on each particle.

a)   b)   c)

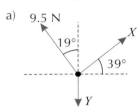   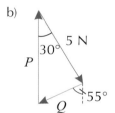   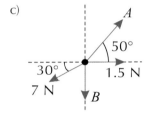

d)   e)   f)

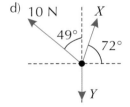   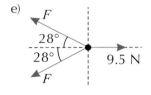   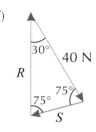

Q5   A particle is acted on by a force of magnitude 9 N in the positive horizontal direction
     and a force of magnitude 10 N at 30° above the positive horizontal. A third force of
     magnitude P N acts on the particle at 60° above the positive horizontal. Find P,
     given that the resultant of the three forces acts at 45° above the positive horizontal.

Q6   Forces of magnitude 1 N and 2 N act at angles of 10°
     and 35° above **i** respectively. A third force of magnitude
     3 N acts at an angle of θ above **i**, where $180° \leq \theta \leq 360°$.
     The resultant of the three forces has no horizontal component.

     a) Find θ.

     b) Calculate the magnitude of the resultant of the three forces.

> **Q6 Hint:** Be careful —
> make sure the angle you
> calculate is in the range
> given for θ. Remember
> $\cos \theta = \cos(360° - \theta)$.

Q7   Forces of magnitude P N and $2P$ N act on a particle vertically upwards and horizontally, as shown. A third force of 20 N acts at an angle θ to the downward vertical. No other forces act on the particle. Given that the particle is in equilibrium, find the values of P and θ.

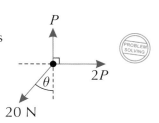

Harder equilibrium problems

You can use everything from the last few pages to answer questions about all sorts of **real-life situations**. Objects hanging from **strings** and objects on **inclined planes** are some common examples of where you might see forces in equilibrium.

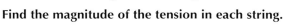

Example 1

The diagram shows a body of mass 8 kg held in equilibrium by two light, inextensible strings. One string is horizontal, and the other string makes an angle of 30° with the vertical.

Find the magnitude of the tension in each string.

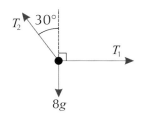

The components in each direction must sum to zero because the body is in equilibrium. The 8g force acting downwards is the body's weight, and T_1 and T_2 are the tensions in the two strings.

1.   Resolving vertically ($\uparrow$):

    Tip: Remember to use $g = 9.8$ ms^{-2} unless you're told otherwise.

$T_2 \cos 30° - 8g = 0$

$T_2 \cos 30° = 8g$

$T_2 = 8g \div \cos 30° = 90.528... = $ 90.5 N (to 3 s.f.)

2.   Resolving horizontally ($\rightarrow$):

$T_1 - T_2 \sin 30° = 0$

$T_1 = T_2 \sin 30° = 90.528... \times \sin 30°$
$\qquad = 45.264... = $ 45.3 N (to 3 s.f.)

Inclined planes

When you're resolving forces on an object that is on an **inclined plane**, it's usually best to resolve **parallel** and **perpendicular to the slope**.

Mostly, you'll be resolving an object's **weight**, because weight always acts **vertically downwards**, and you'll need to use its **components parallel** and **perpendicular to the slope**.

These are:

•   Component of weight **parallel** to the plane: $mg \sin \theta$

•   Component of weight **perpendicular** to the plane: $mg \cos \theta$

where mg is the weight of the object and θ is the angle of the incline of the slope.

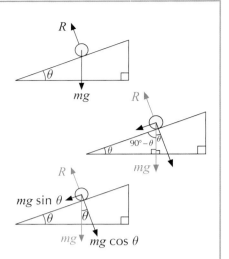

Resolving an Object's Weight

- You want to find the **components** of an object's weight **parallel** and **perpendicular** to the plane.

- Using **right-angled triangles**, the angle between the object's weight and its component perpendicular to the plane is equal to θ.

- You can **resolve** as usual to find the components of the weight using **trigonometry**.

- You may have to resolve **other forces** as well as the weight, depending on their **direction**.

Example 2

A stone of mass 0.1 kg rests on a smooth plane inclined at 20° to the horizontal. It is held in equilibrium by a force, F, acting parallel to the plane, as shown. Find the magnitude of force F and the normal reaction, R, of the plane on the stone.

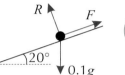

1. Resolving parallel to the plane ($\nearrow$):

   $F - 0.1g \sin 20° = 0$

   $F = 0.98 \sin 20° = \boxed{0.335 \text{ N (to 3 s.f.)}}$

2. Resolving perpendicular to the plane ($\nwarrow$):

   $R - 0.1g \cos 20° = 0$

   $R = 0.98 \cos 20° = \boxed{0.921 \text{ N (to 3 s.f.)}}$

Example 3

Two brothers are fighting over a sledge of weight 100 N. The sledge lies on a smooth slope inclined at an angle of 35° to the horizontal.

One brother tries to pull the sledge up the slope with a force of magnitude 70 N, while the other tries to pull the sledge down the slope with a force of magnitude F.

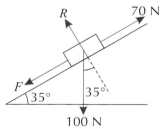

a) **Find the magnitude of the normal reaction force, R, on the sledge.**

   Resolving perpendicular to the plane ($\nwarrow$): $R - 100 \cos 35° = 0$

   $\Rightarrow R = 100 \cos 35° = \boxed{81.9 \text{ N (to 3 s.f.)}}$

b) **The sledge remains stationary. Find the magnitude of the force F.**

   Resolving parallel to the plane ($\nearrow$): $70 - F - 100 \sin 35° = 0$

   $\Rightarrow F = 70 - 100 \sin 35° = \boxed{12.6 \text{ N (to 3 s.f.)}}$

Example 4

A rock of mass 9 kg rests on a smooth plane inclined at 35° to the horizontal. The rock is held in equilibrium by a horizontal force of magnitude 10 N directed towards the plane and the tension in a string parallel to the plane.

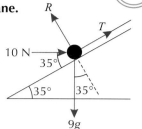

a) **Find the normal reaction force, *R*, between the plane and rock.**

1. Draw a diagram showing all of the forces acting on the rock — find the angle between the 10 N force and the slope of the plane using alternate angles.

2. Resolve perpendicular to the plane ($\nwarrow$): $R - 10 \sin 35° - 9g \cos 35° = 0$

$$R = 10 \sin 35° + 9g \cos 35° = \boxed{78.0 \text{ N (3 s.f.)}}$$

b) **Find the magnitude of the tension in the string.**

Resolve parallel to the plane ($\nearrow$): $T + 10 \cos 35° - 9g \sin 35° = 0$

$$T = 9g \sin 35° - 10 \cos 35° = \boxed{42.4 \text{ N (3 s.f.)}}$$

Example 5

The diagram shows a block of mass 30 kg at rest on a smooth plane inclined at an angle α to the horizontal. The block is held in equilibrium by a force of 147 N, acting at an angle of 60° to the plane, as shown.

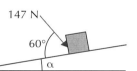

a) **Show that sin α = 0.25.**

1. Draw a diagram showing all of the forces acting on the block:

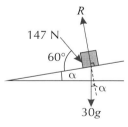

2. Resolving parallel to the plane ($\nearrow$): $147 \cos 60° - 30g \sin \alpha = 0$

$(30 \times 9.8) \sin \alpha = 147 \times 0.5$

$\Rightarrow \sin \alpha = 73.5 \div 294 = \boxed{0.25}$ as required

b) **Find the normal reaction, *R*, of the plane on the block.**

1. First you need to find the value of α: $\alpha = \sin^{-1}(0.25) = 14.4775...°$

2. Now resolving perpendicular to the plane ($\nwarrow$): $R - 147 \sin 60° - 30g \cos \alpha = 0$

$R = 147 \sin 60° + 30g \cos(14.4775...°)$
$= \boxed{412 \text{ N (to 3 s.f.)}}$

Q1 Each of the diagrams below shows a particle held in equilibrium by two light, inextensible strings. In each case, find the magnitude of the missing tension, *T*, and the mass of the particle, *m*.

a)

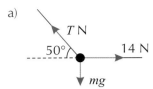

b)

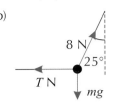

c)

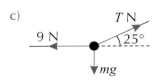

d)

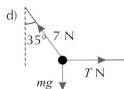

Q2 The diagram below shows a particle suspended from two light, inextensible strings. The particle is in equilibrium. Find the weight of the particle, *W*, and the angle *x*.

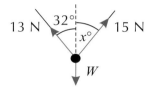

Q3 A particle of weight 10 N rests on a smooth inclined plane. The plane is inclined at an angle *x*° to the horizontal. A force of magnitude 8 N acting along the line of greatest slope of the plane holds the particle in equilibrium.

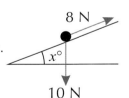

a) Calculate the size of the angle *x*.

b) Calculate the magnitude of the normal reaction force exerted by the plane on the particle.

Q4 A particle rests on a smooth plane inclined at 45° to the horizontal. A force acting up the plane, parallel to the slope, holds the particle in equilibrium. The magnitude of the normal reaction force exerted by the plane on the particle is 25 N.

Q4 Hint: Use the fact that cos 45° = sin 45°.

a) Find the magnitude of the force which holds the particle at rest.

b) Find the mass of the particle.

Q5 A smooth wire is threaded through a bead of mass *m* kg and inclined at an angle of 60° to the horizontal. The bead is held at rest by a force of magnitude 4.2 N acting parallel to the wire.

a) Find the mass of the bead.

b) Find the magnitude of the normal reaction from the wire on the bead.

Q6 A particle with a mass of 5 kg rests on a smooth plane inclined at 10° to the horizontal, as shown in the diagram below. The particle is held in place by a light, inextensible string inclined at an angle of 30° to the plane.

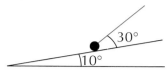

a) Calculate the magnitude of the tension in the string.

b) Calculate the magnitude of the normal reaction of the plane on the particle.

Q7 The diagram below shows a 2 kg block held at rest on a smooth inclined plane by a horizontal force of 14.7 N. The plane is inclined at an angle of θ to the horizontal.

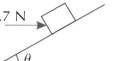

Show that tan θ = 0.75.

Q8 A particle of mass m is held at rest on a smooth plane inclined at 12° to the horizontal by a light, inextensible string. The string is inclined at 45° to the horizontal. The magnitude of the normal reaction force from the plane on the particle is 15 N. Find:

a) the magnitude of the tension, T, in the string,

b) the mass, m, of the particle in kg.

Q9 A particle, Q, of mass m kg, rests on a smooth plane which makes an angle of 60° to the vertical. It is held in equilibrium by a light, inextensible string angled at 10° to the plane, as shown. The magnitude of the tension in the string is 70 N.

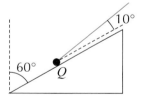

Find the mass of Q and the normal reaction of the plane on Q.

Q10 A brick of mass 2 kg is at rest on a smooth plane inclined at an angle θ to the horizontal. The brick is held in equilibrium by a force of 18 N acting at an angle of 30° to the plane.

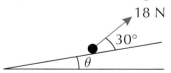

a) Find the size of the angle θ.

b) Find the magnitude of the normal reaction, R, from the plane on the brick.

Q11 A particle is held in equilibrium on a smooth plane by a light, inextensible string. The plane is inclined at 50° to the horizontal and the string is inclined at 70° to the horizontal. The tension in the string has magnitude 5 N. A force, F, also acts on the particle, down the plane, parallel to the slope. Given that the magnitude of the normal reaction of the plane on the particle is four times the magnitude of F, find the weight of the particle.

5.2 Friction

If a body is in contact with a rough surface, and there is a force acting that could cause the body to move, then friction will act between the body and the surface to try to prevent motion.

Learning Objectives (Spec Ref 8.6):
- Understand and use the relationship $F \leq \mu R$.
- Understand the term 'limiting friction'.
- Use the formula for limiting friction to solve problems for a body in equilibrium.

Friction

If an object is in contact with a **rough** surface, then **friction** can act to try to **prevent it moving**. Friction will **only** act if there is a **force** acting on the object which could cause it to **move** along the surface.

There will only be friction if the surface is **rough**. If the surface is **smooth**, no frictional force will act on the object.

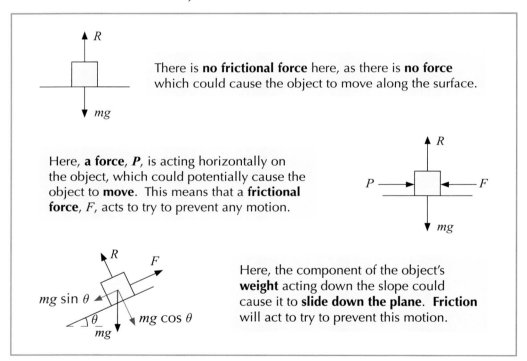

There is **no frictional force** here, as there is **no force** which could cause the object to move along the surface.

Here, **a force**, **P**, is acting horizontally on the object, which could potentially cause the object to **move**. This means that a **frictional force**, *F*, acts to try to prevent any motion.

Here, the component of the object's **weight** acting down the slope could cause it to **slide down the plane**. **Friction** will act to try to prevent this motion.

Friction always acts in the **opposite direction to motion** (or potential motion).

The magnitude of the frictional force can take a **range of possible values** — as the magnitude of the force which is trying to move the object **increases**, the magnitude of the frictional force will **also increase**. The magnitude of the frictional force will only be as big as is necessary to prevent motion. Eventually, the frictional force will reach its **maximum possible value**. At this point, friction is said to be **limiting**.

If the force which is trying to move the object is **greater** than the maximum possible frictional force, the frictional force won't be large enough to prevent motion, and the object will **move**.

The maximum possible magnitude of the frictional force depends on the **coefficient of friction**, μ, between the surface and the object.

μ is a **number greater than or equal to 0**, and is a measure of the effect of friction between the object and the surface — the higher the number, the greater the effect of friction.

The frictional force, F, acting on an object is given by: $\boxed{\boldsymbol{F \leq \mu R}}$

where R is the **normal reaction** of the surface on the object.

When the object starts to **move**, or is on the point of moving (i.e. friction is **limiting**), the frictional force takes its **maximum value**: $\boxed{\boldsymbol{F_{max} = \mu R}}$

An object which is on the point of moving is said to be in '**limiting equilibrium**'.

Example 1

A horizontal force, P, acts on a particle of mass 12 kg, which is at rest on a rough horizontal plane.

Find the range of values that the frictional force, F, can take, given that the coefficient of friction between the particle and the plane is 0.4.

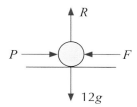

1. Resolving the forces vertically ($\uparrow$): $R - 12g = 0$
                                              $\Rightarrow R = 12g$

2. Using the formula $F \leq \mu R$: $F \leq 0.4 \times 12g$
                                             $\boxed{F \leq 47.04 \text{ N}}$

So in the example above, F can take any value up to 47.04 N, depending on the magnitude of P. If $P \leq 47.04$ N, the particle will remain at rest (and will be on the point of moving if $P = 47.04$ N). If $P > 47.04$ N, then the particle will move and F will remain constant at 47.04 N.

Example 2

A horizontal force of 30 N acts on a 4 kg block which is at rest on a rough horizontal plane.

Given that the block is on the point of moving, find the coefficient of friction between the block and the plane.

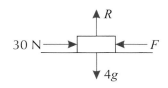

1. Resolving horizontally ($\leftarrow$): $F - 30 = 0 \Rightarrow F = 30$ N

2. Resolving vertically ($\uparrow$): $R - 4g = 0 \Rightarrow R = 4g$

3. The block is on the point of moving, so friction is limiting: $F = \mu R$
                                        $30 = \mu \times 4g$

      Tip: μ is usually given correct to 2 decimal places. $\mu = 30 \div 4g = \boxed{0.77 \text{ (to 2 d.p.)}}$

Example 3

A box of mass 10 kg is on the point of slipping across a rough horizontal plane. A force, Q, acts on the box at an angle of 10° to the horizontal, as shown.

Given that the coefficient of friction between the box and the plane is 0.7, find the magnitude of the normal reaction force from the plane and the magnitude of Q.

1. Draw a diagram to show all the forces acting on the box:

   Tip: F always acts parallel to the surface, no matter what angle other forces act at.

   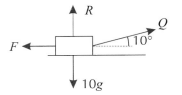

2. Resolving vertically (↑):

   $R + Q \sin 10° = 10g$

   $\Rightarrow Q \sin 10° = 10g - R$ — call this equation ①

3. Resolving horizontally (→):

   $Q \cos 10° = F$

   Tip: The box is on the point of slipping (i.e. in limiting equilibrium), so $F = \mu R$.

   $\Rightarrow Q \cos 10° = \mu R$

   $\Rightarrow Q \cos 10° = 0.7R$ — call this equation ②

4. Dividing equation ① by equation ②:

   $\dfrac{Q \sin 10°}{Q \cos 10°} = \dfrac{10g - R}{0.7R}$

   $\Rightarrow \tan 10° = \dfrac{10g - R}{0.7R}$

   $\Rightarrow 0.7R \tan 10° = 10g - R$

   $\Rightarrow R = \dfrac{10g}{(1 + 0.7 \tan 10°)} = 87.232...$

   $= \boxed{87.2 \text{ N} \ (3 \text{ s.f.})}$

5. Substituting R into equation ②:

   $Q \cos 10° = 0.7 \times 87.232...$

   $\Rightarrow Q = 61.063... \div \cos 10° = \boxed{62.0 \text{ N} \ (3 \text{ s.f.})}$

Example 4

A block of mass 3.2 kg lies at rest on a rough plane inclined at an angle of θ to the horizontal. The block is on the point of sliding. Given that $\mu = 0.75$, find the value of θ.

1. Draw a diagram to show all the forces acting on the block:

   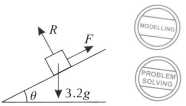

2. Resolving parallel to the plane:

   $F = 3.2g \sin \theta$

3. Resolving perpendicular to the plane:

   $R = 3.2g \cos \theta$

4. The block is on the point of moving, so, using $F = \mu R$:

$$3.2g \sin \theta = 0.75 \times 3.2g \cos \theta$$

$$\frac{3.2g \sin \theta}{3.2g \cos \theta} = 0.75$$

$$\Rightarrow \tan \theta = 0.75$$

$$\Rightarrow \theta = \boxed{36.9°} \text{ (to 3 s.f.)}$$

Make sure you know in which direction the friction is acting. In Example 4, the block is on the point of sliding **down** the slope because of its weight, so friction will act **up** the slope to oppose motion.

Exercise 5.2.1

Q1 A particle of weight W rests on a rough horizontal surface with coefficient of friction μ between them. A horizontal force is applied to the particle such that the particle is on the point of slipping. Find the magnitude of the frictional force, F, on the particle if:

a) $W = 5$ N, $\mu = 0.25$ b) $W = 8$ N, $\mu = 0.3$

c) $W = 15$ N, $\mu = 0.75$ d) $W = 6$ N, $\mu = 0$

e) $W = 17$ N, $\mu = 0.82$ f) $W = 0.5$ N, $\mu = 0.95$

Q2 A particle of weight W is at rest on a rough horizontal surface. A horizontal force P acts on the particle. Given that the particle is on the point of moving, calculate the coefficient of friction if:

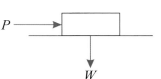

a) $W = 20$ N, $P = 5$ N   b) $W = 15$ N, $P = 8$ N

c) $W = 28$ N, $P = 3.5$ N   d) $W = 13$ N, $P = 6$ N

Q3 A particle of mass 8 kg is at rest on a rough horizontal plane. A horizontal force, P, is applied to the particle. Given that the coefficient of friction between the particle and the plane is 0.45, find the range of possible values for F.

Q4 A brick of mass 3 kg lies at rest on a rough plane, inclined at an angle of θ to the horizontal. The brick is on the point of sliding. Given that $\mu = 0.7$, find the value of θ.

Q5 A sled of mass 8 kg lies at rest on rough horizontal surface. A light, inextensible rope is attached to the sled at an angle of 25° above the horizontal, and the tension in the rope is 38 N. Find the maximum value of μ, to 2 d.p., such that the sled remains at rest.

Q6 A particle of mass 12 kg is placed on a rough horizontal surface. A horizontal force of magnitude 50 N is applied to the particle. The coefficient of friction between the particle and the surface is 0.5.

a) Will the 50 N force cause the particle to move?

b) What is the maximum possible magnitude of force that can be applied horizontally to the particle, such that the particle will remain in equilibrium?

Q7 A pull-along toy of weight 8 N rests on a rough horizontal surface with coefficient of friction $\mu = 0.61$ between the toy and the surface. A light, inextensible string is attached to the toy, at an angle of α to the horizontal, as shown. Find the maximum possible tension in the string given that the toy remains stationary when:

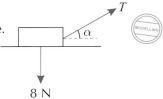

a) $\alpha = 0°$ b) $\alpha = 35°$ 8 N

Q8 A box of mass 2 kg is at rest on a rough plane inclined at an angle of θ to the horizontal. A force of 12 N acts up the plane on the box, which is on the point of moving up the slope.

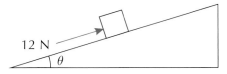

> **Q8 Hint:** To find $\sin \theta$ given $\cos \theta$, draw a right-angled triangle and use trigonometry and Pythagoras' theorem.

Given that $\cos \theta = \dfrac{4}{5}$, find the coefficient of friction between the box and the plane.

Q9 A horizontal wire is threaded through a bead of mass m kg. A force of magnitude 4 N is applied to the bead at an angle of 25° to the horizontal, as shown. The bead is on the point of sliding along the wire. Given that the coefficient of friction between the wire and the bead is 0.15, find:

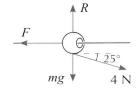

a) the magnitude of R, the normal reaction of the wire on the bead,

b) the value of m.

Q10 A stone of mass 8 kg is at rest on a rough slope inclined at 23° to the horizontal. A force of magnitude 9 N acts on the stone at an angle of 10° to the slope, as shown. Calculate the coefficient of friction, μ, given that the force of 9 N is only just large enough to stop the stone sliding down the slope.

Q11 An object is placed on a rough plane inclined at an angle α to the horizontal. The coefficient of friction between the object and the plane is μ. Show that the object will be at rest on the plane if $\tan \alpha \leq \mu$.

Q12 A sledge of mass 20 kg is at rest on a rough slope inclined at 29° to the horizontal. The coefficient of friction between the slope and the sledge is 0.1. A force, T, acts on the sledge at an angle of 15° to the slope, as shown. Calculate the magnitude of T, given that this force is only just large enough to stop the sledge sliding down the slope.

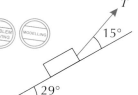

Q13 A wire is threaded through a bead of mass 0.5 kg and inclined at an angle of 10° to the horizontal. The coefficient of friction between the wire and the bead is 0.25. A force of P N is applied to the bead, at an angle of 45° to the wire, as shown.

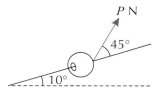

Calculate the magnitude of the normal reaction to the bead, R, given that P is only just large enough to stop the bead sliding down the slope.

5.3 Newton's Laws of Motion

You've seen Newton's three laws before, so there's nothing new here. You need to be able to combine what you learned in Year 1 with what you've seen so far in this chapter.

Learning Objectives (Spec Ref 8.2 & 8.4):
- Use Newton's laws of motion in situations that require resolving forces.
- Solve problems involving friction when a particle is moving.
- Solve problems involving connected particles, friction forces and inclined planes.

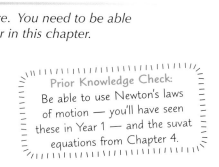

Prior Knowledge Check:
Be able to use Newton's laws of motion — you'll have seen these in Year 1 — and the *suvat* equations from Chapter 4.

Newton's laws of motion

Here's a quick recap of Newton's three laws of motion:

Newton's first law: A body will stay at **rest** or maintain a **constant velocity** unless a **resultant force** acts on the body.

Newton's second law: The **overall resultant force** (F_{net}) acting on a body is equal to the **mass** of the body multiplied by the body's **acceleration**. i.e. $F_{net} = ma$

Newton's third law: For **two bodies**, A and B, the force exerted by A on B is **equal in magnitude** but **opposite in direction** to the force exerted by B on A.

Example 1

A particle of weight 18 N is being pulled along a smooth horizontal surface by a force of 7 N acting at an angle of 25° to the horizontal, as shown. Find the speed of the particle after 3 seconds, given that it starts from rest.

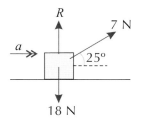

1. Resolve forces horizontally ($\rightarrow$):

$$F_{net} = 7 \cos 25°$$

2. Use Newton's second law to find the acceleration, a:

$$F_{net} = ma$$
$$7 \cos 25° = \frac{18}{g}a$$
$$6.344... = 1.836... \times a$$
$$a = 3.454... \text{ ms}^{-2}$$

Tip: You're told the weight, so use the formula $W = mg$ to find the mass.

3. Use one of the *suvat* equations to find the speed after three seconds:

$$u = 0, \quad v = v, \quad a = 3.454..., \quad t = 3$$

$$v = u + at$$
$$= 0 + 3.454... \times 3$$
$$= \boxed{10.4 \text{ ms}^{-1} \text{ (to 3 s.f.)}}$$

Example 2

Two forces, given by the vectors (12**i** – 4**j**) N and (–3**i** + 16**j**) N, act on a particle of mass 3 kg, causing it to accelerate from rest.

a) **Find the acceleration of the particle as a vector.**

   1. Find the resultant force on the particle:
             $F_{net} = (12\mathbf{i} - 4\mathbf{j}) + (-3\mathbf{i} + 16\mathbf{j}) = 9\mathbf{i} + 12\mathbf{j}$

   2. Using Newton's second law (with vectors) to find acceleration:

$$F_{net} = ma$$
$$9\mathbf{i} + 12\mathbf{j} = 3a$$
$$\Rightarrow a = \boxed{(3\mathbf{i} + 4\mathbf{j})\ ms^{-2}}$$

b) **Find the velocity vector of the particle after 7 seconds.**

   1. List the variables:
             $u = 0 \quad v = v \quad a = 3\mathbf{i} + 4\mathbf{j} \quad t = 7$

   2. Use the equation $v = u + at$:

$$v = u + at$$
$$v = 0 + (3\mathbf{i} + 4\mathbf{j}) \times 7$$
$$= \boxed{(21\mathbf{i} + 28\mathbf{j})\ ms^{-1}}$$

c) **How far does the particle travel in the first 4 seconds?**

   1. Find the magnitude of the acceleration:
             $|a| = \sqrt{3^2 + 4^2} = 5\ ms^{-2}$

   2. List the variables:
             $s = s \quad u = 0 \quad a = 5 \quad t = 4$

   3. Use the equation $s = ut + \frac{1}{2}at^2$:

$$s = ut + \frac{1}{2}at^2$$
$$s = (0 \times 4) + \frac{1}{2} \times 5 \times 4^2 = \boxed{40\ m}$$

> **Tip:** You could solve part c) by finding the displacement as a vector, and then working out its magnitude — you would get the same answer either way.

d) **A third force K is applied to the particle, which now moves with acceleration (7i – 2j) ms⁻². Find the force K in terms of i and j.**

   1. Use Newton's second law to find the new resultant force:

$$F_{net} = ma$$
$$F_{net} = 3(7\mathbf{i} - 2\mathbf{j}) = 21\mathbf{i} - 6\mathbf{j}$$

   2. Subtract the two original forces from F_{net} to find K:

$$(12\mathbf{i} - 4\mathbf{j}) + (-3\mathbf{i} + 16\mathbf{j}) + K = (21\mathbf{i} - 6\mathbf{j})$$
$$K = (21\mathbf{i} - 6\mathbf{j}) - (12\mathbf{i} - 4\mathbf{j}) - (-3\mathbf{i} + 16\mathbf{j})$$
$$= \boxed{(12\mathbf{i} - 18\mathbf{j})\ N}$$

Q1   A particle of mass 4 kg is accelerated from rest across a smooth, horizontal plane by a horizontal force of 20 N. Find the distance travelled by the particle after 2.5 seconds.

Q2   A particle of mass 2 kg is accelerated from rest across a smooth surface by a constant force of $(4\mathbf{i} - 9\mathbf{j})$ N. Calculate the velocity vector of the particle after 3 seconds.

Q3   A particle of mass 3 kg is being accelerated across a horizontal plane by a force of 10 N acting at an angle of 45° to the horizontal, as shown in the diagram below.

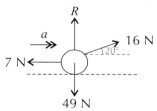

Find the magnitude of:

a) the acceleration of the particle,

b) the normal reaction with the plane.

Q4   A particle of weight 49 N initially at rest on a horizontal plane is acted on by a constant horizontal resistive force of 7 N and a force of 16 N acting at an angle of 20° to the horizontal.

R

a →→

7 N ←   120°   → 16 N

49 N

a) Find the acceleration of the particle.

b) Find the speed of the particle after 7 seconds.

c) Find the magnitude of the normal reaction with the plane.

Q5   A particle of mass 5 kg is acted on by two forces, $(6\mathbf{i} - 10\mathbf{j})$ N and $(4\mathbf{i} + 5\mathbf{j})$ N.

a) Find the magnitude of the acceleration of the particle.

b) A third force, of $(-6\mathbf{i} + 2\mathbf{j})$ N, begins to act on the particle. Describe the effect this has on the magnitude of the acceleration of the particle.

Q6   Three forces are acting on a particle of mass 10 kg.

a) Two of the forces are given by $(6\mathbf{i} - 2\mathbf{j})$ N and $(5\mathbf{i} + 5\mathbf{j})$ N and the resultant force is $(7\mathbf{i} + \mathbf{j})$ N. Find the third force in vector form.

b) Find the particle's velocity vector 8 seconds after it begins accelerating from rest.

c) A fourth force of $(-7\mathbf{i} - \mathbf{j})$ N begins to act on the particle. Describe the effect this has on the particle's motion.

Friction and inclined planes

Inclined planes

For objects on an inclined plane, resolve forces **parallel** and **perpendicular** to the plane, rather than horizontally and vertically. The normal reaction force is always perpendicular to the surface.

Remember that weight always acts **vertically downwards**, so you need to find the **components** of the weight in these directions.

Example 1

A particle of mass 600 g is propelled up the line of greatest slope of a smooth plane inclined at 30° to the horizontal.

Immediately after the propelling force has stopped, the particle has speed 3 ms⁻¹. Find:

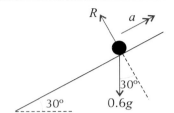

a) **the distance the particle travels before coming instantaneously to rest.**

1. First, resolve parallel to the plane (⤤) to find a:

    > **Tip:** The particle is slowing down, so its acceleration is negative (i.e. it's decelerating).

    $F_{net} = ma$
    $-0.6g \sin 30° = 0.6a$
    $a = -4.9 \text{ ms}^{-2}$

2. Use one of the constant acceleration equations:

    $v^2 = u^2 + 2as$
    $0 = 3^2 + 2(-4.9)s$
    $s = 0.918 \text{ m (3 s.f.)}$

b) **the magnitude of the normal reaction from the plane.**

Now resolve perpendicular to the plane (⤡):
The particle is moving parallel to the plane, so the acceleration perpendicular to the plane is zero.

$F_{net} = ma$
$R - 0.6g \cos 30° = 0.6 \times 0$
$R = 5.09 \text{ N (3 s.f.)}$

Frictional forces

You've already covered friction on pages 88-91, but back then you were only concerned with objects which were being held in **equilibrium**.

When a **moving** object is acted on by a frictional force, friction is **limiting**, and the frictional force (F) is at its maximum value: $F = \mu R$, where μ is the coefficient of friction and R is the normal reaction between the object and the surface.

Friction **opposes** motion, so it will always act in the **opposite direction** to the direction an object is moving in.

You'll need to use Newton's laws and $F = \mu R$ to solve problems involving objects which are accelerating and being acted on by friction.

Example 2

A block of mass 12 kg is being accelerated across a rough, horizontal plane by a force of magnitude 60 N, as shown. Given that the magnitude of the acceleration is 1.5 ms^{-2}, find the coefficient of friction between the block and the plane.

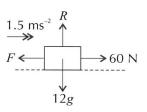

1. Resolve forces horizontally ($\rightarrow$), to find the frictional force, F.

   $F_{net} = ma$

   $60 - F = 12 \times 1.5$

   $F = 42$ N

2. Resolve forces vertically ($\uparrow$) to find the normal reaction, R.

   $F_{net} = ma$

   $R - 12g = 12 \times 0$

   $R = 12g = 117.6$ N

   Tip: Don't get confused between F and F_{net}. F is the frictional force and F_{net} is the overall resultant force.

3. The block is moving, so F takes its maximum possible value.

   $F = \mu R$

   $42 = \mu \times 117.6$

   $\mu = \boxed{0.36 \text{ (2 d.p.)}}$

Example 3

A small body of weight 20 N is released from rest on a rough plane angled at 15° to the horizontal.

Given that the body accelerates down the plane at a rate of 0.44 ms^{-2}, find the coefficient of friction between the body and the plane.

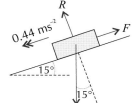

1. Resolve parallel to the plane ($\leftarrow$):

   $F_{net} = ma$

   $20 \sin 15° - F = \dfrac{20}{g} \times 0.44$

   $F = 4.278...$ N

   Tip: The body is accelerating down the plane, so the frictional force acts up the slope.

2. Resolve perpendicular to the plane ($\nwarrow$):

   $F_{net} = ma$

   $R - 20 \cos 15° = \dfrac{20}{g} \times 0$

   $R = 20 \cos 15° = 19.318...$ N

3. The body is sliding, i.e. friction is limiting:

   $F = \mu R$

   $4.278... = \mu \times 19.318...$

   $\mu = \boxed{0.22 \text{ (to 2 d.p.)}}$

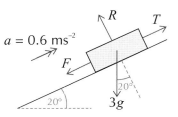

Example 4

A mass of 3 kg is being pulled up a plane inclined at 20° to the horizontal by a rope parallel to the surface. Given that the mass is accelerating at 0.6 ms⁻² and the coefficient of friction between the mass and the plane is 0.4, find T, the tension in the rope.

1. Resolve perpendicular to the plane ($\nwarrow$):

   $F_{net} = ma$

   $R - 3g \cos 20° = 3 \times 0$

   $R = 3g \cos 20° = 27.626...$ N

2. The mass is sliding, so $F = \mu R$:

   $F = 0.4 \times 27.626... = 11.050...$ N

3. Resolve parallel to the plane ($\nearrow$):

   $F_{net} = ma$

   $T - F - 3g \sin 20° = 3 \times 0.6$

   $T = 1.8 + 11.050... + 3g \sin 20°$

   $= \boxed{22.9 \text{ N (3 s.f.)}}$

Exercise 5.3.2

Q1 A particle of mass 300 g is propelled up the line of greatest slope of a smooth plane inclined at 17° to the horizontal. Immediately after the propelling force has stopped, the particle has speed 7 ms⁻¹. Find:

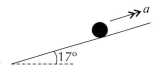

   a) the distance the particle travels before momentarily coming to rest.

   b) the magnitude of the normal reaction from the plane.

Q2 A wooden block of mass 1.5 kg is placed on a smooth plane inclined at 25° to the horizontal, as shown on the right. The block is released from rest and begins to accelerate down the slope.

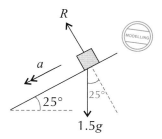

   a) What is the magnitude of the block's acceleration?

   b) Assuming that the block's acceleration is constant, find the speed of the block 3 seconds after it is released.

Q3 A horizontal force of magnitude 26 N is acting on a box of mass 4 kg, causing the box to accelerate across a rough, horizontal plane at a rate of 1.2 ms⁻².

   a) Draw a labelled diagram to show the forces acting on the box.

   b) Calculate the normal reaction, R, of the plane on the box.

   c) Use Newton's second law to find the magnitude of the frictional force acting on the box.

   d) Find the coefficient of friction, μ, between the box and the plane.

Q4 A box of mass 7 kg is accelerated across a rough horizontal plane by a horizontal force, P. The coefficient of friction, μ, between the box and the plane is 0.2 and the box accelerates at a rate of 0.8 ms^{-2}.

a) Draw a labelled diagram to show the forces acting on the box.

b) Calculate the normal reaction, R, of the plane on the box.

c) Calculate the magnitude of P.

Q5 A taut rope is pulling a block up a rough inclined plane angled at 40° to the horizontal. The rope is parallel to the plane. The coefficient of friction between the block and the surface is 0.35 and the tension in the rope is 70 N.

a) Draw a diagram to show the forces acting on the block.

b) Given that the block is accelerating at a rate of 3.2 ms^{-2}, find the mass of the block.

Q6 A block of mass 1 kg slides down a rough plane of length 2 m, which is inclined at an angle of 50° to the horizontal. The coefficient of friction between the block and the surface is 0.4.

a) Draw a diagram to show the forces acting on the block.

b) If the block is released from rest at the top of the plane, find how long it will take to reach the bottom of the plane.

Q7 A block with mass 2 kg is released from rest at the top of a rough plane which is inclined at an angle of 28° to the horizontal. The block travels 0.5 m down the line of greatest slope of the plane in the first two seconds after being released. Calculate the coefficient of friction, μ, between the block and the plane.

Q8 A rock weighing 5000 N is being pulled up a rough inclined plane which is at an angle of 10° to the horizontal, as shown. The coefficient of friction between the rock and the plane is 0.1. The rock accelerates up the plane at a rate of 0.35 ms^{-2}.

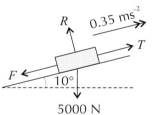

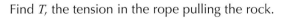

Find T, the tension in the rope pulling the rock.

Q9 A package of mass 9 kg is moving up the line of greatest slope of a rough plane inclined at an angle of 22° to the horizontal. The package is being pushed up the slope by a force of magnitude 110 N acting horizontally. Given that the package is accelerating up the slope at a rate of 1.3 ms^{-2}, find μ, the coefficient of friction between the package and the plane.

Q10 A block of mass 5 kg is at rest on a rough plane inclined at 35° to the horizontal. The coefficient of friction between the block and the plane is 0.4. Given that the block is being held in equilibrium by a force D acting parallel to the plane, find the range of possible values of the magnitude of D.

Q11 A block with mass 0.5 kg is pushed up a rough plane inclined at an angle of 20° to the horizontal by a force P N, which acts at an angle of 15° to the plane, as shown.

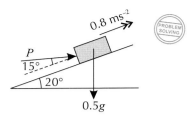

The block is accelerating up the plane at a rate of 0.8 ms⁻² and the coefficient of friction between the plane and the block is 0.3. Find the magnitude of the force P.

Connected particles, pegs and pulleys

You also need to be able to resolve forces and calculate friction in situations with **connected particles**. You should remember from Year 1 that when particles are connected by a **taut, inextensible string** or a **rigid rod**, it will exert an **equal tension** force or **thrust** force respectively on both particles. The particles will also have the same **magnitude** of **acceleration**.

Normally, the way to approach these problems is to resolve forces on each particle **separately** and form a pair of **simultaneous equations**, although sometimes it will be easier to treat the **whole system** as **one object**.

Example 1

Two particles, A and B, of mass 6 kg and 8 kg respectively, are connected by a light, inextensible string. The particles are accelerating up a rough slope which is inclined at an angle of 20° to the horizontal. The force causing the acceleration has magnitude 200 N and acts on A in a direction parallel to the slope. The coefficient of friction between each particle and the slope is 0.6.

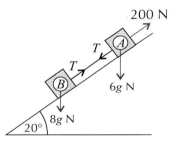

Find the acceleration of A.

The particles are connected, so the acceleration of A will be the same as the acceleration of the two particles combined.

1. Treat the two particles as one combined particle with mass 6 kg + 8 kg = 14 kg, and resolve perpendicular to the plane (↖).

$F_{net} = ma$

$R - 14g \cos 20° = 0$

$R = 14g \cos 20°$ N

2. The particles are moving, so the maximum frictional force is acting on the particles.

$F = \mu R = 0.6 \times 14g \cos 20°$

$\quad = 8.4g \cos 20°$

3. Again, treat the two particles as one combined particle, but now resolve parallel to the plane (↗).

$F_{net} = ma$

$200 - 14g \sin 20° - F = 14a$

$200 - 14g \sin 20° - 8.4g \cos 20° = 14a$

$a = \boxed{5.41 \text{ ms}^{-2} \text{ (3 s.f.)}}$

> **Tip:** The total frictional force acting on the two particles is the sum of the individual frictional forces: $F = F_A + F_B$

Example 2

Particles A and B, of mass 4 kg and 10 kg respectively, are
connected by a light inextensible string which passes over
a fixed smooth pulley. A force of 15 N acts on A at an angle
of 25° to a rough horizontal plane, as shown. The coefficient
of friction between A and the plane is 0.7. B is released from
rest and falls d m vertically to the ground in 2 seconds.

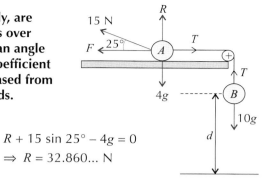

a) **Find d.**

1. Resolve vertically for A (↑)
   to find the normal reaction, R.

   $R + 15 \sin 25° - 4g = 0$
   $\Rightarrow R = 32.860...$ N

2. The particles are moving,
   so F takes its maximum value:

   $F = \mu R = 0.7 \times 32.860... = 23.002...$ N

3. Resolve horizontally for A (→):

   $T - 23.002... - 15 \cos 25° = 4a$
   $T = 4a + 36.597...$ — equation ①

4. Resolve vertically for B (↓):

   $10g - T = 10a$
   $\Rightarrow T = 98 - 10a$ — equation ②

5. Substitute equation ① into equation ②
   to work out the acceleration.

   $4a + 36.597... = 98 - 10a$
   $\Rightarrow a = 4.385...$ ms^{-2}

6. Using a constant acceleration equation:

   $s = d, \ u = 0, \ t = 2, \ a = 4.385...$
   $s = ut + \frac{1}{2}at^2$

   Tip: Don't round the numbers in any of
   the intermediate steps of a calculation, or
   your final answer might not be correct.

   $d = (0 \times 2) + \frac{1}{2} \times 4.385... \times 2^2$
   $= \boxed{8.77 \text{ m (to 3 s.f.)}}$

b) **When B hits the ground, A carries on moving along the plane. The resistive
   forces acting on A remain the same as in part a), and A does not hit the pulley.
   How long does it take A to stop after B hits the ground?**

1. First, find the speed of A
   when B hits the ground.

   $u = 0, \ v = v, \ a = 4.385..., \ t = 2$
   $v = u + at$
   $v = 0 + (4.385... \times 2) = 8.771...$ ms^{-1}

2. Next, resolve horizontally for A (→)
   to find its deceleration after the string has
   gone slack and there is no tension force.

   $-23.002... - 15 \cos 25° = 4a$
   $-36.597... = 4a$
   $\Rightarrow a = -9.149...$ ms^{-2}

3. Now find the time taken for A to stop:

   $u = 8.771..., \ v = 0, \ a = -9.149..., \ t = t$
   $v = u + at$

   Tip: Don't confuse the *suvat*
   variables from before B hits the
   ground with those from after.

   $0 = 8.771... + -9.149... \times t$
   $\Rightarrow t = \frac{8.771...}{9.149...} = \boxed{0.959 \text{ s (to 3 s.f.)}}$

Example 3

A block of mass 3 kg is held in equilibrium on a rough plane inclined at 30° to the horizontal. It is attached via a light, inextensible string to a mass of *M* kg hanging vertically beneath a fixed smooth pulley, as shown. The coefficient of friction between *A* and the plane is 0.4.

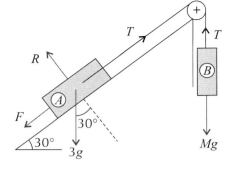

a) **Find *M*, given that *A* is on the point of sliding up the plane.**

A is "on the point of sliding" — this is another way of describing **limiting equilibrium**, so the frictional force takes its maximum value: $F = \mu R$.

This is really a **statics** question — the particles aren't moving, so acceleration is zero in all directions.

1. Resolve perpendicular to the plane (↖) for *A*:

    $R - 3g \cos 30° = 3 \times 0$
    $R = 3g \cos 30°$

2. The friction is limiting, so:

    $F = \mu R = 0.4 \times 3g \cos 30°$
    $\quad\quad = 10.184... \text{ N}$

3. Resolve vertically (↓) for *B*:

    $Mg - T = M \times 0$
    $\Rightarrow T = Mg$

4. Resolve parallel to the plane (↗) for *A*:

    $T - F - 3g \sin 30° = 3 \times 0$
    $Mg - 10.184... - 3g \sin 30° = 0$
    $\Rightarrow M = \boxed{2.54 \text{ kg (to 3 s.f.)}}$

b) **What would *M* be if *A* were on the point of sliding down the plane?**

Resolve parallel to the plane (↗) for *A*:

$T + F - 3g \sin 30° = 3 \times 0$
$Mg + 10.184... - 3g \sin 30° = 0$
$M = \boxed{0.461 \text{ kg (to 3 s.f.)}}$

Tip: You've already done all the hard work in part a), so in b), just repeat the very last step and resolve parallel to the plane, with the frictional force acting in the opposite direction.

Example 4

Two particles, A and B, of masses 4 kg and 3 kg respectively, are joined by a light inextensible string which passes over a smooth fixed pulley. The particles are positioned as shown in the diagram. The system is released from rest and A begins to move down the slope and B begins to move up the slope.

Given that the coefficient of friction between each particle and the surface is 0.2, find the magnitude of the acceleration of A.

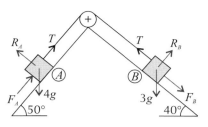

1. The particles are moving, so friction is limiting:

    Tip: Find R_A and R_B by resolving perpendicular to each plane.

    $F_A = \mu R_A = 0.2 \times 4g \cos 50°$
    $\qquad = 5.039...$ N

    $F_B = \mu R_B = 0.2 \times 3g \cos 40°$
    $\qquad = 4.504...$ N

2. Resolve parallel to the plane ($\swarrow$) for A:

    $4g \sin 50° - F_A - T = 4a$
    $24.989... - T = 4a$ — call this equation ①

3. Resolve parallel to the plane ($\nwarrow$) for B:

    $T - 3g \sin 40° - F_B = 3a$
    $T - 23.402... = 3a$
    $T = 3a + 23.402...$ — call this equation ②

4. Substitute equation ② into equation ①:

    $24.989... - 3a - 23.402... = 4a$
    $\Rightarrow a = $ 0.227 ms⁻² (to 3 s.f.)

Exercise 5.3.3

Q1 A light, inextensible string passing over a smooth pulley connects boxes A and B, of mass 10 kg and 8 kg respectively, as shown in the diagram. The system is released from rest and the boxes begin to accelerate at a rate of 0.5 ms⁻². Find:

    a) the tension in the connecting string, T.

    b) the coefficient of friction between A and the surface.

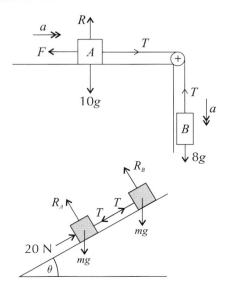

Q2 Two identical objects are connected by a rigid rod. The objects are being pushed up a uniform rough slope inclined at an angle θ to the horizontal by a force of 20 N acting parallel to the slope. Calculate the thrust force in the rod.

Q3   A truck of mass 2 tonnes is moving along a rough, horizontal plane ($\mu = 0.8$), and towing a car of mass 0.8 tonnes up a smooth plane, angled at 25° to the horizontal, as shown.

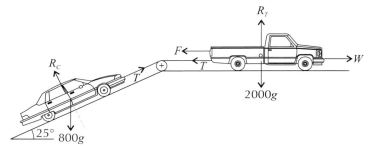

The chain between the truck and the car is modelled as a light, inextensible string passing over a fixed, smooth pulley. The car is initially 25 m from the pulley and is towed 10 m towards the pulley in the first 30 seconds after starting from rest.

The truck and the car move with constant acceleration. You may assume that the frictional force between the truck and the horizontal plane takes its maximum value.

Q3 Hint: Start by finding the acceleration of the truck and the car.

a) Find the tension in the chain.

b) Calculate W, the driving force of the truck.

c) The chain connecting the truck to the car snaps. Assuming that all other forces remain constant, calculate the instantaneous acceleration of the truck.

Q4   A light, inextensible string attaches a block P of mass 60 kg to a block Q of mass 20 kg over a fixed, smooth pulley. P lies on a rough plane ($\mu = 0.1$) inclined at an angle of 50° to the horizontal, and Q hangs vertically below the pulley, as shown.

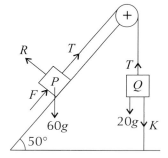

The system is held in limiting equilibrium with P on the point of sliding down the plane by a second light, inextensible string attached to Q at one end and the horizontal ground at the other.

a) Find the tension in the second string, K.

b) The string fixing Q to the ground is cut.
Given that Q does not hit the pulley, find the speed of P 5 seconds after it starts moving.

Q4b) Hint: When the string is cut, the tension force K will disappear.

Q5   Particles A and B, of mass 8 kg and 9 kg respectively, are connected by a light, inextensible string which passes over a fixed, smooth pulley. A force of 60 N acts on A at an angle of 40° to the rough, horizontal plane that A rests on, away from the pulley. Particle A is held 20 cm from the pulley and, when released from rest, accelerates towards the pulley at a rate of 0.4 ms^{-2}.

a) Find μ, the coefficient of friction between A and the plane.

b) Find the speed of A when it hits the pulley.

c) When A hits the pulley, the string breaks and B falls freely.
Given that B was initially released from a position 60 cm above the horizontal ground, find the speed of B when it hits the ground.

Q5c) Hint: While the particles are connected, they'll have the same speed.

Q6   Two particles, A and B, with mass 8 kg and 5 kg respectively, are attached to either end of a light, inextensible string, which passes over a fixed, smooth pulley. Particle A lies on a rough plane inclined at an angle of 25° to the horizontal, and particle B lies on a rough plane inclined at an angle of 20° to the horizontal, as shown in the diagram below. When released from rest, the particles accelerate at a constant rate of 0.3 ms⁻².

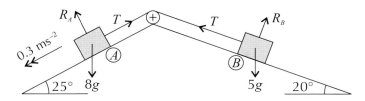

Find the coefficient of friction, μ, between each particle and the plane, given that it is the same for both particles.

Q7   Two blocks, P and Q, with masses 2 kg and 3 kg respectively, are joined by a light, inextensible string, as shown on the right. They lie on a rough plane ($\mu = 0.4$) inclined at an angle α to the horizontal, where $\tan \alpha = \frac{3}{4}$.

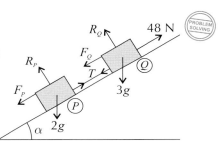

The blocks start from rest and are accelerated up the slope by a string attached to Q, where the tension in the string has a magnitude of 48 N.

a) Find the magnitude of the acceleration of the blocks.

b) After three seconds, the string connecting the blocks is cut. Assuming that all other forces remain constant, find the time taken for block P to come to rest.

c) Will P remain at rest? Justify your answer.

Q8   Particles A and B, of mass 0.2 kg and 0.9 kg respectively, are connected by a light, inextensible string. The string passes over a smooth pulley fixed to the apex of a wedge. A rests on a rough plane ($\mu_A = 0.7$) inclined at an angle of 40° to the horizontal, and B rests on a different rough plane ($\mu_B = 0.05$) inclined at an angle of 20° to the horizontal, as shown in the diagram below.

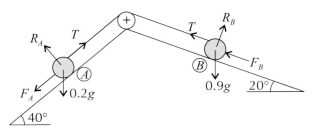

The particles are held at rest with A 35 cm from the pulley.

a) Given that A begins to accelerate up the slope when the particles are released from rest, find the tension in the string.

b) Find the speed of A when it reaches the pulley.

Review Exercise

Q1 A force of magnitude 8 N acts on an object that rests on a plane inclined at 11° to the horizontal, as shown. The component of the force in the direction parallel to the plane is 6.5 N.

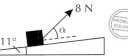

a) Find the angle between the direction of the force and the incline of the plane.

b) Find the horizontal component of the force.

Q2 The diagrams below show a particle on the point of slipping on a rough surface. Calculate the coefficient of friction, μ, between each particle and the surface shown.

a)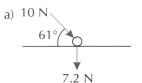

b)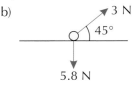

c)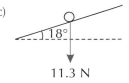

Q3 A horizontal force P, acting on a 2 kg mass, generates an acceleration of 0.3 ms⁻².

a) Given that the mass is in contact with a rough horizontal plane which resists motion with a force of 1 N, find P.

b) Find the coefficient of friction, μ, to 2 d.p.

Q4 Three forces are acting on a particle of mass 2.5 kg.

a) Two of the forces are given by $(4\mathbf{i} - 7\mathbf{j})$ N and $(6\mathbf{i} + 4\mathbf{j})$ N. The resultant force is $(5\mathbf{i} + \mathbf{j})$ N. Find the third force in vector form.

b) Find the distance travelled by the particle, 4 seconds after it begins accelerating from rest.

Q5 A brick of mass 1.2 kg accelerates down a rough plane inclined at 25° to the horizontal at a rate of 0.3 ms⁻². Find the coefficient of friction between the brick and the plane.

Q6 An army recruit of weight 600 N steps off a tower and accelerates down a "death slide" wire as shown. The recruit hangs from a light rope held between her hands and looped over the wire. The coefficient of friction between the rope and wire is 0.5. Given that the wire is 20 m long and makes an angle of 30° to the horizontal throughout its length, find how fast the recruit is travelling when she reaches the end of the wire.

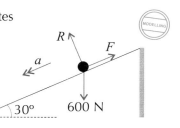

Q7 Two particles of mass 3 kg and 4 kg are connected by a light, inextensible string passing over a fixed, smooth pulley. The 3 kg mass is on a smooth slope angled at 40° to the horizontal and the 4 kg mass hangs vertically below the pulley. Find:

a) the acceleration of the particles immediately after being released from rest,

b) the tension in the string,

c) the magnitude of force acting on the 3 kg mass in a direction parallel to the plane which would hold the particles in equilibrium.

Exam-Style Questions

Q1 A block of mass m kg is placed on a slope inclined at an angle of 28° to the horizontal. It is attached to one end of a light, inextensible string which passes smoothly over a pulley at the top of the slope, such that the string between the block and the pulley is parallel to the slope. A mass of $2m$ kg is attached to the other end, and hangs freely.

   a) Assuming that the slope is smooth, find the acceleration of the block up the slope.

   [3 marks]

   b) It is found through experimentation that the actual acceleration is 3.8 ms^{-2}. Find the coefficient of friction between the block and the slope.

   [3 marks]

Q2 A toy boat is pulled by two strings. The first string pulls at a bearing of 315° and the second pulls at a bearing of 075°. A third force of $(-3\mathbf{i} - \mathbf{j})$ N resists the motion, where $\mathbf{i}$ is due east and $\mathbf{j}$ is due north. The resultant force on the boat is $(5\mathbf{i} + 3\mathbf{j})$ N. Find the magnitude of each of the two forces exerted by the strings, giving your answers to 3 s.f.

   [5 marks]

Q3 A sled of mass m kg lies on a rough slope inclined at an angle of 30° to the horizontal. The sled is prevented from sliding on the slope by a rope held parallel to the slope.

   The coefficient of friction between the sled and the slope is $\frac{1}{2\sqrt{3}}$.

   a) Show that $\frac{1}{4} mg \le T \le \frac{3}{4} mg$, where T is the tension in the rope.

   [4 marks]

   b) A child of mass $2m$ kg then gets on the sled and the rope is released. Find the velocity of the sled after 3 seconds.

   [4 marks]

Q4 Two blocks A and B, with masses 5 kg and 2 kg respectively, lie on rough slopes, as shown. The blocks are attached to the ends of a light inextensible string which runs over a fixed, smooth pulley at the top of the two slopes. The angle between the slopes is 90° and the slope that A rests on is inclined at angle θ to the horizontal. The coefficient of friction between the blocks and the slopes is 0.2 and A is on the point of moving up the slope.

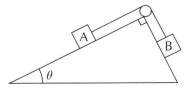

   a) Show that $\tan \theta = \frac{5}{27}$.

   [5 marks]

   b) Find the magnitude of the force P exerted on the pulley by the string.

   [3 marks]

6.1 Moments

You've seen that a force applied to a particle can cause the particle to accelerate in a straight line in the direction of the force. A force can also have a turning effect, usually when a body is pivoted at a point.

Learning Objectives (Spec Ref 9.1):

- Find the moment of a force about a point.
- Find the sum of moments about a point.
- Find missing distances and forces in calculations involving rigid bodies in equilibrium.
- Find the centre of mass of a non-uniform rod or beam.

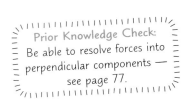
Prior Knowledge Check:
Be able to resolve forces into perpendicular components — see page 77.

Moments

A **moment** is the **turning effect** a force has **around a point**.

- The **larger the magnitude** of the force, and the **greater the distance** between the force and the pivot, the **greater the moment**.

- Moments are either **clockwise** or **anticlockwise** — you should always state the **direction** as well as the **magnitude** of a moment.

You can use the following formula to find the moment of a force about a point:

$$\text{Moment} = \frac{\text{Magnitude}}{\text{of Force}} \times \frac{\text{Perpendicular Distance from}}{\text{the line of action of the force}}$$
$$\text{to the pivot}$$

Tip: The 'line of action' of the force is just the direction that the force acts in.

Or, more concisely: **Moment = Fd.**

If the force is measured in newtons and the distance is measured in metres, then the moment is measured in newton-metres, **Nm**.

Example 1

A 2 m long plank is attached to a ship at one end, *O*. The plank is horizontal, and a bird lands on the other end, applying a downward force of magnitude 15 N, as shown. Model the plank as a light rod and find the turning effect of the bird on the plank.

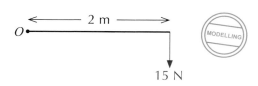

Use the formula, making *O* the pivot point:

$$\text{Moment} = Fd$$
$$= 15 \times 2$$
$$= \boxed{30 \text{ Nm clockwise}}$$

Tip: Modelling the plank as a light rod means that you don't have to worry about its weight.

Example 2

A spanner is attached to a bolt at a point, *O*. A force of 20 N is applied at an angle of 60° to the other end of the spanner, as shown on the right. Find the turning effect of the force upon the bolt.

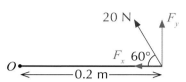

> **Tip:** 'Find the turning effect' means the same as 'find the moment'.

1. Resolve the force to find its component acting perpendicular to the spanner.

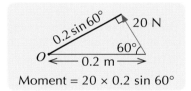

F_x acts through *O*, so its moment is zero (it has no turning effect).

$F_y = 20 \sin 60°$

2. F_y is a perpendicular distance of 0.2 m from *O*, so, using the formula:

Moment = $20 \sin 60° \times 0.2$

= 3.46 Nm (3 s.f.) anticlockwise

In Example 2 above, instead of finding the component of the force acting perpendicular to the spanner, you could have found the perpendicular distance to the line of action of the force:

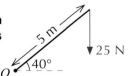

Moment = $20 \times 0.2 \sin 60°$

Example 3

A force of 25 N acts upon a light rod of length 5 m, pivoted at *O*, as shown on the right. The 25 N force acts vertically downwards, and the rod makes an angle of 40° with the horizontal. What is the turning effect about *O*?

1. Find the perpendicular distance, *d*, between the line of action of the force and the pivot point:

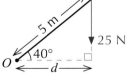

So *d* = 5 cos 40°

2. Calculate the moment:

Moment = $25 \times 5 \cos 40°$

= 95.8 Nm (3 s.f.) clockwise

You could have resolved the force to find the component acting perpendicular to the rod, as in Example 2:

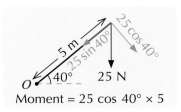

Moment = $25 \cos 40° \times 5$

Finding the sum of moments about a point

- If there are **two or more** forces acting on a rod or beam,
  then you can find the **sum of the moments** about a particular point.

- If the sum of the moments about a particular point is **not zero**,
  the rod will **turn** clockwise or anticlockwise about **that point**.

- The direction that the rod turns (i.e. clockwise or anticlockwise) is called the **sense** of rotation.

- If the sum of the moments about a particular point is **zero**,
  then the rod **won't rotate** about that point.

- If the rod is **in equilibrium**, then the sum of the moments about **any point** must be **zero**.

Example 4

The diagram shows the light rod AB. A force of magnitude 5 N
acts vertically downwards at point C. A force of magnitude
4 N acts at point B, making an angle of 30° with the rod.

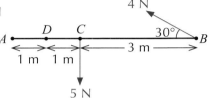

a) **The rod is pivoted at point A.**
   Show that there is no overall turning effect about this point.

   Taking moments about A (with clockwise being
   the positive direction), and finding their sum:

   Sum of moments = $(5 \times 2) - (4 \sin 30° \times 5)$
   $= 10 - 10 = $ 0 Nm

   Tip: The 4 sin 30° term is negative
   because the moment is anticlockwise.

   Total moment is zero, so there is
   no overall turning effect about A.

b) **The rod is now pivoted at point D. Given that the forces acting at B and C are the same
   as in part a), will the rod rotate clockwise or anticlockwise about this point?**

   Taking moments about D (with clockwise being
   the positive direction), and finding their sum:

   Sum of moments = $(5 \times 1) - (4 \sin 30° \times 4)$
   $= 5 - 8 = $ –3 Nm

   The sum of moments is negative,
   so the rod will rotate anticlockwise .

Exercise 6.1.1

Q1   For each of the following light rods, find the moment of the force about A.

a)
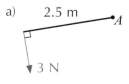

b)
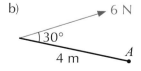

c)
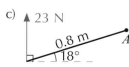

d)
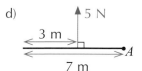

e)

f)
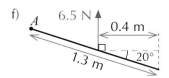

Q2 A light rod, *AB*, has length 4 m. A force of magnitude 5 N is applied to *A* at an angle of 40° above the rod, as shown. A second force of magnitude 3 N is applied vertically upwards at the rod's midpoint. Find the sum of the moments of the forces acting on the rod about *B*.

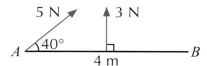

Hint: Remember to choose either anticlockwise or clockwise as the positive direction.

Q3 For each of the following light rods, find the sum of the moments about *X*.

a)
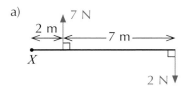

b)
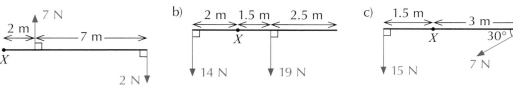

c)
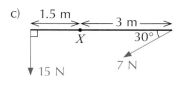

d)
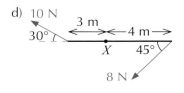

e)

f)
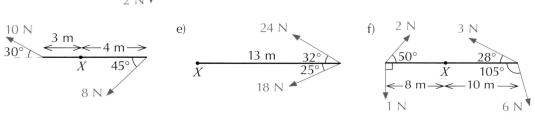

Q4 A light rod, *AB*, has length 6.8 m and is pivoted at *A*. A particle of mass 4.7 kg is placed in the centre of the rod, and a particle of mass 0.75 kg is placed on the rod 1.1 m from *B*. Find the sum of the moments about *A* of the forces acting on the rod when the rod is horizontal.

Q4 Hint: Recall that weight = *mg*.

Q5 Two children sit on a light horizontal see-saw of length 3 m, pivoted at its centre. One child, of mass 25 kg, sits on one end, and the other child, whose mass is 30 kg, sits on the other end. Find the overall turning effect about the centre of the see-saw.

Q6 The diagram below shows the light rod *AB*. Find the range of possible values for *X*, given that *AB* rotates clockwise about the point *O*.

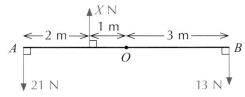

Q7 The diagram below shows the light rod *PQ*. Find the range of possible values for *d* which will cause *PQ* to rotate anticlockwise about the point *O*.

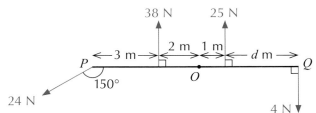

Moments in equilibrium

A rigid body which is in **static equilibrium** will **not move**. This means that there is **no resultant force** in **any direction** — any forces acting on the body will cancel each other out.

It also means that the **sum of the moments** on the body **about any point** is **zero**.

So, for a body in equilibrium:

> Total Clockwise Moment = Total Anticlockwise Moment

By **resolving forces** and **equating clockwise and anticlockwise moments**, you can solve problems involving bodies in equilibrium.

It's a good idea to take moments about a point where an **unknown force** is acting — the moment of that force about the point will be zero so it won't appear in the equation.

Example 1

Two weights of 30 N and 45 N are placed on a light 8 m beam. The 30 N weight is at one end of the beam, as shown, whilst the other weight is a distance d from the midpoint, M.

The beam is held in equilibrium by a light, inextensible wire with tension T attached at M. Find T and the distance d.

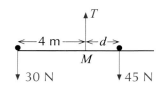

1. First resolve forces vertically
   (forces 'up' = forces 'down'):

   $T = 30 + 45 = \boxed{75 \text{ N}}$

2. Then take moments about M
   (moments clockwise = moments anticlockwise):

   $45d = 30 \times 4$

   $d = 120 \div 45 = \boxed{2.67 \text{ m (3 s.f.)}}$

Example 2

The diagram below shows a light rod AB, of length 10 m. Particles of mass M_A kg and M_B kg are placed at A and B respectively. The rod is supported in equilibrium by two vertical reaction forces of magnitude 145 N and 90 N, as shown in the diagram. Find the values of M_A and M_B.

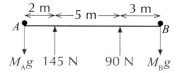

1. Taking moments about A
   (moments clockwise = moments anticlockwise):

   $M_B g \times 10 = (145 \times 2) + (90 \times 7)$

   $\Rightarrow M_B = 920 \div 98 = 9.387... = \boxed{9.39 \text{ kg (3 s.f.)}}$

2. You know that there is no resultant force acting on the rod. So, resolving forces vertically ('forces up' = 'forces down'):

   $145 + 90 = M_A g + M_B g$

   $\Rightarrow M_A + M_B = 235 \div 9.8 = 23.979...$

   $\Rightarrow M_A = 23.979... - 9.387... = \boxed{14.6 \text{ kg (3 s.f.)}}$

Centres of mass

The **centre of mass** (**COM**) of an object is the point where the object's **weight** can be considered to act.

The mass of a **uniform beam** is spread evenly along the length of the beam, and so the centre of mass is at its **midpoint**:

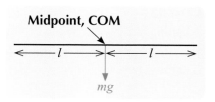

The centre of mass of a **non-uniform beam** could be at **any point** along the beam. When you're **taking moments** and **resolving forces** for a heavy (i.e. not light) beam, you need to remember to include the **weight** of the beam in your calculations.

Example 3

A 6 m long uniform beam AB of weight 40 N is supported at A by a vertical reaction R. AB is held horizontally by a vertical wire attached 1 m from the other end. A particle of weight 30 N is placed 2 m from the support R. Find the tension T in the wire and the force R.

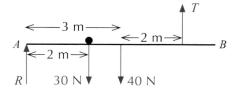

1. Taking moments about A: Clockwise moments = Anticlockwise moments

$$(30 \times 2) + (40 \times 3) = 5T$$
$$\Rightarrow T = 180 \div 5 = \boxed{36 \text{ N}}$$

Tip: This is the weight of the beam, acting at its centre.

2. Resolving vertically: $T + R = 30 + 40$
$$R = 70 - T = 70 - 36 = \boxed{34 \text{ N}}$$

The point of tilting

If a rod is '**about to tilt**' about a particular point of support, then any **normal reactions** acting at any other supports along the rod will be **zero**. The **tension** in any strings supporting the rod at any other point will also be **zero**.

Example 4

A non-uniform wooden plank of mass M kg rests horizontally on supports at A and B, as shown. When a bucket of water of mass 18 kg is placed at point C, the plank is in equilibrium, and is on the point of tilting about B. Find the value of M and the magnitude of the reaction at B.

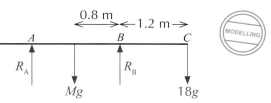

The plank is on the point of tilting about B, so the reaction at A, R_A, is zero.

1. Taking moments about B: $(18g \times 1.2) + 0 = Mg \times 0.8$
$$\Rightarrow M = (18 \times 9.8 \times 1.2) \div (9.8 \times 0.8)$$
$$= \boxed{27 \text{ kg}}$$

Tip: $R_A = 0$, so the moment of the force is zero.

2. Resolving vertically: $R_A + R_B = Mg + 18g$
$$0 + R_B = 27g + 18g \Rightarrow R_B = \boxed{441 \text{ N}}$$

Laminas

A **lamina** is a flat 2D object (its thickness can be ignored).

The centre of mass of a **uniform rectangular** lamina is at the symmetrical centre of the rectangle.

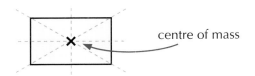

centre of mass

Example 5

A uniform lamina, *ABCD*, of weight 8 N, is pivoted at point *A*. The lamina is held in equilibrium by a vertical force *F* acting at point *C*, as shown.

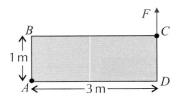

a) **Find the horizontal and vertical distances of the centre of mass of the lamina from *A*.**

The centre of mass is at the centre of the lamina.

Horizontal distance = 3 ÷ 2 = 1.5 m

Vertical distance = 1 ÷ 2 = 0.5 m

b) **Find the magnitude of the force *F*.**

1. Both the lamina's weight and *F* act vertically, so the perpendicular distance from each force to the pivot is just the horizontal distance.

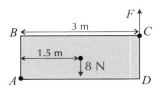

2. Taking moments about *A*:

$8 \times 1.5 = F \times 3$

$\Rightarrow F = 12 \div 3 = 4 \text{ N}$

If there are forces acting **at angles** to the sides of the lamina, it's usually easier to resolve them **perpendicular** and **parallel** to the lamina's sides. But remember that **both components** will have a turning effect on the lamina.

Example 6

A uniform rectangular lamina of mass 12 kg is pivoted at one corner at *A*. A light, inextensible string attached at the opposite corner applies a tension force *T* to the lamina as shown.

Given that the string holds the lamina in equilibrium at an angle of 20° to the horizontal, find the tension in the string.

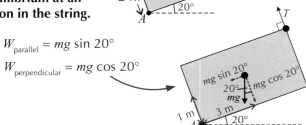

1. Find the components of the weight parallel and perpendicular to the longer side of the lamina.

$W_{\text{parallel}} = mg \sin 20°$

$W_{\text{perpendicular}} = mg \cos 20°$

2. Taking moments about *A*:

$(mg \cos 20° \times 3) = (mg \sin 20° \times 1) + (T \times 6)$

$\Rightarrow 6T = mg(3 \cos 20° - \sin 20°)$

$\Rightarrow T = 19.6(2.4770...) = 48.6 \text{ N} \ \ (3 \text{ s.f.})$

Q1 For each of the following diagrams, find the values of x and y, given that the light rod AB is in equilibrium:

a)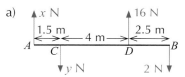

b)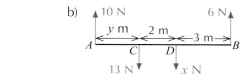

Q2 A uniform rod, AB, of length 5 m, rests horizontally in equilibrium on supports at C and D. If the magnitude of the normal reaction at C is 49 N, find:

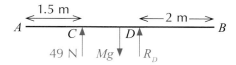

a) the magnitude of the normal reaction at D,

b) the mass of the rod.

Q3 A uniform rod, AB, of mass 9 kg, is held in equilibrium by a fixed vertical wire at C and a support at D, as shown. When an object of mass 3 kg is placed at B, the rod is still horizontal and in equilibrium, but is on the point of tilting clockwise about D.

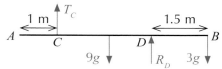

Find the length of the rod, AB.

Q4 A uniform beam, AB, has length 5 m and mass 8 kg. It is held horizontally in equilibrium by vertical ropes at B and the point C, 1 m from A.

a) Find the tension in each rope.

b) When a particle of mass 16 kg is placed on the beam, the beam remains horizontal and in equilibrium, but is on the point of tilting anticlockwise about C. Find the distance of the particle from A.

Q5 The diagram below shows a light rod held horizontally in equilibrium by two vertical strings. Find U and l, giving your answers in N and m respectively.

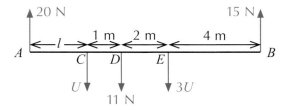

Q6 A light rod, AB, of length 4 m, supports an object of weight 4 N at its midpoint. It rests in equilibrium in a horizontal position on vertical supports at C and D, where $AC = 1$ m and $AD = 3.5$ m. Find:

a) the magnitude of the reaction force at C,

b) the magnitude of the reaction force at D.

Q7 A non-uniform rod, AB, has length 4.8 m and mass 500 g. It rests horizontally in equilibrium on vertical supports at C and D, where $AC = 1.6$ m and $AD = 4.2$ m, and is held by a light, inextensible, vertical string attached at A. The normal reaction at D is twice that at C, and the tension in the string is 1 N.

   a) Find the magnitudes of the normal reactions at C and D.

   b) Find the distance of the centre of mass of the rod from A.

Q8 A light rod, AB, has an object of mass 11 kg attached to it, 13 m from A. The rod is held in equilibrium by two light, inextensible strings. The strings are attached to the rod at A and B, making angles with the horizontal of 38° and α respectively, as shown on the right. Find:

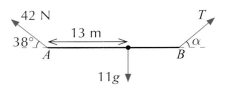

   a) the length of the rod,   b) the value of α,

   c) the magnitude of T, the tension in the string attached at B.

Q9 A non-uniform rod, AB, of length 6 m, is held horizontally in equilibrium by two light, inextensible strings, as shown. The centre of mass of the rod is 2.7 m from A. Find:

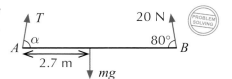

   a) the mass of the rod,   b) the value of α,

   c) the magnitude of the tension in the string at A.

Q10 A painter of mass 80 kg stands on a horizontal non-uniform 4 m plank, AB, of mass 20 kg. The plank rests on supports 1 m from each end, at C and D. The painter places paint pots, of mass 2.5 kg, 0.2 m from each end of the plank.

   a) He stands at the centre of mass of the plank and finds that the reaction forces at C and D are in the ratio $4:1$. Find the distance of the centre of mass of the plank from A.

   b) He uses up all the paint in the pot near A, and discards the pot. He then stands on the plank at a point between D and B, and the plank is on the point of tilting about D. How far is he from B?

Q11 A uniform rectangular lamina $ABCD$ of weight 6 N is pivoted at point A and acted on by a force F at point C. F has magnitude 10 N, and acts at an angle of θ to the horizontal, as shown. Find the sum of the moments about A if:

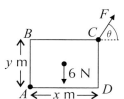

   a) $x = 10$, $y = 6$, $\theta = 90°$ b) $x = 1$, $y = 5$, $\theta = 0$

   c) $x = 4$, $y = 8$, $\theta = 270°$ d) $x = 7$, $y = 6$, $\theta = 180°$

   e) $x = 5$, $y = 5$, $\theta = 30°$ f) $x = 1$, $y = 11$, $\theta = 120°$

Q12 A uniform rectangular lamina of mass m has corners at the following coordinates: A (0, 0), B (–2, 8), C (2, 9), D (4, 1). The lamina is pivoted at A. A horizontal force of 8 N acts on the lamina in the negative x-direction at D, and a vertical force of 11 N pulls upwards on the lamina at C.

   a) Draw a diagram to show this information, given that gravity acts in the negative y-direction.

   b) Given that the system is in equilibrium, find m.

6.2 Reaction Forces and Friction

When an object is resting against a surface, the surface will exert a normal reaction on the object perpendicular (or normal) to the surface and, if the surface is rough, friction will oppose any motion. However, if the object is fixed by a hinge, the reaction force might not act perpendicular to the surface.

Learning Objectives (Spec Ref 8.6 & 9.1):
- Solve problems involving rigid bodies that are freely hinged to a surface.
- Solve problems involving rigid bodies under the influence of a frictional force.

Prior Knowledge Check:
Be able to calculate frictional forces. See p.88-91.

Reaction forces

If a **rigid body** is fixed to a **surface** by a **hinge** or **pivot**, you can deal with the reaction force on the body from the hinge by **splitting it up** into two **components**, **parallel** and **perpendicular** to the **surface**.

When a body is **freely hinged**, the reaction force is the force in the hinge that helps keep the body in **equilibrium**. It's **not the same** as the normal reaction, which acts when a body is in contact with a **surface**, and which always acts **perpendicular** to the surface.

Example 1

A uniform rod, *AB*, of mass 2 kg and length 1.2 m, is freely hinged on a vertical wall. The rod is held horizontally in equilibrium by a light, inextensible string attached at *C*, 0.4 m from *B*, which makes an angle of 45° with the rod, as shown.

Find the tension in the string and the magnitude of the reaction force on the rod at *A*.

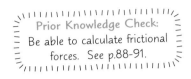

1. Taking moments about *A*:

$T \sin 45° \times (1.2 - 0.4) = 2g \times 0.6$

$T \sin 45° = 14.7 \Rightarrow T = 20.788...$
$= \boxed{20.8 \text{ N (3 s.f.)}}$

2. Split the reaction into horizontal and vertical components, R_H and R_{V}, and draw a diagram — you can work out in which directions the components act by considering the other forces.

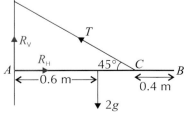

The rod is in equilibrium so the horizontal and vertical components of all the forces acting on the rod must sum to zero.

- The downward force of the rod's weight ($2g = 19.6$ N) is greater than the upward vertical component of the tension ($T \sin 45° = 14.7$ N), so the reaction will act **upwards.**

- The horizontal component of the tension in the string acts on the rod to the left, so the horizontal component of the reaction will act to the **right**.

3. Resolving horizontally: $\qquad$ $R_{\text{H}} = T\cos 45° = (20.788...)\cos 45° = 14.7$ N

4. Resolving vertically: $\qquad$ $R_{\text{V}} + T\sin 45° = 2g \Rightarrow R_{\text{V}} = 4.9$ N

5. Use Pythagoras' theorem to find R, the magnitude of the reaction at A.

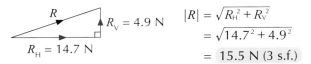

$|R| = \sqrt{R_{\text{H}}^2 + R_{\text{V}}^2}$
$= \sqrt{14.7^2 + 4.9^2}$
$= \boxed{15.5 \text{ N (3 s.f.)}}$

Example 2

A non-uniform rod, AB, of length 6 m and mass 0.1 kg, is freely hinged on a vertical wall. The rod is supported by a light strut at an angle of 70° to the wall, as shown. The strut exerts a thrust of 16 N at the midpoint of the rod. A particle of weight 2 N rests at B, and the rod is horizontal and in equilibrium.

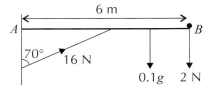

Find the distance of the centre of mass of the rod from A, and the magnitude and direction of the reaction force on the rod at A.

1. Let x be the distance of the centre of mass of the rod from A. Take moments about A.

$(0.1g \times x) + (2 \times 6) = 16\cos 70° \times 3$
$0.1gx = 4.416...$
$\Rightarrow x = 4.507... = \boxed{4.51 \text{ m (3 s.f.)}}$

2. Split the reaction into its horizontal and vertical components, R_{H} and R_{V}, and draw a diagram.

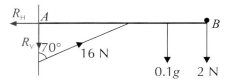

- The horizontal component of the thrust in the strut acts on the rod to the right, so the horizontal component of the reaction will act to the **left**.

- The upward vertical component of the thrust in the strut (16 cos 70° = 5.472... N) is greater than the downward force of the two weights (0.1g + 2 = 2.98 N), so the reaction will act **downwards**.

3. Resolving horizontally: $\qquad$ $R_{\text{H}} = 16\sin 70° = 15.035...$ N

4. Resolving vertically: $\qquad$ $R_{\text{V}} + 0.1g + 2 = 16\cos 70° \Rightarrow R_{\text{V}} = 2.492...$ N

5. Using Pythagoras' theorem to find the magnitude:

$|R| = \sqrt{R_{\text{H}}^2 + R_{\text{V}}^2} = \sqrt{(15.035...)^2 + (2.492...)^2}$
$= \boxed{15.2 \text{ N (3 s.f.)}}$

6. Use trigonometry to find the direction (the direction of a force is measured anticlockwise from the horizontal):

Angle clockwise from the downwards vertical:
$\theta = \tan^{-1}\left(\dfrac{15.035...}{2.492...}\right) = 80.58...°$

So direction = 270° − 80.58...° = $\boxed{189° \text{ (3 s.f.)}}$

Q1 A uniform rod, *AB*, of mass 3 kg and length 4 m, is freely hinged to a vertical wall at *A*. The rod is held horizontal in equilibrium by a light vertical wire attached to the rod 1 m from *A*, as shown. The reaction force, *R*, at the hinge, acts vertically downwards.

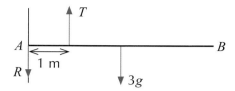

a) Find the magnitude of the tension in the wire.

b) Find the magnitude of the reaction force, *R*, acting on the rod at *A*.

Q1 Hint: The only other forces acting on the rod are vertical, so *R* must also be vertical.

Q2 A uniform rod, *AB*, of mass 0.6 kg and length 0.8 m, is freely hinged to a vertical wall at *A*. The rod is held horizontally and in equilibrium by a light wire attached to the rod 0.6 m from *A*. The wire makes an angle of 60° with the rod, as shown.

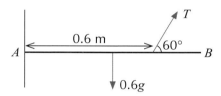

a) Find the magnitude of the tension in the wire.

b) Find the magnitude and direction of the reaction force acting on the rod at *A*.

Q3 A non-uniform beam, *AB*, of mass 1.5 kg and length 2.4 m, is freely hinged to a vertical wall at *A*. The centre of mass of the beam is 0.6 m from *A*. One end of a light, inextensible string is attached to *B*, and the other end is fixed to the wall, directly above *A*, as shown below.

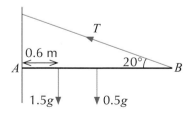

The string makes an angle of 20° with the beam. A body of mass 0.5 kg is placed at the beam's midpoint. The beam is horizontal and in equilibrium. Find:

a) the tension in the string.

b) the magnitude and direction of the reaction force acting on the beam at *A*.

Q4   A non-uniform rod, *AB*, of mass 1.8 kg and length 7 m, is freely hinged to a vertical wall at *A*. A light strut, fixed to the wall, supports the rod at its midpoint, so the rod is kept horizontal and in equilibrium. The strut makes an angle of 71° with the wall, and the thrust in the strut has magnitude 95 N. A force of magnitude 3.5 N is applied to the rod at *B*, at an angle of 80° to the rod, as shown below.

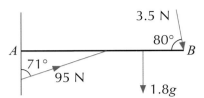

a) Find the distance of the centre of mass of the rod from *A*.

b) Find the magnitude and direction of the reaction force acting on the rod at *A*.

Q5   A uniform plank, *AB*, of mass 1.75 kg and length 8 m, is freely hinged to a vertical wall at *A*. An object of mass 2.25 kg is placed on the plank at *B*. The plank is kept horizontal and in equilibrium by a light wire fixed at its midpoint, at an angle of 30° above the plank, and a light strut fixed at *C*, 2 m along the plank from *A*, at an angle of 30° to the wall, as shown. The thrust in the strut has magnitude 110 N.

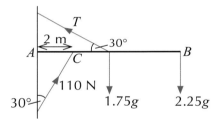

a) Find *T*, the magnitude of the tension in the wire.

b) Calculate the magnitude and direction of the reaction force acting on the plank at *A*.

Q6   A uniform beam, *AB*, of mass 2 kg and length 1.6 m, is freely hinged to a vertical wall at *A*. The beam is held horizontally in equilibrium by a force of magnitude 30 N applied at *B*, at an angle α to the horizontal, as shown.

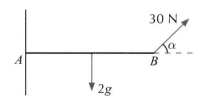

a) Find the value of α.

b) Find the magnitude and direction of the reaction force in the hinge at *A*.

Q7   A pub sign is suspended from a uniform rod, *AB*, of mass 2 kg and length 1 m by a pair of light, inextensible strings attached 20 cm from each end. The rod is held in equilibrium by a light wire attached at *B*, which makes an angle of 25° with the horizontal. Given that the tension in each string has a magnitude of 8 N, find the magnitude of the tension in the wire, T_W, and the magnitude and direction of the reaction force on the rod at *A*.

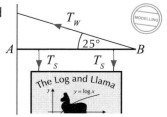

Friction

You saw in Chapter 5 that if a body is in contact with a **rough** surface, then a **frictional force** will act between the body and the surface to oppose motion. The frictional force can take a range of values, and will reach its maximum ($F = \mu R$) when the body is **on the point of moving**, or in 'limiting equilibrium'.

So if you have a rigid body resting on a rough surface, you will have a **normal reaction** force acting **perpendicular** to the surface, and a **frictional force** acting **parallel** to it, in the **opposite** direction to any potential motion.

Example 1

A non-uniform rod, AB, rests against a rough vertical wall at A. The rod is held in limiting equilibrium perpendicular to the wall by a light, inextensible string attached at B at an angle of $22°$ above the rod.

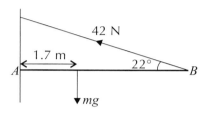

The tension in the string is 42 N, the length of the rod is 5.5 m and the centre of mass of the rod is 1.7 m from A.

Find the mass of the rod, m, and the coefficient of friction, μ, between the wall and the rod.

1. Taking moments about A:

    $mg \times 1.7 = 42 \sin 22° \times 5.5$
    $\Rightarrow m = 86.534... \div 16.66 = 5.194...$
    $= \boxed{5.19 \text{ kg (3 s.f.)}}$

2. Now draw a diagram showing the forces at A.

    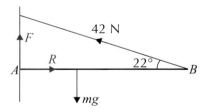

    *   The normal reaction of the wall on the rod acts **perpendicular** to the wall and the frictional force acts **parallel** to the wall, in the opposite direction to potential motion at the wall.

    *   The weight of the rod ($mg = 50.902...$ N) is greater than the upwards vertical component of the tension in the string ($42 \sin 22° = 15.733...$ N), so potential movement is downwards at A — so the frictional force at A acts **upwards**.

3. Resolving horizontally:

    $R = 42 \cos 22° = 38.941...$ N

4. Resolving vertically:

    $F + 42 \sin 22° = mg$
    $\Rightarrow F = 50.902... - 15.733... = 35.168...$ N

5. The rod is in limiting equilibrium, so friction is at its maximum:

    $F = \mu R$
    $35.168... = \mu \times 38.941... \Rightarrow \boxed{\mu = 0.90 \text{ (2 d.p.)}}$

> **Tip:** R is the normal reaction of the wall on the rod — don't confuse it with the reaction in the hinge in the examples in the previous section. There's no hinge here — it's friction which keeps the rod from slipping on the wall.

'Ladder' questions

You might see a question where a rigid body rests at an angle against the ground and a wall — a simple example of a situation like this is a **ladder**.

In these questions, you'll need to consider the **normal reaction** of the **ground**, the **normal reaction** of the **wall**, and any **frictional forces** which may be acting. The question will tell you whether the ground and wall are **rough** or **smooth** — this lets you know whether you need to take friction into account in your calculations.

There are four possible combinations of surfaces for ladder-style questions:

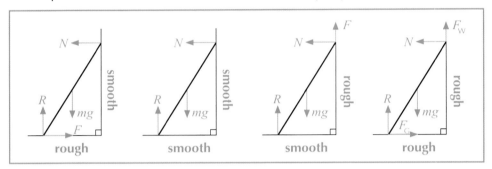

Friction acts to prevent motion. In each case, think about which way the ladder would slip — the frictional force will act in the opposite direction.

Example 2

A ladder rests against a smooth vertical wall at an angle of 65° to rough horizontal ground. The ladder has mass 4.5 kg and length $5x$ m. A cat of mass 1.3 kg sits on the ladder at C, $4x$ m from the base. The ladder is in limiting equilibrium. Modelling the ladder as a uniform rod and the cat as a particle, find the coefficient of friction between the ground and the ladder.

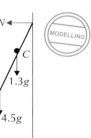

1. Draw a diagram to show the forces acting between the ladder and the ground, and the ladder and the wall:

   - N is the normal reaction at the wall and R is the normal reaction at the ground.
   - The wall is smooth, so there is no frictional force.
   - The ground is rough, so there is a frictional force between it and the ladder.

2. Take moments about the base of the ladder.

   $N \sin 65° \times 5x = (4.5g \cos 65° \times 2.5x) + (1.3g \cos 65° \times 4x)$
   $(4.531...)xN = (46.593..)x + (21.536...)x$
   $\Rightarrow N = (68.130...)x \div (4.531...)x = 15.034...$ N

3. Resolving vertically:

   $R = 1.3g + 4.5g = 56.84$ N

4. Resolving horizontally:

   $F = N = 15.024...$ N

5. Using the fact that the ladder is in limiting equilibrium:

   $F = \mu R$
   $15.034... = \mu \times 56.84$
   $\Rightarrow \mu = 15.034... \div 56.84 = \boxed{0.26 \text{ (2 d.p.)}}$

Example 3

A uniform ladder of mass 11 kg and length 4 m rests against a smooth vertical wall, at an angle of 58° to rough horizontal ground. The coefficient of friction between the ladder and the ground is 0.45. A bucket of water is hung 3 m from the base of the ladder.

What is the maximum possible mass of the bucket of water for which the ladder remains in equilibrium?

1. Draw a diagram to show what's going on:

2. Resolving vertically: $R = 11g + mg = g(11 + m)$

3. Resolving horizontally: $F = N$

4. When the bucket is at its maximum mass, the ladder is on the point of slipping — i.e. in limiting equilibrium. $F = \mu R \Rightarrow N = 0.45R = 0.45g(11 + m)$

5. Taking moments about the base of the ladder:

$$N \sin 58° \times 4 = (11g \cos 58° \times 2) + (mg \cos 58° \times 3)$$
$$1.8g(11 + m) \sin 58° = 22g \cos 58° + 3mg \cos 58°$$
$$19.8 \sin 58° - 22 \cos 58° = m(3 \cos 58° - 1.8 \sin 58°)$$
$$\Rightarrow m = 5.133... \div 0.06327... = \boxed{81.1 \text{ kg (3 s.f.)}}$$

Example 4

A uniform ladder of length 6 m and mass 16 kg is held against a rough vertical wall by a horizontal force of magnitude 50 N, applied at a distance of x m from the base of the ladder. Given that the ladder is inclined at an angle of 70° to the smooth horizontal ground, and that the coefficient of friction between the ladder and the wall is 0.6, find the range of possible values for x so that the ladder remains in equilibrium.

To solve this, you need to find the value of x when the ladder is about to slide towards the wall, and when it is on the point of sliding towards the floor.

First consider the situation where the ladder is about to slide towards the ground.

1. Draw a diagram to show the forces on the ladder:

2. Resolving forces horizontally: $N = 50$ N

3. The ladder is in limiting equilibrium, so $F = \mu R$: $F = \mu N \Rightarrow F = 0.6 \times 50 = 30$ N

4. Taking moments about the base of the ladder:

$$(50 \sin 70° \times x) + (16g \cos 70° \times 3)$$
$$= (N \sin 70° \times 6) + (F \cos 70° \times 6)$$
$$(50 \sin 70°)x + 470.4 \cos 70° = 300 \sin 70° + 180 \cos 70°$$
$$(50 \sin 70°)x = 300 \sin 70° + 180 \cos 70° - 470.4 \cos 70°$$
$$x = 182.58... \div 46.984... = \boxed{3.886... \text{ m}}$$

Now consider the situation where the ladder is on the point of sliding towards the wall.

5. Draw a new diagram showing the forces on the ladder:

6. Resolving forces horizontally: $N = 50 \text{ N} \Rightarrow F = 30 \text{ N}$

7. Taking moments about the base of the ladder:

$(50 \sin 70° \times x) + (16g \cos 70° \times 3)$
$\qquad\qquad + (F \cos 70° \times 6) = (N \sin 70° \times 6)$

> **Tip:** The calculation here is almost identical to the one before, except that the friction term has changed sign.

$(50 \sin 70°)x + 470.4 \cos 70° + 180 \cos 70° = 300 \sin 70°$

$(50 \sin 70°)x = 300 \sin 70° - 180 \cos 70° - 470.4 \cos 70°$

$x = 59.457... \div 46.984... = 1.265... \text{ m}$

So the range of values of x for which the ladder is in equilibrium is: 1.265... m $\le x \le$ 3.886... m

Bodies supported along their lengths

Rather than leaning against a wall, a rigid body may be held in equilibrium by resting on **supports** at points along its length. You can solve problems like this just as before, by **resolving forces** and **taking moments**.

You need to know whether the **ground** and **supports** are **rough** or **smooth**, and you should also remember that the **normal reaction** at a **support** will always act **perpendicular** to the body.

Example 5

A uniform rod, *AB*, of length 3.3 m and weight 10 N, rests with *A* on rough horizontal ground. The rod is supported by a smooth peg at *C*, where *AC* = 2.4 m, in such a way that the rod makes an angle of 28° with the ground. A particle of weight 25 N is placed at *B*.

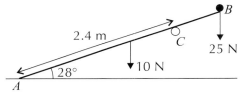

Given that the rod is in limiting equilibrium, find the magnitude of the normal reaction, *N*, at the peg and the magnitude of the frictional force, *F*, between the rod and the ground.

1. Draw a diagram to show the forces acting on the rod:

> **Tip:** The rod's weight acts at its midpoint, 1.65 m from *A*.

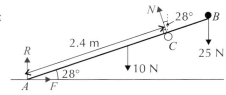

2. Taking moments about *A*:

$2.4N = (10 \cos 28° \times 1.65) + (25 \cos 28° \times 3.3)$
$\Rightarrow N = 36.421... = 36.4 \text{ N (3 s.f.)}$

3. Resolving horizontally:

$F = N \sin 28° = (36.421...) \sin 28°$
$\qquad = 17.1 \text{ N (3 s.f.)}$

Exercise 6.2.2

Q1 A uniform rod, *AB*, of mass 12 kg and length 16 m, rests against a rough, vertical wall at *A*. The rod is held horizontally in limiting equilibrium by a light wire attached at *B*, at an angle of 20° to the rod, as shown.

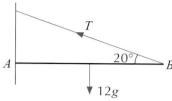

a) Find the magnitude of the tension in the wire.

b) Find the coefficient of friction between the wall and the rod.

Q2 A uniform ladder of mass 11 kg and length 7 m rests against a rough vertical wall, at an angle of 60° to smooth, horizontal ground, as shown. A horizontal force of magnitude 35 N is applied to the base of the ladder, keeping it in limiting equilibrium, with the ladder on the point of sliding up the wall.

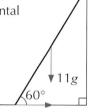

a) Find the magnitude of the normal reaction of the wall on the ladder.

b) Find the frictional force between the wall and the ladder.

c) Find the coefficient of friction between the wall and the ladder.

Q3 A uniform beam, *AB*, of mass 1.6 kg and length 1.5 m, rests with *A* on rough, horizontal ground. The beam is supported by a smooth peg at *C*, where *AC* = 1.1 m, so that it makes an angle of 20° with the horizontal, as shown.

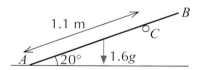

The beam is on the point of slipping. Find:

a) the magnitude of the normal reaction of the peg on the beam,

b) the magnitude of the normal reaction of the ground on the beam,

c) the magnitude of the frictional force between the ground and the beam,

d) the coefficient of friction between the ground and the beam.

Q4 Eliza is holding a nail in place against a rough wall. The nail is modelled as a uniform rod with length 5 cm and mass 2 grams. Eliza applies a force *D* with her finger, acting at an angle of $\theta°$ to the horizontal, such that the nail is horizontal and in equilibrium, and is on the point of slipping down the wall. Given that the coefficient of friction between the nail and the wall is $\mu = 0.7$, calculate the magnitude of the force *D* and the angle θ.

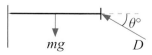

Q5 A uniform rod, AB, of mass 20 kg and length 2 m, is held horizontally in equilibrium against a rough wall by a light wire fixed to the wall at point C, which is 1 m above point A. The other end of the wire is attached at B.

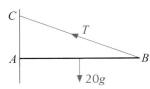

Given that the rod is on the point of slipping down the wall, find the tension in the wire and the coefficient of friction between the rod and the wall.

Q6 A uniform ladder of mass 10 kg and length 6 m rests with one end on rough, horizontal ground and the other end against a smooth, vertical wall. The coefficient of friction between the ground and the ladder is 0.3, and the ladder makes an angle of 65° with the ground. A girl of mass 50 kg begins to climb the ladder. How far up the ladder can she climb before the ladder slips?

Q7 A uniform ladder of length 4 m and weight 80 N rests against a smooth, vertical wall on rough horizontal ground. The ladder makes an angle of 50° with the horizontal, and the coefficient of friction between the ground and the ladder is 0.75. A horizontal force, D, is exerted on the ladder, 3 m from its base. Given that the ladder is on the point of slipping down the wall, find the magnitude of D, stating whether the force acts towards or away from the wall.

Q8 A uniform ladder of mass 9 kg and length 4.8 m rests in limiting equilibrium with one end on rough, horizontal ground and the other end against a rough, vertical wall. The normal reactions at the wall and the ground have magnitude 22 N and 75 N respectively. Find:

a) the angle that the ladder makes with the ground,

b) the coefficient of friction between the wall and the ladder,

c) the coefficient of friction between the ground and the ladder.

Q9 A non-uniform plank, AB, of mass 5.4 kg and length 11 m, rests with A against a rough, vertical wall. A wire with tension of magnitude 86 N is fixed to B, at an angle of 10° to the plank, keeping the plank horizontal. A particle of mass M kg rests on the plank at B, as shown. The plank is in limiting equilibrium.

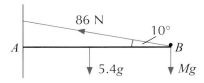

Given that the coefficient of friction between the wall and the plank is 0.55, find:

a) the value of M,

b) the distance of the centre of mass of the plank from A.

Q10 Robert holds an 8 m uniform ladder in place against a smooth vertical wall by applying a horizontal force of K N to it, 1 m from the base of the ladder. The ladder weighs 100 N, and makes an angle of 75° with the rough horizontal floor, where $\mu = 0.1$. Given that the ladder remains at rest, find the range of possible values for the magnitude of the force K.

Q11 A uniform beam, AB, of weight W N rests in limiting equilibrium at an angle of 30° to the horizontal on a rough peg at A and a smooth peg at C, where $AC = 0.75AB$. The reaction forces at A and C are both perpendicular to the beam.

Q11 Hint: The reaction forces at A and C both act perpendicular to the beam, so resolve forces parallel and perpendicular to the beam, rather than horizontally and vertically.

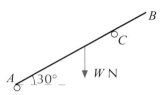

Find the coefficient of friction between the peg and the beam at A.

Q12 A uniform beam AB of weight 12 N and length 5 m rests on a smooth surface at A and a rough peg at C, 4 m from A. The beam makes an angle of 40° with the horizontal.

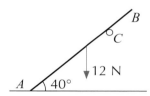

Given that the beam is in equilibrium, find the range of possible values of the coefficient of friction between the beam and the peg.

Q13 A uniform ladder of mass 25 kg and length 9 m rests with one end on rough, horizontal ground and the other end against a smooth, vertical wall. The ladder makes an angle of 68° with the horizontal, as shown. A window cleaner of mass 76 kg stands two-thirds of the way up the ladder, and the ladder is in equilibrium. Find the range of possible values of the coefficient of friction between the ground and the ladder.

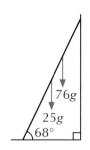

Q14 A uniform beam, AB, of weight 50 N and length 2 m, rests with A on rough, horizontal ground, as shown. The beam is supported at an angle of 35° to the ground by a smooth peg at C, where $AC = 1.4$ m. A horizontal force of magnitude 10 N is applied to the beam at B.

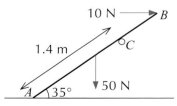

Find the range of values of the coefficient of friction between the ground and the beam for which the beam will remain in equilibrium.

Review Exercise

Q1 A horizontal uniform rod AB of length 12 m and mass 1.6 kg is acted on by an upward vertical force of magnitude 23 N at B. Find the sum of the moments about A.

Q2 The diagram shows a light rod held horizontally in equilibrium by two vertical strings. Find the magnitudes of the forces P and Q.

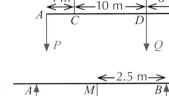

Q3 A non-uniform rod of mass 1.5 kg rests horizontally in equilibrium on supports at A and B, as shown. When a downwards force of magnitude F N is applied to the rod at C, the rod remains horizontal and in equilibrium, but is on the point of tilting about B, where the normal reaction has magnitude 44 N. Given that the distance between B and the centre of mass of the rod is 2.5 m, find:

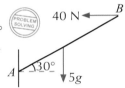

a) the value of F, b) the distance between the points B and C.

Q4 A non-uniform beam, AB, of mass 5 kg and length b m, is freely hinged to a vertical wall at A. The beam is held in equilibrium at an angle of 30° to the horizontal by a force of magnitude 40 N, applied horizontally at B, as shown. Find the distance of the centre of mass of the beam from A. Give your answer in surd form in terms of b and g.

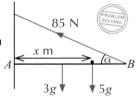

Q5 A uniform rod, AB, of mass 3 kg and length 1.2 m, rests horizontally in equilibrium with A against a rough, vertical wall. A wire is attached to the rod at B. The other end of the wire is attached to the wall, 0.9 m directly above A. A particle of mass 5 kg rests on the rod, x m from A, as shown, and the tension in the wire has magnitude 85 N. Find:

a) the value of x,

b) the range of possible values for the coefficient of friction between the wall and rod at A.

Q6 A uniform ladder of mass 20 kg rests with one end on rough, horizontal ground, and the other end against a smooth, vertical wall. The ladder makes an angle of 60° with the horizontal, and is on the point of slipping.

a) Show that the coefficient of friction between the ladder and the ground is $\frac{\sqrt{3}}{6}$.

b) A person of mass 60 kg stands three-quarters of the way up the ladder. Find the magnitude of the minimum horizontal force which must be applied to the base of the ladder to keep it in limiting equilibrium.

Q7 A uniform beam, AB, of mass 14 kg and length 15 m, rests with A on rough, horizontal ground. The beam is supported by a smooth peg at C, where $AC = 13$ m, so that it makes an angle of 18° with the horizontal, as shown. The beam is on the point of slipping. Find the coefficient of friction between the ground and the beam at A.

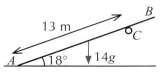

Q1 A uniform lamina has sides of length 5 cm and 3 cm, and a mass of 2 kg.
It is pivoted at point A, as shown, and is held in equilibrium at an angle α
to the horizontal by a horizontal force of 26 N.

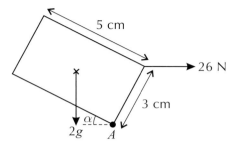

Find the angle α, giving your answer to 3 significant figures.

[4 marks]

Q2 A uniform rod AB of mass m is freely hinged to a fixed vertical wall at A. A particle
of mass $0.5m$ is attached to the end of the rod at B. The particle is held in equilibrium
with the rod at an angle of $30°$ to the horizontal by a force F acting at an angle of $60°$
to the rod at B as shown below.

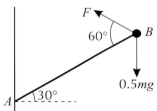

a) Find the magnitude of F.

[2 marks]

b) Find the magnitude (in terms of mg) and direction of the force acting on the rod at A.

[6 marks]

Q3 A ladder is leaning against a rough vertical wall and is resting on rough horizontal ground
at an angle of $45°$ to the horizontal. The ladder has mass m and length $2l$.

A man of mass $3m$ stands at a point $\frac{2}{3}l$ up the ladder. The coefficient of friction
between the ladder and the wall is 2μ and between the ladder and the ground is 3μ.

a) Show that $mg = \frac{R}{4}(1 + 6\mu^2)$, where R is the reaction force
between the ladder and the ground.

[3 marks]

b) Given that the ladder is on the point of slipping, show that $\mu = 0.11$ to 2 d.p.

[4 marks]

Practice Paper

Q1   The density of air pollution particles, p mg m^{-3}, recorded d metres from a major road is shown in the table below.

Distance from road, d metres	5	45	100	175	200	220	260	300
Pollution particle density, p mg m^{-3}	0.55	0.39	0.42	0.24	0.13	0.26	0.05	0.09

   a) Calculate the product moment correlation coefficient for the data.

   [1 mark]

   b) Interpret your answer to part a).

   [2 marks]

   c) Stating your hypotheses clearly, test at the 1% significance level whether or not there is a negative correlation between the distance from the road and the density of air pollution particles.

   [3 marks]

Q2   At a nature reserve, it is estimated that 10% of toads are rare natterjack toads. A random sample of 80 toads from the nature reserve is selected.

   a) Use a normal approximation to find the probability that there are more than 5 but fewer than 10 natterjack toads in the sample.

   [3 marks]

   b) Explain why a normal approximation is justified in this case.

   [1 mark]

Q3   For the events A and B:

$$P(A) = 0.36, \quad P(B) = 0.18, \quad P(A \cap B') = 0.2952$$

   a) Find $P(A' \cap B')$.

   [2 marks]

   b) Show that events A and B are independent.

   [2 marks]

   For another event C, $P(C'|A) = 0.25$ and $P(C'|A') = 0.5$.

   c) Find $P(C)$.

   [3 marks]

Q4 The number of bacterial cells, P, left in a petri dish t minutes after exposure to a disinfectant is recorded every 5 minutes for an hour starting at $t = 0$, then every 10 minutes for the following hour. It is found that the relationship between P and t can be modelled by the equation $P = ab^t$, where a and b are constants.

The regression line of $\log P$ on t is $\log P = 7.17 - 0.45t$.

a) Find the values of a and b.

[3 marks]

b) State the range of values of t for which it is suitable to use the regression line to find an estimate for P.

[1 mark]

Q5 The heights of the palm trees on a tropical island are normally distributed. The probability that a randomly selected palm tree is shorter than 4.5 m is 0.5793 and the probability that it is taller than 5.5 m is 0.0626.

a) Find the mean and standard deviation of the palm trees on the island to 2 d.p.

[4 marks]

A random sample of 15 palm trees on a second island are found to have a mean height of 4.7 m. The variance in height of the trees on the second island is the same as on the first island.

b) Using your rounded answers to part a), test whether or not the mean heights of the palm trees on the two islands are different at the 5% significance level. State your hypotheses clearly.

[5 marks]

Q6 A non-uniform rod AB with length 2 m and mass 3 kg is held in equilibrium by two smooth supports at C, 0.4 m from A, and D, 0.2 m from B, as shown below. The reaction force at D has twice the magnitude of the reaction force at C.

a) Find the distance of the centre of mass of the rod from B.

[4 marks]

A particle with mass m kg is placed on the rod 0.15 m from A.

b) Given that the rod is now on the point of turning about C, calculate the magnitude of the reaction force at C to 3 significant figures.

[5 marks]

Practice Paper

Q7   A tennis ball is projected with velocity $(5\mathbf{i} + 12\mathbf{j})$ ms⁻¹ from a platform x m above the ground.

a) Calculate the amount of time, in seconds, that the tennis ball spends
at a height greater than its initial point of projection.

[3 marks]

A wall of height 6.5 m stands at a horizontal distance of 9 m from the point of projection.

b) Given that the ball just goes over the wall on its descent, find x.

[4 marks]

Q8   The acceleration of a particle P over time t is given by $\mathbf{a} = [12t\mathbf{i} - 2\mathbf{j}]$ ms⁻²,
where $\mathbf{i}$ and $\mathbf{j}$ are unit vectors due east and north respectively.

Initially, P moves with velocity $\mathbf{v} = -\mathbf{i}$ ms⁻¹, and after 1 second,
the particle's displacement is $\mathbf{r} = (\mathbf{i} + 3\mathbf{j})$ m.

Find the position vector of the particle P at time t.

[4 marks]

Q9   Two particles A and B, with masses of 4 kg and 5 kg respectively, are attached
to the ends of a light, inextensible string which passes over a smooth, fixed pulley.

Particle A lies on a rough plane inclined at an angle α to the horizontal,
where $\tan \alpha = \frac{3}{4}$, and particle B hangs freely below the pulley, as shown.

The particles are released from rest, and accelerate at a rate of 2 ms⁻².

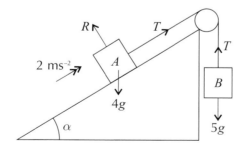

a) Find the coefficient of friction, μ, between A and the rough plane.

[5 marks]

After two seconds, the string is cut. At the instant that the string
is cut, A is 1.2 m down the plane from the pulley.

b) Show that A does not hit the pulley in the subsequent motion.

[5 marks]

Answers

Chapter 1: Correlation and Regression

1.1 Regression

Exercise 1.1.1 — Correlation and linear regression

Q1 **a)** Number of shots is the explanatory variable and number of goals is the response variable.

    b) b = 0.2 > 0, so this is positive correlation.

    c) Use $x = 5$ in the regression line:
$y = 0.2(5) - 1.1 = -0.1$

    d) This estimate is unreliable because 5 shots is an extrapolation — there is no evidence that the relationship continues outside the data range. The estimate must be unreliable in this case because it is impossible to score a negative number of goals in a football match.

Exercise 1.1.2 — Linear regression with coded data

Q1 Substitute the expressions defining p and q into the equation of the regression line for q on p. This gives you an equation involving just x and y.
$q = 40 + 2p$, so $y - 50 = 40 + 2(x - 7)$

Now rearrange this so it is in the form $y = a + bx$, where a and b are constants.
$y = 40 + 2x - 14 + 50 = 76 + 2x$
So the equation of the regression line of y on x is
$y = 76 + 2x$.

Q2 **a)** Substitute expressions for x and y into the regression equation: $t - 29 = 22.4 - 4.8\frac{s}{10}$
This means that: $t = 51.4 - 0.48s$

    b) When $s = 9$,
$t = 51.4 - 0.48(9) = 51.4 - 4.32 = 47.08$
The smallest observed value of x is 1, which corresponds to $s = 10$, so $s = 9$ is an extrapolated value and the estimate may not be accurate.
You could also say that s = 9 corresponds to a value of x = 0.9, which is less than the smallest x-value.

Q3 Take logs of both sides of the equation $y = ab^x$ to get:
$\log y = x\log b + \log a$
Comparing this to the equation of a straight line:
gradient $= \log b = 0.032 \Rightarrow b = 10^{0.032} = 1.08$ (3 s.f.)
intercept $= \log a = 0.315 \Rightarrow a = 10^{0.315} = 2.07$ (3 s.f.)
(So $y \approx 2.07 \times 1.08^x$)

Q4 Take logs of both sides of the equation $p = at^b$ to get:
$\log p = b \log t + \log a$
Comparing this to the equation of a straight line:
gradient $= b = 0.1596 = 0.160$ (3 s.f.)
intercept $= \log a = 1.1723$
$\Rightarrow a = 10^{1.1723} = 14.869... = 14.9$ (3 s.f.)
(So $p \approx 14.9t^{0.160}$)

1.2 The Product Moment Correlation Coefficient

Exercise 1.2.1 — Finding the PMCC

Q1 **a)** $r = 0.852$ is close to 1, so there appears to be a strong positive correlation between the variables.

    b) $r = -0.0551$ is very close to zero, so there appears to be little or no correlation between the variables.

    c) $r = -0.483$ is just closer to 0 than -1, so there appears to be a fairly weak negative correlation between the variables.

Q2 Input the x and y values into the correct statistical function on your calculator to calculate
$r = 0.427$ to 3 s.f.
This is just closer to 0 than 1, so there appears to be a fairly weak positive correlation between the heights and weights of the teenage boys.

Q3 Input the p and q values into the correct statistical function on your calculator to calculate
$r = -0.419$ to 3 s.f.
This is just closer to 0 than -1, so there appears to be a fairly weak negative correlation between p and q.

Q4 Input the a and s values into the correct statistical function on your calculator to calculate
$r = -0.723$ to 3 s.f.
This is quite close to -1, and so there is a fairly strong negative correlation between the age of a patient (a) and their score on the memory test (s). The older a patient is (i.e. the higher the value of a), the lower their score on the memory test tends to be (i.e. the lower the value of s).
Remember that when you're asked to interpret a correlation in context, you can't just describe it — you need to relate it back to the context.

Exercise 1.2.2 — PMCC hypothesis testing

Q1 The test statistic is $r = 0.5749$.
This is a one-tailed test, so the hypotheses are H_0: $\rho = 0$ and H_1: $\rho > 0$.
Test for significance using $\alpha = 0.025$ and sample size 12.
Using the critical values table, the critical value is 0.5760, so you would reject H_0 if $r \geq 0.5760$.
Since $0.5749 < 0.5760$, there is insufficient evidence at the 2.5% level of significance to reject H_0 and to support the alternative hypothesis that there is positive correlation between the ages and weights of the baby elephants.

Q2 a) Input the values into the correct statistical function on your calculator. This gives $r = 0.9940$ to 4 d.p.

b) The test statistic is $r = 0.9940$.
This is a one-tailed test, so the hypotheses are H_0: $\rho = 0$ and H_1: $\rho > 0$.
Test for significance using $\alpha = 0.025$ and sample size 8.
Using the critical values table, the critical value is 0.7067, so you would reject H_0 if $r \geq 0.7067$.
Since $0.9940 > 0.7067$ the result is significant.
There is evidence at the 2.5% level of significance to reject H_0 and to support the alternative hypothesis that the length and width of leaves are positively correlated.

Q3 a) This is a two-tailed test, so the hypotheses are H_0: $\rho = 0$ and H_1: $\rho \neq 0$.
$\alpha = 0.05$, so you want the critical value for $\frac{\alpha}{2} = \frac{0.05}{2} = 0.025$.
Test for significance with $\alpha = 0.025$ and sample size 9.
Using the critical values table the critical value is 0.6664, so the critical region is $r \geq 0.6664$ or $r \leq -0.6664$.

b) Input the values into the correct statistical function on your calculator. This gives $r = -0.6628$ to 4 d.p.

c) You would reject H_0 if $r \geq 0.6664$ or $r \leq -0.6664$.
$r = -0.6628$ is outside the critical region so there is insufficient evidence to reject H_0 and to support the alternative hypothesis that kidney function and weight are correlated.

Review Exercise — Chapter 1

Q1 a) Explanatory variable = number of hours spent designing the cover, response variable = number of books sold in the first year.

b) Gradient of regression line = $429.5 > 0$, so there is positive correlation between the variables.

c) The gradient of 429.5 suggests that for every additional hour spent on the cover design, the sales in the first year will increase by around 429.5.

d) Use $h = 6$ in the regression line:
$b = 1374.7 + 429.5(6) = 3951.7 \approx 3950$ (3 s.f.)
This is interpolation so the estimate should be reliable.

Q2 Substitute expressions for x and y into the regression equation:
$y = 1.8x + 50 \Rightarrow \frac{n}{2000} = 1.8(c - 150) + 50$
$\Rightarrow n = 3600(c - 150) + 100\,000$
So the regression line of n on c is:
$n = 3600c - 440\,000$

Q3 Take logs of both sides of the equation $y = kb^x$ to get:
$\log y = x\log b + \log k$
Comparing this to the equation of a straight line:
gradient $= \log b = 0.0963$
$\Rightarrow b = 10^{0.0963} = 1.25$ (3 s.f.)
intercept $= \log k = 0.3873$
$\Rightarrow k = 10^{0.3873} = 2.44$ (3 s.f.)
(So $y \approx 2.44 \times 1.25^x$)

Q4 r must be positive and fairly close to zero, so $r = 0.313$ is the most likely value.

Q5 $r = -0.701$ (3 s.f.)
This shows fairly strong negative correlation between x and y.

Q6 The test statistic is $r = 0.5152$.
This is a one-tailed test, so the hypotheses are H_0: $\rho = 0$ and H_1: $\rho > 0$.
Test for significance using $\alpha = 0.025$ and sample size 15.
Using the critical values table, the critical value is 0.5140, so you would reject H_0 if $r \geq 0.5140$.
Since $0.5152 > 0.5140$, there is evidence at the 2.5% level of significance to reject H_0 and to support the alternative hypothesis that there is positive correlation between the amount spent on food and the amount spent on petrol.

Q7 The test statistic is $r = 0.7126$.
This is a two-tailed test, so the hypotheses are H_0: $\rho = 0$ and H_1: $\rho \neq 0$.
$\alpha = 0.01$, so you want the critical value for $\frac{\alpha}{2} = \frac{0.01}{2} = 0.005$.
Test for significance with $\alpha = 0.005$ and sample size 12. Using the critical values table, the critical value is 0.7079.
$0.7126 > 0.7079$, so there is evidence at the 1% level of significance to reject H_0 and support the alternative hypothesis that there is some correlation between the age of a painting and its value.

Exam-Style Questions — Chapter 1

Q1 a) Input the x and y values into the correct statistical function on your calculator to calculate $r = 0.986$ to 3 s.f.
[1 mark for correct answer]

b) r is close to 1 so there is a strong positive correlation between the amount of time and the amount of money spent. The longer a customer spent in the supermarket, the more money they spent — and vice versa.
[2 marks available — 1 mark for identifying strong positive correlation, 1 mark for relating to context of question]

c) Use $t = 24$ in the regression line:
$p = 1.53(24) - 18.32 = 18.4$
So the customer is predicted to spend £18.40.
[1 mark for correct answer]

Q2 Substitute the expressions defining X and Y into the equation of the regression line of Y on X. This gives an equation involving just x and y.
$\log y = 0.64 - 0.1x$
$\Rightarrow 10^{\log y} = 10^{0.64 - 0.1x}$
$\Rightarrow y = 10^{0.64} \times (10^{-0.1})^x$
$\Rightarrow y = 4.37 \times 0.794^x$ (3 s.f.)
So $p = 4.37$ and $q = 0.794$ (3 s.f.)
[4 marks available — 1 mark for removing logs, 1 mark for splitting $10^{0.64-0.1x}$ into two powers of 10, 1 mark for p, 1 mark for q]

Q3 a) Take logs of both sides of the equation $b = kd^m$ to get $\log b = m \log d + \log k$

Comparing this to the equation of a straight line:
gradient $= m = 0.71$
intercept $= \log k = 0.56 \Rightarrow k = 10^{0.56} = 3.63$ (3 s.f.)
[3 marks available — 1 mark for equation for log b in terms of log d and log k, 1 mark for m, 1 mark for k]

b) When $d = 100$, $b = kd^m$
$= 3.63 \times 100^{0.71}$
$= 95$ (to nearest whole number)
[2 marks available — 1 mark for correct method, 1 mark for correct answer]

Q4 a) Input the x and y values into the correct statistical function on your calculator to calculate $r = -0.861$ to 3 s.f.
[1 mark for correct answer]

b) The test statistic is $r = -0.861$.
This is a two-tailed test, so the hypotheses are H_0: $\rho = 0$ and H_1: $\rho \neq 0$.
$\alpha = 0.05$, so you want the critical value for $\frac{\alpha}{2} = \frac{0.05}{2} = 0.025$.
Test for significance with $\alpha = 0.025$ and sample size 8. Using the critical values table the critical value is -0.7067.
$-0.861 < -0.7067$, so there is sufficient evidence at the 5% level of significance to reject H_0 and support the alternative hypothesis that there is some correlation between height and the time taken to complete the race.
[3 marks available — 1 mark for correct hypotheses, 1 mark for correct critical value, 1 mark for correct conclusion]

Chapter 2: Probability

2.1 Conditional Probability

Exercise 2.1.1 — Conditional probability

Q1 **a)** $P(A') = 1 - P(A) = 1 - 0.3 = 0.7$

  b) $P(A \cup B) = P(A) + P(B) - P(A \cap B)$, so
  $P(A \cap B) = P(A) + P(B) - P(A \cup B)$
  $= 0.3 + 0.5 - 0.7 = 0.1$

  c) $P(A) = P(A \cap B) + P(A \cap B')$, so
  $P(A \cap B') = P(A) - P(A \cap B) = 0.3 - 0.1 = 0.2$

Q2 The probability that neither X nor Y occurs is
  $P(X' \cap Y')$
  Using $P(X \cup Y) + P(X' \cap Y') = 1$,
  $P(X' \cap Y') = 1 - P(X \cup Y)$
  Since X and Y are independent, $P(X \cap Y) = P(X)P(Y)$
  $P(X \cup Y) = P(X) + P(Y) - P(X)P(Y)$
  $= 0.8 + 0.15 - (0.8 \times 0.15) = 0.83$
  So $P(X' \cap Y') = 1 - 0.83 = 0.17$

Q3 **a)** $P(G|H) = \dfrac{P(G \cap H)}{P(H)} = \dfrac{0.24}{0.63} = \dfrac{24}{63} = \dfrac{8}{21}$

  You could give the answer as a decimal instead, but using a fraction means you can give an exact answer.

  b) $P(H|G) = \dfrac{P(G \cap H)}{P(G)} = \dfrac{0.24}{0.7} = \dfrac{24}{70} = \dfrac{12}{35}$

Q4 **a)** $P(B|A) = \dfrac{P(A \cap B)}{P(A)} = \dfrac{0.34}{0.68} = 0.5$

  b) $P(A|C) = \dfrac{P(A \cap C)}{P(C)} = \dfrac{0.16}{0.44} = \dfrac{16}{44} = \dfrac{4}{11}$

  c) $P(C'|B) = \dfrac{P(B \cap C')}{P(B)} = \dfrac{0.49}{1 - 0.44} = 0.875$

Q5 **a)** $P(J \cap K) = P(J)P(K|J) = 0.4 \times 0.2 = 0.08$
  $P(K) = \dfrac{P(J \cap K)}{P(J|K)} = \dfrac{0.08}{0.64} = 0.125$
  $P(J \cup K) = P(J) + P(K) - P(J \cap K)$
  $= 0.4 + 0.125 - 0.08 = 0.445$

  b) $P(J \cup K) + P(J' \cap K') = 1$, so
  $P(J' \cap K') = 1 - P(J \cup K) = 1 - 0.445 = 0.555$

Q6 Let F = 'over 6 feet tall' and G = 'can play in goal'.

  a) $P(G|F) = \dfrac{P(F \cap G)}{P(F)}$

  $P(F \cap G) = \dfrac{2}{11}$ and $P(F) = \dfrac{5}{11}$

  So, $P(G|F) = \dfrac{P(F \cap G)}{P(F)} = \dfrac{\frac{2}{11}}{\frac{5}{11}} = \dfrac{2}{5}$

  b) $P(F|G) = \dfrac{P(F \cap G)}{P(G)}$ and $P(G) = \dfrac{3}{11}$.

  So $P(F|G) = \dfrac{P(F \cap G)}{P(G)} = \dfrac{\frac{2}{11}}{\frac{3}{11}} = \dfrac{2}{3}$

Q7 **a)** $P(Y) = 1 - P(Y') = 1 - 0.72 = 0.28$

  b) $P(X \cap Y) = P(Y)P(X|Y) = 0.28 \times 0.75 = 0.21$

  c) $P(X \cap Z) = P(X)P(Z|X) = 0.44 \times 0.25 = 0.11$

  d) $P(Y|Z') = \dfrac{P(Y \cap Z')}{P(Z')} = \dfrac{0.2}{1 - 0.61} = \dfrac{20}{39}$

  e) $P(X \cap Y \cap Z) = P(Z)P(X \cap Y|Z)$

  $= \dfrac{61}{100} \times \dfrac{7}{61} = \dfrac{7}{100} = 0.07$

  There are lots of ways to write an expression for $P(X \cap Y \cap Z)$ — e.g. $P(X \cap Y)P(Z|X \cap Y)$ or $P(Y \cap Z)P(X|Y \cap Z)$. You have to choose the way that makes best use of the information in the question.

Q8 **a)** $P(M|A) = \dfrac{P(M \cap A)}{P(A)} = \dfrac{\frac{10}{100}}{\frac{33}{100}} = \dfrac{10}{33}$

  b) $P(A|E \cap M) = \dfrac{P(A \cap E \cap M)}{P(E \cap M)} = \dfrac{\frac{2}{100}}{\frac{9}{100}} = \dfrac{2}{9}$

  c) $P(E|M') = \dfrac{P(E \cap M')}{P(M')} = \dfrac{\frac{39}{100}}{\frac{60}{100}} = \dfrac{39}{60} = \dfrac{13}{20}$

  d) $P(A|E') = \dfrac{P(A \cap E')}{P(E')} = \dfrac{\frac{18}{100}}{\frac{52}{100}} = \dfrac{18}{52} = \dfrac{9}{26}$

  e) $P(M|A \cap E) = \dfrac{P(M \cap A \cap E)}{P(A \cap E)} = \dfrac{\frac{2}{100}}{\frac{15}{100}} = \dfrac{2}{15}$

  You could also use the number of outcomes rather than the probabilities in the calculations above — like you saw in Example 2 on p.13.

Q9 **a)** Let S = 'swims', T = 'plays tennis' and F = 'plays football'.
  3 members play tennis, football and swim.
  6 play tennis and football, so 6 − 3 = 3 members play tennis and football but don't swim.
  4 play football and swim, so 4 − 3 = 1 member plays football and swims but doesn't play tennis.
  11 play football, so 11 − 3 − 3 − 1 = 4 members only play football.
  Number who don't play football, tennis or swim
  = 2 × number who only play football
  = 2 × 4 = 8
  Draw a Venn diagram with the information you have so far, and let x be the number of members who swim and play tennis but don't play football.

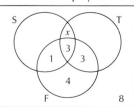

Now find the missing values in terms of x:
15 members swim,
so $15 - 3 - 1 - x = \underline{11 - x}$ only swim.
12 members play tennis, so
$12 - 3 - 3 - x = \underline{6 - x}$ only play tennis.
The diagram becomes:

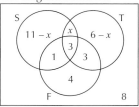

There are 30 members in total, so:
$11 - x + x + 6 - x + 1 + 3 + 3 + 4 + 8 = 30$
$\Rightarrow x = 6$
The complete Venn diagram is then:

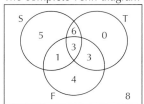

b) $P(S|T) = \dfrac{6 + 3}{6 + 3 + 3 + 0} = \dfrac{9}{12} = \dfrac{3}{4}$
You could also use the probability formula:
$P(S|T) = \dfrac{P(S \cap T)}{P(T)}.$

Exercise 2.1.2 — Using conditional probability

Q1 Draw a tree diagram using the information from the question:

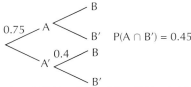

Then $P(B|A') = P(A \cap B') \div P(A) = 0.45 \div 0.75 = 0.6$
Each pair of branches sums to 1, so fill in the diagram:

$P(A' \cap B) = P(A') \, P(B|A') = 0.25 \times 0.4 = 0.1$
$P(A \cap B) = P(A) \, P(B|A) = 0.75 \times 0.4 = 0.3$
$P(B) = P(A \cap B) + P(A' \cap B) = 0.3 + 0.1 = 0.4$
$P(A) \, P(B) = 0.75 \times 0.4 = 0.3 = P(A \cap B),$
so A and B are independent.
You can see this from the diagram — the probability of B happening is the same whether A happens or not.

Q2 a)

	Action	Comedy	Total
Under 20	16	10	26
20 and over	6	8	14
Total	22	18	40

or in terms of the probabilities,

	Action	Comedy	Total
Under 20	0.4	0.25	0.65
20 and over	0.15	0.2	0.35
Total	0.55	0.45	1

b) You're told that they saw a comedy, so look at the Comedy column — the total is 18 (or 0.45). The Under 20 entry in this column is 10 (or 0.25), so $P(\text{Under 20}|\text{Comedy}) = \dfrac{10}{18} \left(\text{or } \dfrac{0.25}{0.45} \right) = \dfrac{5}{9}$

Q3 a) (i) The circles for R and T do not overlap, so they are mutually exclusive (i.e. $P(R \cap T) = 0$).
(ii) Adding up the probabilities on the Venn diagram:
$P(R) = 0.25, P(S) = 0.2, P(T) = 0.46$
$P(R)P(S) = 0.25 \times 0.2 = 0.05 = P(R \cap S)$
so R and S are independent.
$P(S)P(T) = 0.2 \times 0.46 = 0.092 \neq P(S \cap T)$
so S and T are not independent.
$P(R)P(T) = 0.25 \times 0.46 = 0.115 \neq P(R \cap T)$
so R and T are not independent.

b) (i) $P(R|S) = \dfrac{P(R \cap S)}{P(S)} = \dfrac{0.05}{0.2} = 0.25$
(ii) $P(R|S \cap T') = \dfrac{P(R \cap S \cap T')}{P(S \cap T')}$
$P(R \cap S \cap T') = P(R \cap S) = 0.05$
$P(S \cap T') = P(S) - P(S \cap T)$
$\qquad = 0.2 - 0.11 = 0.09$
So $P(R|S \cap T') = \dfrac{P(R \cap S \cap T')}{P(S \cap T')} = \dfrac{0.05}{0.09} = \dfrac{5}{9}$

Q4 a) $P(X \cap Y) = P(X)P(Y) = 0.84 \times 0.68 = 0.5712$
b) $P(Y' \cap Z') = P(Y')P(Z') = 0.32 \times 0.52 = 0.1664$
c) Since Y and Z are independent,
$P(Y|Z) = P(Y) = 0.68$
d) Since Z' and Y' are independent,
$P(Z'|Y') = P(Z') = 1 - 0.48 = 0.52$
e) Since Y and X' are independent,
$P(Y|X') = P(Y) = 0.68$

Q5 a) $P(S) = 0.45$, $P(P|S) = 0.6$, $P(P|S') = 0.2$

$P(S \cap P) = P(S)P(P|S)$
$= 0.45 \times 0.6 = 0.27$
$P(S \cap P') = P(S) - P(S \cap P)$
$= 0.45 - 0.27 = 0.18$
$P(S') = 1 - P(S)$
$= 1 - 0.45 = 0.55$
$P(S' \cap P) = P(S')P(P|S')$
$= 0.55 \times 0.2 = 0.11$
$P(S' \cap P') = P(S') - P(S' \cap P)$
$= 0.55 - 0.11 = 0.44$

So the Venn diagram looks like this:

b) $P(P) = 0.27 + 0.11 = 0.38$

$P(S|P) = \dfrac{P(S \cap P)}{P(P)} = \dfrac{0.27}{0.38} = \dfrac{27}{38} = 0.711$ (3 s.f.)

Q6 Let S = 'owns smartphone' and let C = 'has contract costing more than £25 a month'. Then you know the following probabilities: $P(S) = 0.62$, $P(C) = 0.539$ and $P(C'|S) = 0.29$, and you want to find $P(S|C)$.
Using the conditional probability formula:

$P(S|C) = \dfrac{P(S \cap C)}{P(C)}$.

Use a tree diagram to help you find $P(S \cap C)$. You don't need to label all the branches, just the ones that help you answer the question:

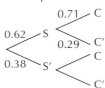

So $P(S \cap C) = 0.62 \times 0.71 = 0.4402$, and so:

$P(S|C) = \dfrac{P(S \cap C)}{P(C)} = \dfrac{0.4402}{0.539} = 0.817$ (3 s.f.)

Q7 Let R = red counter, W = white counter, B = blue counter.
There are $10 + 15 + 11 = 36$ counters in the bag initially.
The first counter that is drawn from the bag isn't replaced, so there will be 35 counters in the bag when the second counter is drawn.
The tree diagram is:

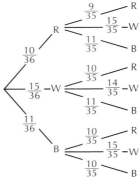

P(2nd counter blue | 1st counter not red)

$= \dfrac{P(\text{2nd counter blue} \cap \text{1st counter not red})}{P(\text{1st counter not red})}$

$= \dfrac{P(\text{2nd counter blue} \cap \text{1st counter white})}{P(\text{1st counter white or blue})}$

$+ \dfrac{P(\text{2nd counter blue} \cap \text{1st counter blue})}{P(\text{1st counter white or blue})}$

$= \dfrac{\frac{15}{36} \times \frac{11}{35} + \frac{11}{36} \times \frac{10}{35}}{\frac{15}{36} + \frac{11}{36}} = \dfrac{55}{182}$

2.2 Modelling with Probability

Exercise 2.2.1 — Modelling assumptions and probability

There are many possible answers to these questions — here are some examples:

Q1 – He has assumed that the probability of it landing on each face is equally likely — given that the shape is a cuboid, this is probably not a very good assumption.

– He has assumed that he throws it the same way each time and that his throw gives an equal probability of each face coming up, which might not be the case.

Q2 – She has assumed that the volunteer is equally likely to choose any of the 10 cards, but some people may tend to choose cards in a particular way, e.g. from the middle or from the ends more often.

– She has assumed that the card is put back at random, and that the volunteer can't see and track the card before choosing the second one — if they could, they might intentionally try to choose the same one twice, which would affect the probability.

Q3 – They assumed that their estimate of the probability (using the relative frequency from their data) is valid for children from any other school — there are likely to be lots of reasons why this is not the case. For example, children in urban areas may be more or less likely to walk than children in rural areas.

– The model doesn't account for the age of the child — it might be that older children are more likely to walk while younger children get driven to school.

– The teacher has assumed that the probability holds on any particular day, but factors like weather will affect the probability — children would probably be more likely to walk to school on warm, sunny days than on cold, rainy days.

Review Exercise — Chapter 2

Q1 $P(C|D) = \dfrac{P(C \cap D)}{P(D)} = \dfrac{0.15}{0.24} = 0.625$

$P(D|C) = \dfrac{P(D \cap C)}{P(C)} = \dfrac{P(C \cap D)}{P(C)} = \dfrac{0.15}{0.4} = 0.375$

Q2 **a)** Total number of outcomes
= 34 + 15 + 27 + 44 = 120
$P(A \cap B) = \dfrac{15}{120} = \dfrac{1}{8}$

b) $P(A \cup B') = \dfrac{34}{120} + \dfrac{15}{120} + \dfrac{44}{120} = \dfrac{93}{120} = \dfrac{31}{40}$

c) $P(A|B) = \dfrac{15}{15 + 27} = \dfrac{15}{42} = \dfrac{5}{14}$

d) $P(B|A') = \dfrac{27}{27 + 44} = \dfrac{27}{71}$

Q3 Let R = 'flower is red', Y = 'flower is yellow', T = 'flower is tall' and S = 'flower is short'.
From the question: P(R) = 0.35, P(T) = 0.46 and P(S|Y) = 0.4.
The flowers are either red or yellow, so
P(Y) = 1 – 0.35 = 0.65.
The flowers are either tall or short, so
P(S) = 1 – 0.46 = 0.54.

a) $P(S|Y) = \dfrac{P(S \cap Y)}{P(Y)}$, so

P(short yellow flower) = P(S ∩ Y) = P(S|Y)P(Y)
= 0.4 × 0.65
= 0.26

b) $P(S|R) = \dfrac{P(S \cap R)}{P(R)}$
To find P(S ∩ R), use P(S) = P(S ∩ R) + P(S ∩ Y).
So P(S ∩ R) = P(S) – P(S ∩ Y)
= 0.54 – 0.26 = 0.28
So $P(S|R) = \dfrac{P(S \cap R)}{P(R)} = \dfrac{0.28}{0.35} = 0.8$

Q4 Let C = 'catches bus' and L = 'is late'.
From the question:
P(C) = 0.6 so P(C') = 1 – 0.6 = 0.4.
P(L|C) = 0.1, so P(L'|C) = 1 – 0.1 = 0.9
Putting what you know on a tree diagram gives:

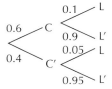

To complete the tree diagram, you need to find P(L|C') and P(L'|C').
From the question, P(arrives on time) = 0.92.
So P(C ∩ L') + P(C' ∩ L') = 0.92
P(C ∩ L') = P(L' ∩ C) = P(L'|C) × P(C)
= 0.9 × 0.6 = 0.54
So P(C' ∩ L') = 0.92 – 0.54 = 0.38
and $P(L'|C') = \dfrac{P(L' \cap C')}{P(C')} = \dfrac{P(C' \cap L')}{P(C')} = \dfrac{0.38}{0.4} = 0.95$
P(L|C') = 1 – P(L'|C') = 1 – 0.95 = 0.05
So the complete tree diagram is:

$$
\begin{array}{c}
0.6 \ \diagdown \ C \begin{cases} 0.1 \nearrow L \\ 0.9 \searrow L' \end{cases} \\
0.4 \ \diagdown \ C' \begin{cases} 0.05 \nearrow L \\ 0.95 \searrow L' \end{cases}
\end{array}
$$

So P(Asmaa is late given that she rides her bike)
= P(L|C') = 0.05.

Q5 E.g. Let event W = the day was on a weekend, and let event S = sold more than 150 cups of coffee.
Then from the question, $P(S|W) = \dfrac{3}{10}$
and $P(W' \cap S') = \dfrac{1}{2}$.
The day is picked at random,
so $P(W) = \dfrac{2}{7}$, $P(W') = \dfrac{5}{7}$.
$P(W' \cap S) = P(W') - P(W' \cap S') = \dfrac{5}{7} - \dfrac{1}{2} = \dfrac{3}{14}$
$P(W \cap S) = P(W) \times P(S|W) = \dfrac{2}{7} \times \dfrac{3}{10} = \dfrac{3}{35}$
$P(S) = P(W' \cap S) + P(W \cap S) = \dfrac{3}{14} + \dfrac{3}{35} = \dfrac{3}{10}$
So P(S) = P(S|W), so S and W are independent.
You might have done this a different way —
there are lots of possible ways to show it.

Q6 From the question you know that:
$P(F \cap H) = 0.08$, $P(F) = 0.37$ and $P(B) = 0.25$.
Draw a table and fill it in showing this information:

	B	C	H	Total
F			0.08	0.37
S				
Total	0.25			1

You also know that $P(S|B) = \frac{2}{5}$ and $P(F|C) = \frac{1}{3}$. So:

$P(S \cap B) = P(S|B) \times P(B) = \frac{2}{5} \times 0.25 = \underline{0.1}$
$P(B) = P(F \cap B) + P(S \cap B)$, so
$P(F \cap B) = P(B) - P(S \cap B) = 0.25 - 0.1 = \underline{0.15}$
$P(F) = P(F \cap B) + P(F \cap C) + P(F \cap H)$
So $P(F \cap C) = P(F) - P(F \cap B) - P(F \cap H)$
$\qquad = 0.37 - 0.15 - 0.08 = \underline{0.14}$

$P(F|C) = \dfrac{P(F \cap C)}{P(C)}$

So $P(C) = \dfrac{P(F \cap C)}{P(F|C)} = 0.14 \div \frac{1}{3} = \underline{0.42}$

$P(C) = P(F \cap C) + P(S \cap C)$, so
$P(S \cap C) = P(C) - P(F \cap C) = 0.42 - 0.14 = \underline{0.28}$
$P(S) = 1 - P(F) = 1 - 0.37 = \underline{0.63}$
Also $P(S) = P(S \cap B) + P(S \cap C) + P(S \cap H)$
So $P(S \cap H) = P(S) - P(S \cap B) - P(S \cap C)$
$\qquad = 0.63 - 0.1 - 0.28 = \underline{0.25}$
$P(H) = P(F \cap H) + P(S \cap H) = 0.08 + 0.25 = \underline{0.33}$

You can now fill in the table:

	B	C	H	Total
F	0.15	0.14	0.08	0.37
S	0.1	0.28	0.25	0.63
Total	0.25	0.42	0.33	1

Q7 **a)** E.g. He has assumed that each puzzle is equally likely to be solved first, but one of them might be easier than the others. / Most people are likely to attempt the first puzzle first, which might make it more likely to be solved first.

b) E.g. Ariel has assumed that there is a probability of 0.5 that tomorrow will be sunny and a probability of 0.5 that it will be rainy, but she has not taken into account the possibility of other weather conditions or the season/recent weather.

Exam-Style Questions — Chapter 2

Q1 **a)** **(i)** $P(\text{female} \mid 11\text{-}13) = \frac{15}{25} = \frac{3}{5}$ *[1 mark]*

 (ii) $P(\text{male} \mid \text{under 17}) = \frac{10+14}{25+30} = \frac{24}{55}$ *[1 mark]*

 b) Let x be the number of 11-year-old girls in the 11-13 age group.
 $P(11 \text{ years old} \mid \text{girl in 11-13 group}) = \frac{x}{15} = 0.2$
 [1 mark]
 $\Rightarrow x = 3$. So there are three 11-year-old girls.
 [1 mark]

 c) If a competitor is selected at random,
 $P(\text{male}) = \frac{32}{75}$, $P(17\text{-}18) = \frac{20}{75} = \frac{4}{15}$
 and $P(\text{male} \cap 17\text{-}18) = \frac{8}{75} = 0.106....$
 $P(\text{male}) \times P(17\text{-}18) = \frac{32}{75} \times \frac{4}{15} = \frac{128}{1125} = 0.113...$
 So $P(\text{male}) \times P(17\text{-}18) \neq P(\text{male} \cap 17\text{-}18)$, so the events are not independent.
 [2 marks available — 1 mark for attempting to compare P(male) × P(17-18) with P(male ∩ 17-18), 1 mark for correct conclusion]

Q2 $P(B|A \cap C') = \dfrac{\text{number of outcomes in } B \cap (A \cap C')}{\text{number of outcomes in } A \cap C'}$
$\qquad\qquad = \dfrac{x}{x + 0.2} = 0.2$

$\Rightarrow x = 0.2x + 0.04 \Rightarrow 0.8x = 0.04 \Rightarrow x = 0.05$

$P(A \cup B) = 0.7 \Rightarrow 0.2 + 0.05 + y + 0.1 + 0.15 = 0.7$
$\qquad\qquad\qquad \Rightarrow y = 0.2$

$z = 1 - P(A \cup B) = 1 - 0.7 = 0.3$
[5 marks available — 1 mark for correct expression for P(B|A ∩ C') in terms of x, 1 mark for correct value of x, 1 mark for a correct method to find y, 1 mark for correct value of y, 1 mark for correct value of z]

Chapter 3: The Normal Distribution

3.1 The Normal Distribution

Exercise 3.1.1 — The normal distribution

These questions are done using a calculator with an upper bound of 9999 or a lower bound of −9999 where needed.

Q1 **a)** $P(X < 50) = 0.9772$ (4 d.p.)
  b) $P(X \leq 43) = 0.7257$ (4 d.p.)

Q2 **a)** $P(X \geq 28) = 0.0512$ (4 d.p.)
  b) $P(X > 25) = 0.3415$ (4 d.p.)

Q3 **a)** $P(X > 107) = 0.9801$ (4 d.p.)
  b) $P(X > 115) = 0.7854$ (4 d.p.)

Q4 **a)** $P(X \leq 15) = 0.2525$ (4 d.p.)
  b) $P(X < 12) = 0.0478$ (4 d.p.)

Q5 **a)** $P(52 < X < 63) = 0.3399$ (4 d.p.)
  b) $P(57 \leq X < 66) = 0.0801$ (4 d.p.)

Q6 **a)** $P(0.45 \leq X \leq 0.55) = 0.1747$ (4 d.p.)
  b) $P(0.53 < X < 0.58) = 0.0970$ (4 d.p.)
  c) $P(0.65 < X \leq 0.7) = 0.0928$ (4 d.p.)

Q7 **a)** $P(240 < X \leq 280) = 0.8176$ (4 d.p.)
  b) $P(232 < X < 288) = 0.9381$ (4 d.p.)
  c) $P(255 \leq X < 264) = 0.2357$ (4 d.p.)

Exercise 3.1.2 — The standard normal distribution, Z

These questions are done using a calculator with an upper bound of 9999 or a lower bound of −9999 where needed.

Q1 **a)** $P(Z \leq 1.87) = 0.9693$ (4 s.f.)
  b) $P(Z < 0.99) = 0.8389$ (4 s.f.)
  c) $P(Z > 2.48) = 0.006569$ (4 s.f.)
  d) $P(Z \geq 0.14) = 0.4443$ (4 s.f.)
  e) $P(Z > -0.24) = 0.5948$ (4 s.f.)
  f) $P(Z > -1.21) = 0.8869$ (4 s.f.)
  g) $P(Z < -0.62) = 0.2676$ (4 s.f.)
  h) $P(Z \leq -2.06) = 0.01970$ (4 s.f.)

Q2 **a)** $P(1.34 < Z < 2.18) = 0.07549$ (4 s.f.)
  b) $P(0.76 \leq Z < 1.92) = 0.1962$ (4 s.f.)
  c) $P(-1.45 \leq Z \leq 0.17) = 0.4940$ (4 s.f.)
  d) $P(-2.14 < Z < 1.65) = 0.9344$ (4 s.f.)
  e) $P(-1.66 < Z \leq 1.66) = 0.9031$ (4 s.f.)
  f) $P(-0.34 \leq Z < 0.34) = 0.2661$ (4 s.f.)
  g) $P(-3.25 \leq Z \leq -2.48) = 0.005992$ (4 s.f.)
  h) $P(-1.11 < Z < -0.17) = 0.2990$ (4 s.f.)
  i) $P(-0.27 \leq Z \leq -0.05) = 0.08648$ (4 s.f.)
  For some of these questions, you could have used the symmetry of the distribution to work out the answer.

Exercise 3.1.3 — Converting to the Z distribution

Q1 **a)** Standard deviation = $\sqrt{100} = 10$ and mean = 106.
  So $P(X \leq 100) = P\left(Z \leq \dfrac{100 - 106}{10}\right)$
  $= P(Z \leq -0.6) = 0.2743$ (4 d.p.)

  b) $P(X > 122) = P\left(Z > \dfrac{122 - 106}{10}\right)$
  $= P(Z > 1.6) = 0.0548$ (4 d.p.)

  c) $P(X \geq 112) = P\left(Z \geq \dfrac{112 - 106}{10}\right)$
  $= P(Z \geq 0.6) = 0.2743$ (4 d.p.)

Q2 **a)** $P(X \geq 9) = P\left(Z \geq \dfrac{9 - 11}{2}\right)$
  $= P(Z \geq -1) = 0.8413$ (4 d.p.)

  b) $P(10 \leq X \leq 12) = P\left(\dfrac{10 - 11}{2} \leq Z \leq \dfrac{12 - 11}{2}\right)$
  $= P(-0.5 \leq Z \leq 0.5) = 0.3829$ (4 d.p.)

  c) $P(7 < X < 11) = P\left(\dfrac{7 - 11}{2} < Z < \dfrac{11 - 11}{2}\right)$
  $= P(-2 \leq Z \leq 0) = 0.4772$ (4 d.p.)

Q3 **a)** $P(240 < X < 280)$
  $= P\left(\dfrac{240 - 260}{15} < Z < \dfrac{280 - 260}{15}\right)$
  $= P(-1.3333 < Z < 1.3333) = 0.8176$ (4 d.p.)

  b) $P(232 < X < 288)$
  $= P\left(\dfrac{232 - 260}{15} < Z < \dfrac{288 - 260}{15}\right)$
  $= P(-1.867 < Z < 1.867) = 0.9381$ (4 d.p.)

  c) $P(259 < X \leq 269)$
  $= P\left(\dfrac{259 - 260}{15} < Z \leq \dfrac{269 - 260}{15}\right)$
  $= P(-0.06... < Z \leq 0.6) = 0.2523$ (4 d.p.)

Exercise 3.1.4 — Finding x-values

These questions are done using a calculator with an upper bound of 9999 or a lower bound of −9999 where needed.

Q1 **a)** $P(X < x) = 0.8944$ for $x = 13$
  b) $P(X \leq x) = 0.0304$ for $x = 10.5$
  c) Using the fact that the area under the curve is 1:
  $P(X < x) = 1 - P(X \geq x) = 1 - 0.2660 = 0.7340$
  $P(X < x) = 0.7340$ for $x = 12.5$
  d) Using the fact that the area under the curve is 1:
  $P(X \leq x) = 1 - P(X > x) = 1 - 0.7917 = 0.2083$
  $P(X \leq x) = 0.2083$ for $x = 11.35$

Q2 **a)** $\Phi(z) = 0.004$ for $z = -2.65$ (2 d.p.)
  b) Using the fact that the area under the curve is 1:
  $P(Z \leq z) = 1 - P(Z > z) = 1 - 0.0951 = 0.9049$
  $\Phi(z) = 0.9049$ for $z = 1.31$ (2 d.p.)

c) $P(-z < Z < z) = 0.9426$, so the remaining area is
$1 - 0.9426 = 0.0574$.
Using symmetry, $P(Z \le -z) = 0.0574 \div 2 = 0.0287$
$\Rightarrow P(Z \le -z) = 0.0287$ for $z = -1.90$ (2 d.p.)
So $z = 1.90$ (2 d.p.)

d) $P(z < Z < -1.25) = 0.0949$
$\Rightarrow P(Z < -1.25) - P(Z \le z) = 0.0949$
$\Rightarrow P(Z \le z) = P(Z < -1.25) - 0.0949$
$\Rightarrow P(Z \le z) = 0.1056 - 0.0949 = 0.0107$
$\Phi(z) = 0.0107$ for $z = -2.30$ (2 d.p.)

Q3 a) $P(53 < X < x) = 0.05$
$\Rightarrow P(X < x) - P(X \le 53) = 0.05$
$\Rightarrow P(X < x) = 0.05 + P(X \le 53)$
$\qquad\qquad = 0.05 + 0.8413 = 0.8913$
$P(X < x) = 0.8913$ for $x = 54.17$ (2 d.p.)

b) $P(x < X < 49) = 0.4312$
$\Rightarrow P(X < 49) - P(X \le x) = 0.4312$
$\Rightarrow P(X \le x) = P(X < 49) - 0.4312$
$\qquad\qquad = 0.5793 - 0.4312 = 0.1481$
$P(X < x) = 0.1481$ for $x = 42.78$ (2 d.p.)

Q4 a) Using the percentage points table,
$p = 0.005$ for $z = 2.5758$

b) Using the percentage points table,
$p = 0.2$ for $z = 0.8416$

c) $P(Z < z) = 0.7 \Rightarrow P(Z \ge z) = 0.3 \Rightarrow z = 0.5244$

d) $P(Z < z) = 0.999 \Rightarrow P(Z \ge z) = 0.001$
$\qquad\qquad\qquad\qquad \Rightarrow z = 3.0902$

Q5 a) Convert X to the standard normal variable:
$P(X > x) = P\left(Z > \dfrac{x-25}{4}\right) = 0.4$

Using the percentage points table,
$p = 0.4$ for $z = 0.2533$.
So $\dfrac{x-25}{4} = 0.2533 \Rightarrow x = 26.0132$

b) Convert X to the standard normal variable:
$P(X < x) = P\left(Z < \dfrac{x-25}{4}\right) = 0.975$

$\Rightarrow P\left(Z \ge \dfrac{x-25}{4}\right) = 1 - 0.975 = 0.025$

Using the percentage points table,
$p = 0.025$ for $z = 1.9600$
So $\dfrac{x-25}{4} = 1.96 \Rightarrow x = 32.84$

Exercise 3.1.5 — Finding the mean and standard deviation of a normal distribution

Q1 a) $P(X < 23) = 0.9332 \Rightarrow P\left(Z < \dfrac{23-\mu}{6}\right) = 0.9332$

$\Phi(z) = 0.9332$ for $z = 1.50$ (2 d.p.)

$\Rightarrow \dfrac{23-\mu}{6} = 1.5 \Rightarrow \mu = 23 - 1.5 \times 6 = 14$

b) $P(X < 57) = 0.9970 \Rightarrow P\left(Z < \dfrac{57-\mu}{8}\right) = 0.9970$

$\Phi(z) = 0.9970$ for $z = 2.75$ (2 d.p.)

$\Rightarrow \dfrac{57-\mu}{8} = 2.75 \Rightarrow \mu = 57 - 2.75 \times 8 = 35$

c) $P(X > 528) = 0.1292$

$\Rightarrow P\left(Z > \dfrac{528-\mu}{100}\right) = 0.1292$

$\Rightarrow P\left(Z \le \dfrac{528-\mu}{100}\right) = 1 - 0.1292 = 0.8708$

$\Phi(z) = 0.8708$ for $z = 1.13$ (2 d.p.)

$\Rightarrow \dfrac{528-\mu}{100} = 1.13$

$\Rightarrow \mu = 528 - 1.13 \times 100 = 415$

d) $P(X < 11.06) = 0.0322$

$\Rightarrow P\left(Z < \dfrac{11.06-\mu}{0.4}\right) = 0.0322$

$\Phi(z) = 0.0322$ for $z = -1.85$ (2 d.p.)

$\Rightarrow \dfrac{11.06-\mu}{0.4} = -1.85$

$\Rightarrow \mu = 11.06 - (-1.85) \times 0.4 = 11.8$

e) $P(X > 1.52) = 0.9938$

$\Rightarrow P\left(Z > \dfrac{1.52-\mu}{0.02}\right) = 0.9938$

$\Rightarrow P\left(Z < \dfrac{\mu-1.52}{0.02}\right) = 0.9938$

$\Phi(z) = 0.9938$ for $z = 2.50$ (2 d.p.)

$\Rightarrow \dfrac{\mu-1.52}{0.02} = 2.5$

$\Rightarrow \mu = 2.5 \times 0.02 + 1.52 = 1.57$

Here you use the fact that $P(Z > z) = P(Z < -z)$ for the standard normal distribution.

Q2 Start with a sketch showing what you know about X.

So, $P(X < 20.17) = 0.95 + 0.025 = 0.975$

$\Rightarrow P\left(Z < \dfrac{20.17-\mu}{3.5}\right) = 0.975$

$\Phi(z) = 0.975$ for $z = 1.96$ (2 d.p.)

$\Rightarrow \dfrac{20.17-\mu}{3.5} = 1.96$

$\Rightarrow \mu = 20.17 - 1.96 \times 3.5 = 13.31$

There are different ways you could do this question. For example, using the symmetry of the graph, you know that μ is exactly in the middle of 6.45 and 20.17, so you can simply find the average of these 2 values.

Q3 a) $P(X < 53) = 0.8944$

$\Rightarrow P\left(Z < \dfrac{53-48}{\sigma}\right) = P\left(Z < \dfrac{5}{\sigma}\right) = 0.8944$

$\Phi(z) = 0.8944$ for $z = 1.25$ (2 d.p.)

$\Rightarrow \dfrac{5}{\sigma} = 1.25 \Rightarrow \sigma = 5 \div 1.25 = 4$

b) $P(X < 528) = 0.7734$

$\Rightarrow P\left(Z < \dfrac{528-510}{\sigma}\right) = P\left(Z < \dfrac{18}{\sigma}\right) = 0.7734$

$\Phi(z) = 0.7734$ for $z = 0.75$ (2 d.p.)

$\Rightarrow \dfrac{18}{\sigma} = 0.75 \Rightarrow \sigma = 18 \div 0.75 = 24$

c) $P(X > 24) = 0.0367$

$\Rightarrow P\left(Z > \frac{24-17}{\sigma}\right) = P\left(Z > \frac{7}{\sigma}\right) = 0.0367$

$\Rightarrow P\left(Z \leq \frac{7}{\sigma}\right) = 0.9633$

$\Phi(z) = 0.9633$ for $z = 1.79$ (2 d.p.)

$\Rightarrow \frac{7}{\sigma} = 1.79 \Rightarrow \sigma = 7 \div 1.79 = 3.91$ (3 s.f.)

d) $P(X < 0.95) = 0.3085$

$\Rightarrow P\left(Z < \frac{0.95-0.98}{\sigma}\right) = P\left(Z < -\frac{0.03}{\sigma}\right) = 0.3085$

$\Phi(z) = 0.3085$ for $z = -0.5$.

$\Rightarrow -\frac{0.03}{\sigma} = -0.5 \Rightarrow \sigma = 0.03 \div 0.5 = 0.06$

e) $P(X > 4.85) = 0.8365$

$\Rightarrow P\left(Z > \frac{4.85-5.6}{\sigma}\right) = P\left(Z > -\frac{0.75}{\sigma}\right) = 0.8365$

$\Rightarrow P\left(Z < \frac{0.75}{\sigma}\right) = 0.8365$

$\Phi(z) = 0.8365$ for $z = 0.98$ (2 d.p.)

$\Rightarrow \frac{0.75}{\sigma} = 0.98$

$\Rightarrow \sigma = 0.75 \div 0.98 = 0.765$ (3 s.f.)

Q4 Start with a sketch showing what you know about X.

So $P(X > 75) = 0.15$

$\Rightarrow P\left(Z > \frac{75-68}{\sigma}\right) = P\left(Z > \frac{7}{\sigma}\right) = 0.15$

Using the percentage points table,
$p = 0.15$ for $z = 1.0364$.

$\Rightarrow \frac{7}{\sigma} = 1.0364 \Rightarrow \sigma = 7 \div 1.0364 = 6.75$ (3 s.f.)

Q5 a) $P(X < 30) = 0.9192 \Rightarrow P\left(Z < \frac{30-\mu}{\sigma}\right) = 0.9192$

$\Phi(z) = 0.9192$ for $z = 1.40$ (2 d.p.)

$\Rightarrow \frac{30-\mu}{\sigma} = 1.4 \Rightarrow 30 - \mu = 1.4\sigma$ ①

$P(X < 36) = 0.9953 \Rightarrow P\left(Z < \frac{36-\mu}{\sigma}\right) = 0.9953$

$\Phi(z) = 0.9953$ for $z = 2.60$ (2 d.p.)

$\Rightarrow \frac{36-\mu}{\sigma} = 2.6 \Rightarrow 36 - \mu = 2.6\sigma$ ②

Subtracting equation ① from equation ② gives:
$36 - 30 - \mu - (-\mu) = 2.6\sigma - 1.4\sigma$
$\Rightarrow 6 = 1.2\sigma \Rightarrow \sigma = 5$
Putting $\sigma = 5$ into equation ① gives:
$\mu = 30 - 1.4 \times 5 = 23$
So $\mu = 23$ and $\sigma = 5$

b) $P(X < 4) = 0.9332 \Rightarrow P\left(Z < \frac{4-\mu}{\sigma}\right) = 0.9332$

$\Phi(z) = 0.9332$ for $z = 1.50$ (2 d.p.)

$\Rightarrow \frac{4-\mu}{\sigma} = 1.5 \Rightarrow 4 - \mu = 1.5\sigma$ ①

$P(X < 4.3) = 0.9987 \Rightarrow P\left(Z < \frac{4.3-\mu}{\sigma}\right) = 0.9987$

$\Phi(z) = 0.9987$ for $z = 3.01$ (2 d.p.)

$\Rightarrow \frac{4.3-\mu}{\sigma} = 3.01 \Rightarrow 4.3 - \mu = 3.01\sigma$ ②

Subtracting equation ① from equation ② gives:
$3.4.3 - 4 - \mu - (-\mu) = 3.01\sigma - 1.5\sigma$
$\Rightarrow 0.3 = 1.51\sigma \Rightarrow \sigma = 0.198675...$
Putting $\sigma = 0.198675...$ into equation ① gives:
$\mu = 4 - 1.5 \times 0.198675... = 3.70$ (2 d.p.)
So $\mu = 3.7$ and $\sigma = 0.2$

c) $P(X < 20) = 0.7881 \Rightarrow P\left(Z < \frac{20-\mu}{\sigma}\right) = 0.7881$

$\Phi(z) = 0.7881$ for $z = 0.80$ (2 d.p.)

$\Rightarrow \frac{20-\mu}{\sigma} = 0.8 \Rightarrow 20 - \mu = 0.8\sigma$ ①

$P(X < 14) = 0.0548 \Rightarrow P\left(Z < \frac{14-\mu}{\sigma}\right) = 0.0548$

$\Phi(z) = 0.0548$ for $z = -1.60$ (2 d.p.)

$\Rightarrow \frac{14-\mu}{\sigma} = -1.6 \Rightarrow \mu - 14 = 1.6\sigma$ ②

Adding equations ① and ② gives:
$20 - 14 - \mu + \mu = 0.8\sigma + 1.6\sigma$
$\Rightarrow 6 = 2.4\sigma \Rightarrow \sigma = 2.5$
Putting $\sigma = 2.5$ into equation ② gives:
$\mu = 1.6 \times 2.5 + 14 = 18$
So $\mu = 18$ and $\sigma = 2.5$

d) $P(X < 696) = 0.9713$

$\Rightarrow P\left(Z < \frac{696-\mu}{\sigma}\right) = 0.9713$

$\Phi(z) = 0.9713$ for $z = 1.90$ (2 d.p.)

$\Rightarrow \frac{696-\mu}{\sigma} = 1.9 \Rightarrow 696 - \mu = 1.9\sigma$ ①

$P(X < 592) = 0.2420$

$\Rightarrow P\left(Z < \frac{592-\mu}{\sigma}\right) = 0.2420$

$\Phi(z) = 0.242$ for $z = -0.70$ (2 d.p.)

$\Rightarrow \frac{592-\mu}{\sigma} = -0.7 \Rightarrow \mu - 592 = 0.7\sigma$ ②

Adding equations ① and ② gives:
$696 - 592 - \mu + \mu = 1.9\sigma + 0.7\sigma$
$\Rightarrow 104 = 2.6\sigma \Rightarrow \sigma = 40$
Putting $\sigma = 40$ into equation ② gives:
$\mu = 0.7 \times 40 + 592 = 620$
So $\mu = 620$ and $\sigma = 40$

e) $P(X > 33) = 0.1056 \Rightarrow P\left(Z > \dfrac{33 - \mu}{\sigma}\right) = 0.1056$

$\Rightarrow P\left(Z \leq \dfrac{33 - \mu}{\sigma}\right) = 1 - 0.1056 = 0.8944$

$\Phi(z) = 0.8944$ for $z = 1.25$ (2 d.p.)

$\Rightarrow \dfrac{33 - \mu}{\sigma} = 1.25 \Rightarrow 33 - \mu = 1.25\sigma$ ①

$P(X > 21) = 0.9599 \Rightarrow P\left(Z > \dfrac{21 - \mu}{\sigma}\right) = 0.9599$

$\Rightarrow P\left(Z < \dfrac{\mu - 21}{\sigma}\right) = 0.9599$

$\Phi(z) = 0.9599$ for $z = 1.75$ (2 d.p.)

$\Rightarrow \dfrac{\mu - 21}{\sigma} = 1.75 \Rightarrow \mu - 21 = 1.75\sigma$ ②

Adding equations ① and ② gives:
$33 - 21 - \mu + \mu = 1.25\sigma + 1.75\sigma$
$\Rightarrow 12 = 3\sigma \Rightarrow \sigma = 4$
Putting $\sigma = 4$ into equation ② gives:
$\mu = 1.75 \times 4 + 21 = 28$
So $\mu = 28$ and $\sigma = 4$

f) $P(X > 66) = 0.3632 \Rightarrow P\left(Z > \dfrac{66 - \mu}{\sigma}\right) = 0.3632$

$\Rightarrow P\left(Z \leq \dfrac{66 - \mu}{\sigma}\right) = 0.6368$

$\Phi(z) = 0.6368$ for $z = 0.35$ (2 d.p.)

$\Rightarrow \dfrac{66 - \mu}{\sigma} = 0.35 \Rightarrow 66 - \mu = 0.35\sigma$ ①

$P(X < 48) = 0.3446 \Rightarrow P\left(Z < \dfrac{48 - \mu}{\sigma}\right) = 0.3446$

$\Phi(z) = 0.3446$ for $z = -0.40$ (2 d.p.)

$\Rightarrow \dfrac{48 - \mu}{\sigma} = -0.4 \Rightarrow \mu - 48 = 0.4\sigma$ ②

Adding equations ① and ② gives:
$66 - 48 - \mu + \mu = 0.35\sigma + 0.4\sigma$
$\Rightarrow 18 = 0.75\sigma \Rightarrow \sigma = 24$
Putting $\sigma = 24$ into equation ② gives:
$\mu = 0.4 \times 24 + 48 = 57.6$
So $\mu = 57.6$ and $\sigma = 24$

Exercise 3.1.6 — The normal distribution in real-life situations

Q1 a) Let $T \sim N(36, 6^2)$ represent the length of time taken to replace red blood cells, in days.
Using a calculator:
$P(T < 28) = 0.0912$ (4 d.p.)

b) $56 \times 0.0912 = 5.1702$
So approximately 5 blood donors replace their blood cells more quickly than Edward.

c) Let b = the number of days taken by Bella.
Then, $P(T > b) = 0.0714$.
$\Rightarrow P(T \leq b) = 1 - 0.0714 = 0.9286$
$P(X \leq x) = 0.9286$ for $x = 44.79$ days (2 d.p.)
Don't forget to say 'days' in your answer — you need to answer the question in the context in which it was asked.

Q2 a) Let $T \sim N(51, 2.1^2)$ represent the personal best time taken to run 400 m in seconds.
Using a calculator:
$P(T > 49.3) = 0.7909$ (4 d.p.)
So, 79.09% are slower than Gary.

b) Let a = the time to beat. Then, $P(T < a) = 0.2$.
$P(T < a) = 0.2$ for $a = 49.2$ s to 3 s.f.

Q3 a) Let V = volume of vinegar in ml.
Then $V \sim N(\mu, 5^2)$.
$P(V < 506) = 0.719 \Rightarrow P\left(Z < \dfrac{506 - \mu}{5}\right) = 0.719$
$\Phi(z) = 0.719$ for $z = 0.58$ (2 d.p.)
$\Rightarrow \dfrac{506 - \mu}{5} = 0.58$
$\Rightarrow \mu = 506 - 0.58 \times 5 = 503.1$ ml

b) Using $\mu = 503.1$ gives
$P(V < 500) = 0.2676$ (4 d.p.)

c) $P(V \geq 500) = 1 - P(V < 500)$
$= 1 - 0.2676 = 0.7324$
$0.7324 \times 1303 = 954.3172$
So approximately 954 bottles contain at least 500 ml.

Q4 a) Let $L \sim N(300, 50^2)$ represent the lifetime of a battery in hours.
Then $P(L < 200) = 0.0228$ (4 d.p.)

b) $P(L > 380) = 0.0548$ (4 d.p.)

c) Assuming that the lifetimes of the batteries are independent, the probability that both last at least 380 hours $= 0.0548 \times 0.0548 = 0.0030$ (2 s.f.).
If two events are independent, it means you can multiply their probabilities together.

d) $P(160 < L < h) = 0.9746$
$\Rightarrow P\left(\dfrac{160 - 300}{50} < Z < \dfrac{h - 300}{50}\right) = 0.9746$
$\Rightarrow P\left(-2.8 < Z < \dfrac{h - 300}{50}\right) = 0.9746$
$\Rightarrow P\left(Z < \dfrac{h - 300}{50}\right) - P(Z \leq -2.8) = 0.9746$
$\Rightarrow P\left(Z < \dfrac{h - 300}{50}\right) = 0.9746 + P(Z \leq -2.8)$
$\Rightarrow P\left(Z < \dfrac{h - 300}{50}\right) = 0.9746 + 0.0026$
$\Rightarrow P\left(Z < \dfrac{h - 300}{50}\right) = 0.9772$
$\Phi(z) = 0.9772$ for $z = 2.00$ (2 d.p.)
So $\dfrac{h - 300}{50} = 2 \Rightarrow h = 2 \times 50 + 300 = 400$

Q5 a) Let H = height in cm. Then $H \sim N(175, \sigma^2)$.
$P(H > 170) = 0.8$
$\Rightarrow P\left(Z > \dfrac{170 - 175}{\sigma}\right) = P\left(Z > -\dfrac{5}{\sigma}\right) = 0.8$
$\Rightarrow P\left(Z < \dfrac{5}{\sigma}\right) = 0.8 \Rightarrow P\left(Z > \dfrac{5}{\sigma}\right) = 0.2$
Using the percentage points table
$P\left(Z > \dfrac{5}{\sigma}\right) = 0.2$ for $z = 0.8416$
$\Rightarrow \dfrac{5}{\sigma} = 0.8416 \Rightarrow \sigma = 5 \div 0.8416$
$= 5.94$ cm (3 s.f.)

b) Lower bound $= 175 - 4 = 171$ and upper bound $= 175 + 4 = 179$.
So $P(171 < H < 179) = 0.4993$.

Q6 a) Let $M \sim N(60, 3^2)$ be the mass of an egg in grams.
$P(M > 60 - m) = 0.9525$
$\Rightarrow P\left(Z > \frac{60 - m - 60}{3}\right) = 0.9525$
$\Rightarrow P\left(Z > \frac{-m}{3}\right) = 0.9525$
$\Rightarrow P\left(Z < \frac{m}{3}\right) = 0.9525$
$\Phi(z) = 0.9525$ for $z = 1.67$ (2 d.p.)
So $\frac{m}{3} = 1.67 \Rightarrow m = 1.67 \times 3 = 5.01$
$= 5$ g to the nearest gram.

b) Let c = the maximum mass of an egg in one of farmer Elizabeth's sponge cakes.
Then, $P(M \leq c) = 0.1$.
So $P\left(Z \leq \frac{c - 60}{3}\right) = 0.1 \Rightarrow P\left(Z \geq \frac{60 - c}{3}\right) = 0.1$
$\Rightarrow \frac{60 - c}{3} = 1.2816$ from percentage points table
$\Rightarrow c = 60 - 3 \times 1.2816 = 56.1552 = 56.2$ (3 s.f.)
So the maximum mass is 56.2 grams.

Q7 Let R = rainfall in cm. Then $R \sim N(\mu, \sigma^2)$.
$P(R < 4) = 0.102 \Rightarrow P\left(Z < \frac{4 - \mu}{\sigma}\right) = 0.102$
$\Rightarrow P\left(Z > \frac{\mu - 4}{\sigma}\right) = 0.102 \Rightarrow P\left(Z \leq \frac{\mu - 4}{\sigma}\right) = 0.898$
$\Phi(z) = 0.898$ for $z = 1.27$ (2 d.p.)
$\Rightarrow \frac{\mu - 4}{\sigma} = 1.27 \Rightarrow \mu - 4 = 1.27\sigma$ ①
$P(R > 7) = 0.648 \Rightarrow P\left(Z > \frac{7 - \mu}{\sigma}\right) = 0.648$
$\Rightarrow P\left(Z < \frac{\mu - 7}{\sigma}\right) = 0.648$
$\Phi(z) = 0.648$ for $z = 0.38$ (2 d.p.)
$\Rightarrow \frac{\mu - 7}{\sigma} = 0.38 \Rightarrow \mu - 7 = 0.38\sigma$ ②
Subtracting equation ② from equation ① gives:
$\mu - \mu - 4 - (-7) = 1.27\sigma - 0.38\sigma$
$\Rightarrow 3 = 0.89\sigma \Rightarrow \sigma = 3.37$ (3 s.f.)
Putting $\sigma = 3.37$ cm into equation ① gives:
$\mu = 1.27 \times 3.37 + 4 = 8.28$ cm (3 s.f.)
So $\mu = 8.28$ cm and $\sigma = 3.37$ cm (3 s.f.)

3.2 Normal Approximation to a Binomial Distribution

Exercise 3.2.1 — Continuity corrections

Q1 a) $P(4.5 < Y < 5.5)$
b) $P(11.5 < Y < 15.5)$
c) $P(Y < 10.5)$
Q2 a) $P(49.5 < Y < 50.5)$
b) $P(Y < 299.5)$
c) $P(Y > 98.5)$
Q3 a) $P(X = 200)$ is approximated by $P(199.5 < Y < 200.5)$
b) $P(X \geq 650)$ is approximated by $P(Y > 649.5)$.
c) $P(X < 300)$ is approximated by $P(Y < 299.5)$.
d) $P(499 \leq X \leq 501)$ is approximated by $P(498.5 < Y < 501.5)$

e) $P(250 \leq X \leq 750)$ is approximated by $P(249.5 < Y < 750.5)$
f) $P(100 \leq X < 900)$ is approximated by $P(99.5 < Y < 899.5)$

Exercise 3.2.2 — Normal approximation to a binomial distribution

Q1 a) n is large (600) and $p = 0.51 \approx 0.5$, so a normal approximation would be suitable.
b) n is large (100) but $p = 0.98$ is not close to 0.5. It might still be OK if np and $n(1 - p)$ are > 5. $np = 98$ but $n(1 - p) = 2$, so a normal approximation would not be suitable.
c) n is large (100) but $p = 0.85$ is not close to 0.5. It might still be OK if np and $n(1 - p)$ are > 5. $np = 85$ and $n(1 - p) = 15$, so a normal approximation would be suitable.
d) n is not large (6), so a normal approximation would not be suitable.

Q2 a) $\mu = np = 350 \times 0.45 = 157.5$
$\sigma^2 = np(1 - p) = 350 \times 0.45 \times 0.55 = 86.625$
b) $\mu = np = 250 \times 0.35 = 87.5$
$\sigma^2 = np(1 - p) = 250 \times 0.35 \times 0.65 = 56.875$
c) $\mu = np = 70 \times 0.501 = 35.07$
$\sigma^2 = np(1 - p) = 70 \times 0.501 \times 0.499$
$= 17.500$ (3 d.p.)

Q3 $X \sim B(200, 0.6)$, so use a normal approximation
$Y \sim N(\mu, \sigma^2)$ with $\mu = np = 200 \times 0.6 = 120$
$\sigma^2 = np(1 - p) = 200 \times 0.6 \times 0.4 = 48$
So approximate X with $Y \sim N(120, 48)$.
This question has been done using a calculator to find the probabilities.
a) Using a continuity correction you're looking for $P(X < 105) \approx P(Y < 104.5) = 0.0126$ (4 d.p.)
b) Using a continuity correction, you're looking for $P(X = 122) \approx P(121.5 < Y < 122.5) = 0.0552$ (4 d.p.)
c) Using a continuity correction, you're looking for $P(110 < X < 130) \approx P(110.5 < Y < 129.5)$
$= 0.8297$ (4 d.p.)

Q4 a) The normal approximation has
$\mu = np = 80 \times 0.8 = 64$
$\sigma^2 = np(1 - p) = 80 \times 0.8 \times 0.2 = 12.8$
Note that np = 64 and n(1 – p) = 16, so this normal approximation is appropriate.
So approximate X with $Y \sim N(64, 12.8)$.
Using a continuity correction you want to find $P(X = 70) \approx P(69.5 < Y < 70.5) = 0.0275$ (4 d.p.)
b) $P(X = 70) = \binom{80}{70}(0.8)^{70}(0.2)^{10} = 0.0277$ (4 d.p.)
Note that the approximation in part a) is correct to 3 d.p.

Q5 a) n is very large and even though p is not close to 0.5, $np = 50 > 5$ and $n(1 - p) = 950 > 5$, so the normal distribution is a suitable approximation for this distribution.

b) The normal approximation has
$\mu = np = 1000 \times 0.05 = 50$
$\sigma^2 = np(1-p) = 1000 \times 0.05 \times 0.95 = 47.5$
So approximate X with $Y \sim N(50, 47.5)$.
You're looking for the probability that $X > 75$.
Using a continuity correction, you're looking
for $P(Y > 75.5) = 0.0001$ (4 d.p.)

3.3 Choosing Probability Distributions

Exercise 3.3.1 — Choosing probability distributions

Q1 a) Most of the data values are in the middle and
the number of values tails off towards the ends.
It is also fairly symmetrical.

b) $\mu \approx 46$. There is a point of inflection at
approximately $s = 50$. This occurs when
$s = \mu + \sigma \implies 50 \approx 46 + \sigma \implies \sigma \approx 4$
*You could have used any of the other conditions involving
μ and σ, so any answer between 3.5 and 4.5 is acceptable.*

Q2 a) $n (> 100)$ is large and $p = 0.65$ is close to 0.5, or
$np > 100 \times 0.65 > 5$ and $n(1-p) > 100 \times 0.35 > 5$.

b) The normal approximation has
$\mu = np = 105 \times 0.65 = 68.25$
$\sigma^2 = np(1-p) = 105 \times 0.65 \times 0.35 = 23.8875$
So approximate X with $Y \sim N(68.25, 23.8875)$.
Using a continuity correction you want to find
$P(X > 80) \approx P(Y > 80.5) = 0.0061$ (4 d.p.)

3.4 Hypothesis Tests of the Mean of a Population

Exercise 3.4.1 — Hypothesis tests of a population mean

Q1 a) Let the mean weight in grams of all plums from
the tree this year be μ.
Then H_0: $\mu = 42$ and H_1: $\mu > 42$. The significance
level is $\alpha = 0.05$ and it is a one-tailed test.
Let $\overline{X}$ be the sample mean of the weight of plums
in grams. Then under H_0, $X \sim N(42, 16)$,
so $\overline{X} \sim N\left(42, \frac{16}{25}\right) = N(42, 0.64)$.

So under H_0, $Z = \dfrac{\overline{X} - 42}{\sqrt{0.64}} \sim N(0,1)$.

Now $\overline{x} = 43.5$, so $z = \dfrac{43.5 - 42}{\sqrt{0.64}} = 1.875$

You're interested in the higher end of the
distribution, so find the critical value, z, such that
$P(Z > z) = 0.05$.
The percentage points table gives a critical value
of 1.6449. So the critical region is $Z > 1.6449$.
Since $1.875 > 1.6449$, the result lies in the critical
region and is significant.
There is significant evidence at the 5% level to
reject H_0 in favour of the alternative hypothesis
that the weight of plums from the tree has
increased.

b) At the 1% level, you'll have a different critical
region, but everything else is the same.
So you're looking for a critical value, z,
such that $P(Z > z) = 0.01$.
The percentage points table gives a critical value
of 2.3263. So the critical region is $Z > 2.3263$.
$1.875 < 2.3263$, so the result is not significant.
There is insufficient evidence at the 1% level to
reject H_0.

Q2 Let the mean of all the weekly winnings after the new
person joins the games be £μ.
Then H_0: $\mu = 24$ and H_1: $\mu \neq 24$. The significance
level is $\alpha = 0.01$, and it is a two-tailed test.
Let $\overline{X}$ be the sample mean of Bree's winnings.
Then under H_0, $X \sim N(24, 4)$,
so $\overline{X} \sim N\left(24, \frac{4}{12}\right) = N\left(24, \frac{1}{3}\right)$.

So under H_0, $Z = \dfrac{\overline{X} - 24}{\sqrt{\frac{1}{3}}} \sim N(0,1)$.

Now $\overline{x} = 22.5$, so $z = \dfrac{22.5 - 24}{\sqrt{\frac{1}{3}}} = -2.5981$ (4 d.p.)

This is a two-tailed test, so the critical region will be
split. You want to find critical values, $\pm z$, such that
$P(Z > z) = \frac{\alpha}{2} = 0.005$.
The percentage points table gives a critical value of
2.5758. The other critical value will be –2.5758.
So the critical region is $Z < -2.5758$ or $Z > 2.5758$.
Since $z = -2.5981 < -2.5758$, the result lies in the
critical region and is significant.
There is significant evidence at the 1% level to reject
H_0 in favour of the alternative hypothesis that Bree's
mean winnings have changed.

Q3 Let the mean mark of all the students
in the school be μ.
Then H_0: $\mu = 70$ and H_1: $\mu < 70$. The significance
level is $\alpha = 0.05$, and it is a one-tailed test.
Let $\overline{X}$ be the sample mean of the scores.
Then under H_0, $X \sim N(70, 64)$,
so $\overline{X} \sim N\left(70, \frac{64}{40}\right) = N(70, 1.6)$.

So under H_0, $Z = \dfrac{\overline{X} - 70}{\sqrt{1.6}} \sim N(0, 1)$.

$\overline{x} = 67.7$, so $z = \dfrac{67.7 - 70}{\sqrt{1.6}} = -1.8183$ (4 d.p.)

You're interested in the lower end of the distribution, so find the critical value, z, such that $P(Z < z) = 0.05$, i.e. $P(Z > -z) = 0.05$.
The percentage points table gives $z = -1.6449$.
So the critical region is $Z < -1.6449$.
Since $-1.8183 < -1.6449$, the result lies in the critical region, so there is significant evidence at the 5% level to reject H_0 in favour of the alternative hypothesis that the mean score this year is lower.

Q4 a) Let the mean weight in grams of all the pigeons in the city centre this year be μ.
Then H_0: $\mu = 300$ and H_1: $\mu > 300$.

b) This is a one-tailed test.

c) Let $\overline{X}$ be the sample mean of the pigeon weights.
Then under H_0, $X \sim N(300, 45^2)$,

so $\overline{X} \sim N\left(300, \dfrac{45^2}{25}\right) = N(300, 81)$.

So under H_0, $Z = \dfrac{\overline{X} - 300}{\sqrt{81}} \sim N(0, 1)$.

$\overline{x} = 314$, so $z = \dfrac{314 - 300}{\sqrt{81}} = 1.5556$ (4 d.p.)

You're interested in the higher end of the distribution, so find the critical value, z, such that $P(Z > z) = 0.01$.
The percentage points table gives a critical value of 2.3263. So the critical region is $Z > 2.3263$.
Since $1.5556 < 2.3263$, the result does not lie in the critical region and is not significant. There is insufficient evidence at the 1% level to reject H_0 in favour of the alternative hypothesis that the mean pigeon weight has gone up.

Q5 Let the mean number of hours that Kyle has spent studying each week this year be μ. Then H_0: $\mu = 32$ and H_1: $\mu > 32$. This is a one-tailed test.

Let $\overline{X}$ be the sample mean number of hours.
Then under H_0, $X \sim N(32, 5^2)$,

so $\overline{X} \sim N\left(32, \dfrac{5^2}{20}\right) = N(32, 1.25)$.

So under H_0, $Z = \dfrac{\overline{X} - 32}{\sqrt{1.25}} \sim N(0, 1)$.

$\overline{x} = 34$, so $z = \dfrac{34 - 32}{\sqrt{1.25}} = 1.7889$ (4 d.p.)

First test at the 5% level:
You're interested in the higher end of the distribution, so find the critical value, z, such that $P(Z > z) = 0.05$.
The percentage points table gives a critical value of 1.6449. So the critical region is $Z > 1.6449$.
Since $1.7889 > 1.6449$, the result lies in the critical region and is significant. There is significant evidence at the 5% level to reject H_0 in favour of the alternative hypothesis that the mean amount of time spent studying has gone up.

Now test at the 1% level:
Again, you're interested in the higher end of the distribution, so find the critical value, z, such that $P(Z > z) = 0.01$.
The percentage points table gives a critical value of 2.3263. So the critical region is $Z > 2.3263$.
$1.7889 < 2.3263$, so the result does not lie in the critical region and is not significant. There is insufficient evidence at the 1% level to reject H_0 in favour of the alternative hypothesis that the mean amount of time spent studying has gone up.

So the null hypothesis can be rejected at the 5% level, but not at the 1% level.

Review Exercise — Chapter 3

These questions are done using a calculator with an upper bound of 9999 or a lower bound of −9999 where needed.

Q1 a) $P(X < 42) = 0.0228$ (4 d.p.)

b) $P(X > 56) = 0.0668$ (4 d.p.)

c) $P(47 < X < 57) = 0.7333$ (4 d.p.)

Q2 a) $P(Z < 0.84) = 0.7995$ (4 d.p.)

b) $P(Z \leq -0.01) = 0.4960$ (4 d.p.)

c) $P(-0.99 < Z \leq -0.74) = 0.0686$ (4 d.p.)

d) $P(-0.55 \leq Z < 0.35) = 0.3457$ (4 d.p.)

Q3 Standard deviation $= \sqrt{6.25} = 2.5$ and mean $= 21$.

a) $P(X \leq 18) = P\left(Z \leq \dfrac{18 - 21}{2.5}\right)$
$= P(Z \leq -1.2) = 0.1151$ (4 d.p.)

b) $P(X > 20) = P\left(Z > \dfrac{20 - 21}{2.5}\right)$
$= P(Z > -0.4) = 0.6554$ (4 d.p.)

c) $P(19 < X < 22) = P\left(\dfrac{19 - 21}{2.5} < Z < \dfrac{22 - 21}{2.5}\right)$
$= P(-0.8 < Z < 0.4)$
$= 0.4436$ (4 d.p.)

d) $P(23 \leq X \leq 25) = P\left(\dfrac{23 - 21}{2.5} \leq Z \leq \dfrac{25 - 21}{2.5}\right)$
$= P(0.8 < Z < 1.6)$
$= 0.1571$ (4 d.p.)

Q4 a) $P(X \leq x) = 0.5$ for $x = 64$

b) Using the fact that the area under the curve is 1:
$P(X \leq x) = 1 - P(X > x) = 1 - 0.9332 = 0.0668$
$P(X \leq x) = 0.0668$ for $x = 55$

c) $P(x \leq X < 75) = 0.6581$
$\Rightarrow P(X < 75) - P(X \leq x) = 0.6581$
$\Rightarrow P(X \leq x) = P(X < 75) - 0.6581$
$= 0.9666 - 0.6581 = 0.3085$
$P(X < x) = 0.3085$ for $x = 61$

Q5 a) $P(X < a) = 0.99$ for $a = 89.0$ (3 s.f.)

b) $|X - 80| < b \implies 80 - b < X < 80 + b$
80 is the mean of X, and a normal distribution is symmetrical, so
$P(80 - b < X < 80 + b) = 0.8$
$\implies P(X \geq 80 + b) = 0.1$
$\implies P\left(Z \geq \dfrac{80 + b - 80}{\sqrt{15}}\right) = P\left(Z \geq \dfrac{b}{\sqrt{15}}\right) = 0.1$
Using the percentage points table,
$\dfrac{b}{\sqrt{15}} = 1.2816$, so $b = 4.96$ (3 s.f.)

Q6 a) Using the fact that the area under the curve is 1:
$P(Z \leq z) = 1 - P(Z > z) = 1 - 0.0359 = 0.9641$
$P(Z \leq z) = 0.9641$ for $z = 1.80$ (2 d.p.)

b) Using the fact that the area under the curve is 1:
$P(Z \leq z) = 1 - P(Z > z) = 1 - 0.01 = 0.99$
$P(Z \leq z) = 0.99$ for $z = 2.33$ (2 d.p.)

c) $P(z \leq Z \leq 0.5) = 0.2902$
$\implies P(Z \leq 0.5) - P(Z \leq z) = 0.2902$
$\implies P(Z \leq z) = P(Z \leq 0.5) - 0.2902$
$\implies P(Z \leq z) = 0.6915 - 0.2902 = 0.4013$
$\Phi(z) = 0.4013$ for $z = -0.25$ (2 d.p.)

Q7 $P(X > 221) = 0.3085 \implies P\left(Z > \dfrac{221 - \mu}{8}\right) = 0.3085$
$\implies P\left(Z \leq \dfrac{221 - \mu}{8}\right) = 1 - 0.3085 = 0.6915$
$\Phi(z) = 0.6915$ for $z = 0.50$ (2 d.p.)
$\implies \dfrac{221 - \mu}{8} = 0.5 \implies \mu = 221 - 0.5 \times 8 = 217$

Q8 $P(X < 15.2) = 0.9783 \implies P\left(Z < \dfrac{15.2 - \mu}{\sigma}\right) = 0.9783$
$\Phi(z) = 0.9783$ for $z = 2.02$ (2 d.p.)
$\implies \dfrac{15.2 - \mu}{\sigma} = 2.02 \implies 15.2 - \mu = 2.02...\sigma$ ①
$P(X > 14.8) = 0.1056 \implies P\left(Z > \dfrac{14.8 - \mu}{\sigma}\right) = 0.1056$
$\implies P\left(Z \leq \dfrac{14.8 - \mu}{\sigma}\right) = 1 - 0.1056 = 0.8944$
$\Phi(z) = 0.8944$ for $z = 1.25$ (2 d.p.)
$\implies \dfrac{14.8 - \mu}{\sigma} = 1.25... \implies 14.8 - \mu = 1.25...\sigma$ ②
Subtracting equation ② from equation ① gives:
$15.2 - 14.8 - \mu - (-\mu) = 2.02...\sigma - 1.25...\sigma$
$\implies 0.4 = 0.77\sigma \implies \sigma = 0.519...$
Putting $\sigma = 0.52$ into equation ① gives:
$15.2 - \mu = 2.02 \times 0.519... \implies \mu = 14.15$ (2 d.p.)
So $\mu = 14.15$ and $\sigma = 0.52$ (2 d.p.)

Q9 Let $M \sim N(55, 4.4^2)$ represent the mass of items made by the factory.

a) Using a calculator:
$P(M < 55) = 0.5$
55 g is the mean, so the probability will be 0.5.

b) $P(M < 50) = 0.1279$ (4 d.p.)

c) $P(M > 60) = 1 - P(M \leq 60) = 1 - 0.8720...$
$= 0.1279$ (4 d.p.)

Q10 $X \sim B(100, 0.45)$, so use a normal approximation
$Y \sim N(\mu, \sigma^2)$ with $\mu = np = 100 \times 0.45 = 45$
$\sigma^2 = np(1 - p) = 100 \times 0.45 \times 0.55 = 24.75$
So approximate X with $Y \sim N(45, 24.75)$.

a) $P(X = 50) \approx P(49.5 < Y < 50.5) = 0.0484$ (4 d.p.)

b) Using a continuity correction you're looking for
$P(X > 50) \approx P(Y > 50.5) = 0.1345$ (4 d.p.)

c) Using a continuity correction you're looking for
$P(X \leq 45) \approx P(Y < 45.5) = 0.5400$ (4 d.p.)

d) Using a continuity correction you're looking for
$P(40 < X \leq 47) \approx P(40.5 < Y \leq 47.5)$
$= 0.5095$ (4 d.p.)

Q11 a) $X \sim B(120, 0.28)$, so $P(X = 34) = 0.0803$ (4 d.p.)
$X \sim B(120, 0.28)$, so use a normal approximation
$Y \sim N(\mu, \sigma^2)$ with $\mu = np = 120 \times 0.28 = 33.6$
$\sigma^2 = np(1 - p) = 120 \times 0.28 \times 0.72 = 24.192$
So approximate X with $Y \sim N(33.6, 24.192)$.
$P(X = 34) \approx P(33.5 < Y < 34.5) = 0.0807$ (4 d.p.)

b) The normal approximation is accurate to 2 d.p.
It differs from the true value by less than 5 ten-thousandths.

Q12 $H_0: \mu = 45$ and $H_1: \mu < 45$. This is a one-tailed test.
Under H_0, $X \sim N(45, 3^2)$,
so $\overline{X} \sim N\left(45, \dfrac{3^2}{16}\right) = N\left(45, \dfrac{9}{16}\right)$.
So under H_0, $Z = \dfrac{\overline{X} - 45}{\sqrt{\dfrac{9}{16}}} \sim N(0, 1)$.
$\overline{x} = 42$, so $z = \dfrac{42 - 45}{\sqrt{\dfrac{9}{16}}} = -4$
You're interested in the lower end of the distribution, so find the critical value, z, such that $P(Z < z) = 0.05$. The percentage points table gives a critical value of -1.6449. So the critical region is $Z < -1.6449$. Since $-4 < -1.6449$, the result lies in the critical region and is significant. There is sufficient evidence at the 5% level to reject H_0 in favour of H_1.

Exam-Style Questions — Chapter 3

Q1 a) $X \sim N(30, 4^2)$
[1 mark for correct answer]

b) 30 is the mean of X, and a normal distribution is symmetrical, so $P(30 - a < X < 30 + a) = 0.4$
$\implies P(X < 30 - a) = 0.3$
$\Phi(z) = 0.3$ for $z = 27.902...$
$\implies 30 - a = 27.902... \implies a = 2.10$ (3 s.f.)
This method uses the lower end of the distribution. You could have used the higher end instead where $P(X > 30 + a) = 0.3$.
[3 marks available — 1 mark for correct method, 1 mark for correct z-value, 1 mark for correct answer]

Q2 a) Let X be the mass of a clementine,
then $X \sim N(\mu, 5.5^2)$.
$$P(X < 80) = P\left(Z < \frac{80 - \mu}{5.5}\right) = 0.8623$$
$\Phi(z) = 0.8623$ for $z = 1.09...$
$$\Rightarrow \frac{80 - \mu}{5.5} = 1.09... \Rightarrow \mu = 74 \text{ g (to nearest gram)}$$
[3 marks available — 1 mark for attempting to convert to standard normal distribution, 1 mark for correct z-value, 1 mark for correct answer to the nearest gram]

b) A normal distribution is symmetrical about the mean so $w = 74 - (80 - 74) = 68$ g.
[1 mark for correct answer — allow for error carried forward from part a)]

Q3 a) Let X be the number of rose plants that have red flowers, then $X \sim B(200, 0.4)$.
[1 mark for correct answer]

b) $X \sim B(200, 0.4)$, so use a normal approximation
$Y \sim N(\mu, \sigma^2)$ with $\mu = np = 200 \times 0.4 = 80$
$\sigma^2 = np(1 - p) = 200 \times 0.4 \times 0.6 = 48$
So approximate X with $Y \sim N(80, 48)$.
Using a continuity correction you're looking for
$P(X \geq 90) \approx P(Y > 89.5) = 0.0852$ (4 d.p.)
[3 marks available — 1 mark for correct normal approximation, 1 mark for correcting for continuity, 1 mark for correct answer]

c) E.g. n is large and p is close to 0.5.
[1 mark for correct justification]
An alternative answer would be to show that np and $n(1 - p)$ are both greater than 5.

Q4 a) Let X be the length of the brown trout in the lake, then $X \sim N(46.0, 9.6^2)$.
$P(40 < X < 50) = 0.3956$ (4 d.p.)
[1 mark for correct answer]

b) Let the mean length of the brown trout in the lake be μ. Then H_0: $\mu = 46.0$ and H_1: $\mu > 46.0$.
The significance level is $\alpha = 0.01$ and this is a one-tailed test.
Let $\overline{X}$ be the sample mean age.
Then under H_0, $X \sim N(46.0, 9.6^2)$,
so $\overline{X} \sim N\left(46.0, \frac{9.6^2}{32}\right) = N(46.0, 2.88)$.
So under H_0, $Z = \dfrac{\overline{X} - 46.0}{\sqrt{2.88}} \sim N(0, 1)$.
$\overline{x} = 51.7$, so $z = \dfrac{51.7 - 46.0}{\sqrt{2.88}} = 3.3588$ (4 d.p.)
You're interested in the higher end of the distribution so find the critical value, z, such that $P(Z > z) = 0.01$. The percentage points table gives a critical value of 2.3263. So the critical region is $Z > 2.3263$. Since $3.3588 > 2.3263$, the result is in the critical region and is significant. There is sufficient evidence at the 1% level to reject H_0 in favour of the alternative hypothesis that the mean length of the brown trout has increased.
[5 marks available — 1 mark for correct hypotheses, 1 mark for identifying test is one-tailed, 1 mark for correct expression for Z in terms of $\overline{X}$, 1 mark for correct z-value, 1 mark for correct conclusion]

Chapter 4: Kinematics

4.1 Projectiles

Exercise 4.1.1 — The two components of velocity

Q1 **a)** Horizontal component:
10 cos 20° = 9.40 ms⁻¹ (3 s.f.)
Vertical component:
10 sin 20° = 3.42 ms⁻¹ (3 s.f.)

b) Horizontal component:
18 cos 65° = 7.61 ms⁻¹ (3 s.f.)
Vertical component:
18 sin 65° = 16.3 ms⁻¹ (3 s.f.)

c) Horizontal component:
−6.8 cos 21.6° = −6.32 ms⁻¹ (3 s.f.)
Vertical component:
6.8 sin 21.6° = 2.50 ms⁻¹ (3 s.f.)

d) Horizontal component:
9.7 cos 19.7° = 9.13 ms⁻¹ (3 s.f.)
Vertical component:
−9.7 sin 19.7° = −3.27 ms⁻¹ (3 s.f.)

e) Horizontal component:
−24 cos 84° = −2.51 ms⁻¹ (3 s.f.)
Vertical component:
−24 sin 84° = −23.9 ms⁻¹ (3 s.f.)

f) Horizontal component:
16 cos 123° = −8.71 ms⁻¹ (3 s.f.)
Vertical component:
16 sin 123° = 13.4 ms⁻¹ (3 s.f.)

g) Horizontal component:
−7.5 cos 27° = −6.68 ms⁻¹ (3 s.f.)
Vertical component:
−7.5 sin 27° = −3.40 ms⁻¹ (3 s.f.)

h) Horizontal component:
−19 cos 31° = −16.3 ms⁻¹ (3 s.f.)
Vertical component:
19 sin 31° = 9.79 ms⁻¹ (3 s.f.)

i) Horizontal component:
6.6 cos (180° − 114°) = 2.68 ms⁻¹ (3 s.f.)
Vertical component:
−6.6 sin (180° − 114°) = −6.03 ms⁻¹ (3 s.f.)

Q2 Horizontal component: 8 cos 35° = 6.55 ms⁻¹ (3 s.f.)
Vertical component: 8 sin 35° = 4.59 ms⁻¹ (3 s.f.)

Q3 Horizontal component = 0 ms⁻¹
Vertical component = 45 ms⁻¹

Q4

$(22 \times 1000) \div 60^2 = 6.1111... = 6.11$ ms⁻¹ (3 s.f.)
Horizontal component = 6.1111... cos α ms⁻¹
Vertical component = 6.1111... sin α ms⁻¹

Q5

speed $= \sqrt{6^2 + 8^2} = 10$ ms⁻¹
$\theta = \tan^{-1}\left(\frac{8}{6}\right) = 53.1°$ (3 s.f.) above the horizontal

Q6

speed $= \sqrt{17^2 + 2.5^2} = 17.2$ ms⁻¹ (3 s.f.)
$\theta = \tan^{-1}\left(\frac{2.5}{17}\right) = 8.37°$ (3 s.f.) below the horizontal

Q7

$\theta = \tan^{-1}\left(\frac{3a}{2a}\right) = \tan^{-1}\left(\frac{3}{2}\right) = 56.3°$ (3 s.f.)
above the negative horizontal.

Exercise 4.1.2 — The constant acceleration equations

Q1 **a)** Resolving vertically, taking up as positive:
$u = 15 \sin 50°$, $v = 0$, $a = -9.8$, $t = t$
$v = u + at$
$0 = 15 \sin 50° - 9.8t$
$t = 15 \sin 50° \div 9.8 = 1.17$ s (3 s.f.)

b) Resolving vertically, taking up as positive:
$s = s$, $u = 15 \sin 50°$, $v = 0$, $a = -9.8$,
$v^2 = u^2 + 2as$
$0 = (15 \sin 50°)^2 - 19.6s$
$s = (15 \sin 50°)^2 \div 19.6 = 6.74$ m (3 s.f.)

Q2 **a)** Resolving horizontally, taking right as positive:
$s = s$, $u = 12 \cos 37°$, $a = 0$, $t = 0.5$
$s = ut + \frac{1}{2}at^2$
$s = 12 \cos 37° \times 0.5 = 4.791... = 4.79$ m (3 s.f.)

b) Resolving vertically, taking up as positive:

$s = s$, $u = 12 \sin 37°$, $a = -9.8$, $t = 0.5$

$s = ut + \frac{1}{2}at^2$

$s = (12 \sin 37° \times 0.5) + (\frac{1}{2} \times -9.8 \times 0.5^2)$

$= 2.385... = 2.39$ m (3 s.f.)

c) $\sqrt{(4.791...)^2 + (2.385...)^2} = 5.35$ m (3 s.f.)

Q3 a) Resolving vertically, taking up as positive:

$s = 0$, $u = 8 \sin 59°$, $a = -9.8$, $t = t$

$s = ut + \frac{1}{2}at^2$

$0 = (8 \sin 59°)t - 4.9t^2$

$0 = t(8 \sin 59° - 4.9t)$

$\Rightarrow t = 0$ or $(8 \sin 59° - 4.9t) = 0$

$\Rightarrow t = 8 \sin 59° \div 4.9$

$= 1.399... = 1.40$ s (3 s.f.)

b) Resolving horizontally, taking right as positive:

$s = s$, $u = 8 \cos 59°$, $a = 0$, $t = 1.399...$

$s = ut + \frac{1}{2}at^2$

$s = 8 \cos 59° \times 1.399... = 5.77$ m (3 s.f.)

Q4 a) $\tan \theta = \frac{\text{opp}}{\text{adj}}$, so draw a right-angled triangle with $\sqrt{3}$ as the 'opposite' side and 1 as the 'adjacent' side. Using Pythagoras' theorem, the hypotenuse will be 2:

So $\sin \theta = \frac{\sqrt{3}}{2}$ and $\cos \theta = \frac{1}{2}$

Resolving vertically, taking up as positive:

$u = 18 \sin \theta = 9\sqrt{3}$, $v = v$, $a = -9.8$, $t = 2$

$v = u + at$

$v = 9\sqrt{3} - 19.6 = -4.011...$

Resolving horizontally, taking right as positive:

$v = u = 18 \cos \theta = 9$

So speed $= \sqrt{(-4.011...)^2 + 9^2} = 9.85$ ms^{-1} (3 s.f.)

You could also have solved this by spotting that θ = 60°, since tan 60° is one of the common values you should know.

b) $\alpha = \tan^{-1}\left(\frac{-4.011...}{9}\right) = -24.0°$ (3 s.f.)

i.e. 24.0° below the horizontal.

Q5 a) Resolving vertically, taking down as positive:

$s = 40$, $u = 0$, $a = 9.8$, $t = t$

$s = ut + \frac{1}{2}at^2$

$40 = 4.9t^2$

$t^2 = 8.163... \Rightarrow t = 2.857... = 2.86$ s (3 s.f.)

b) Resolving horizontally, taking right as positive:

$s = s$, $u = 80$, $a = 0$, $t = 2.857...$

$s = ut + \frac{1}{2}at^2$

$s = 80 \times 2.857... = 229$ m (3 s.f.)

c) E.g. The acceleration should take into account the increased drag from the water — vertical acceleration can no longer be assumed to be equal to g, and horizontal acceleration can no longer be assumed to be 0.

Q6 Resolving vertically, taking down as positive:

$s = h$, $u = 0$, $a = 9.8$, $t = t$

$s = ut + \frac{1}{2}at^2$

$h = 4.9t^2 \Rightarrow t = \sqrt{\frac{h}{4.9}}$

Resolving horizontally:

$s = d$, $u = 145$, $a = 0$, $t = \sqrt{\frac{h}{4.9}}$

$s = ut + \frac{1}{2}at^2$

$d = 145\sqrt{\frac{h}{4.9}}$ m

Q7 Resolving vertically, taking down as positive:

$s = 215$, $u = 0$, $a = 9.8$, $t = t$

$s = ut + \frac{1}{2}at^2$

$215 = 4.9t^2$

$t^2 = 43.877... \Rightarrow t = 6.624...$ s

Resolving horizontally:

$s = 179$, $u = u$, $a = 0$, $t = 6.624...$

$s = ut + \frac{1}{2}at^2$

$179 = u \times 6.624... \Rightarrow u = 27.0$ ms^{-1} (3 s.f.)

Q8 Resolving vertically, taking up as positive:

$s = 11 - 4 = 7$, $u = 20 \sin 45°$, $a = -9.8$, $t = t$

$s = ut + \frac{1}{2}at^2$

$7 = (20 \sin 45°)t - 4.9t^2$

$4.9t^2 - (20 \sin 45°)t + 7 = 0$

Using the quadratic formula:

$t = \frac{20 \sin 45° \pm \sqrt{(-20 \sin 45°)^2 - (4 \times 4.9 \times 7)}}{9.8}$

$= \frac{14.142... \pm \sqrt{62.8}}{9.8}$

$\Rightarrow t = 2.251...$ or $t = 0.634...$

So the object is higher than 11 m above the ground for $2.251... - 0.634... = 1.62$ s (3 s.f.)

Q9 First find the ball's vertical displacement from its starting point when it passes through the first target. Resolving vertically, taking up as positive:

$s = s_1$, $u = 24 \sin 70°$, $a = -9.8$, $t = 3$

$s = ut + \frac{1}{2}at^2$

$s_1 = (24 \sin 70° \times 3) + (\frac{1}{2} \times -9.8 \times 3^2) = 23.557...$ m

Now find the ball's vertical displacement from its starting point when it passes through the second target. Resolving vertically, taking up as positive:

$s = s_2$, $u = 24 \sin 70°$, $a = -9.8$, $t = 4$

$s = ut + \frac{1}{2}at^2$

$s_2 = (24 \sin 70° \times 4) + (\frac{1}{2} \times -9.8 \times 4^2) = 11.810...$ m

So $h = 23.557... - 11.810... = 11.7$ m (3 s.f.)

Q10 First find the value of α by considering the particle's motion from its point of projection to its maximum height. Resolving vertically, taking up as positive:
$s = 2.8 - 0.6 = 2.2$, $u = 7.5 \sin \alpha$, $v = 0$, $a = -9.8$
$v^2 = u^2 + 2as$
$0 = (7.5 \sin \alpha)^2 + (2 \times -9.8 \times 2.2)$
$\sin^2 \alpha = 43.12 \div 56.25$
$\sin \alpha = 0.875... \Rightarrow \alpha = 61.109...°$
Now resolving horizontally, taking right as positive:
$s = s$, $u = 7.5 \cos (61.109...°) = 3.623...$, $a = 0$, $t = 1.2$
$s = ut + \frac{1}{2}at^2 \Rightarrow s = 3.623... \times 1.2 = 4.35$ m (3 s.f.)

Q11 $\tan \theta = \frac{\text{opp}}{\text{adj}}$, so draw a right-angled triangle with 3 as the 'opposite' side and 4 as the 'adjacent' side.
Using Pythagoras' theorem, the hypotenuse will be 5:

So $\sin \theta = \frac{3}{5}$ and $\cos \theta = \frac{4}{5}$.

Now find an expression for the ball's time of flight.
Resolving horizontally, taking right as positive:
$s = 50$, $u = V \cos \theta = \frac{4}{5}V$, $a = 0$, $t = t$
$s = ut + \frac{1}{2}at^2$
$50 = \frac{4}{5}V \times t \Rightarrow t = \frac{5 \times 50}{4V} = \frac{125}{2V}$
Now resolving vertically, taking up as positive:
$s = 0$, $u = V \sin \theta = \frac{3}{5}V$, $a = -9.8$, $t = \frac{125}{2V}$
$s = ut + \frac{1}{2}at^2$
$0 = \frac{3V \times 125}{5 \times 2V} - 4.9\left(\frac{125}{2V}\right)^2 \Rightarrow 0 = 37.5 - \frac{76\,562.5}{4V^2}$
$\frac{76\,562.5}{4V^2} = 37.5 \Rightarrow \frac{76\,562.5}{4 \times 37.5} = V^2$
$V^2 = \frac{76\,562.5}{150} \Rightarrow V = 22.6$ ms^{-1} (3 s.f.)

Q12 a) Resolving vertically, taking down as positive:
$s = 16$, $u = 3 \sin 7°$, $a = 9.8$, $t = t$
$s = ut + \frac{1}{2}at^2$
$16 = (3 \sin 7°)t + 4.9t^2$
$4.9t^2 + (3 \sin 7°)t - 16 = 0$
Using the quadratic formula:
$t = \dfrac{-3 \sin 7° \pm \sqrt{(3 \sin 7°)^2 - (4 \times 4.9 \times -16)}}{9.8}$
$= \dfrac{-0.3656... \pm \sqrt{313.73...}}{9.8}$
$\Rightarrow t = 1.770...$ or $t = -1.844...$
So the particle's time of flight is $t = 1.770...$ s
Resolving horizontally, taking right as positive:
$s = s$, $u = 3 \cos 7°$, $a = 0$, $t = 1.770...$
$s = ut + \frac{1}{2}at^2$
$s = 3 \cos 7° \times 1.770... = 5.27$ m (3 s.f.)

b) Resolving vertically, taking down as positive:
$s = 16$, $u = 3 \sin 7°$, $v = v_y$, $a = 9.8$
$v^2 = u^2 + 2as$
$v_y^2 = (3 \sin 7°)^2 + (2 \times 9.8 \times 16) = 313.733...$
$\Rightarrow v_y = 17.712...$ ms^{-1}
Horizontally, $v_x = u_x = 3 \cos 7°$ ms^{-1}

Using Pythagoras' theorem:
speed $= \sqrt{(3 \cos 7°)^2 + (17.712...)^2}$
$= 18.0$ ms^{-1} (3 s.f.)

Using trigonometry:
$\theta = \tan^{-1}\left(\dfrac{17.712...}{3 \cos 7°}\right)$
$= 80.5°$ (3 s.f.) below the horizontal

Q13 a) Resolving vertically, taking up as positive:
$s = 2.5 - 0.5 = 2$, $u = 19 \sin 28°$, $a = -9.8$, $t = t$
$s = ut + \frac{1}{2}at^2$
$2 = (19 \sin 28°)t - 4.9t^2$
$4.9t^2 - (19 \sin 28°)t + 2 = 0$
Using the quadratic formula:
$t = \dfrac{19 \sin 28° \pm \sqrt{(-19 \sin 28°)^2 - (4 \times 4.9 \times 2)}}{9.8}$
$= \dfrac{8.9199... \pm \sqrt{40.365...}}{9.8}$
$\Rightarrow t = 0.261...$ or $t = 1.558...$
So the ball is 2.5 m above the ground 0.261... s after being hit (when it is rising) and 1.558... s after being hit (when it is on its descent).
It is caught when it is on its descent, so it is in the air for 1.558... s = 1.56 s (3 s.f.)

b) Resolving horizontally, taking right as positive:
$s = s$, $u = 19 \cos 28°$, $a = 0$, $t = 1.558...$
$s = ut + \frac{1}{2}at^2$
$s = 19 \cos 28° \times 1.558... = 26.1$ m (3 s.f.)

c) Resolving vertically, taking up as positive:
$s = 2$, $u = 19 \sin 28°$, $v = v_y$, $a = -9.8$
$v^2 = u^2 + 2as$
$v_y^2 = (19 \sin 28°)^2 + (2 \times -9.8 \times 2) = 40.365...$
$\Rightarrow v_y = 6.353...$ ms^{-1}
Horizontally, $v_x = u_x = 19 \cos 28°$
Using Pythagoras' theorem:
speed $= \sqrt{(19 \cos 28°)^2 + (6.353...)^2}$
$= 17.9$ ms^{-1} (3 s.f.)

Q14 a) Resolving horizontally, taking right as positive:
$u = U\cos 40°$, $v = V\cos 10°$, $a = 0$, $t = 2$
There is no acceleration horizontally, so $u = v$:
$U\cos 40° = V\cos 10° \Rightarrow V = \dfrac{U\cos 40°}{\cos 10°}$
Resolving vertically, taking upwards as positive:
$u = U\sin 40°$, $v = V\sin 10°$, $a = -9.8$, $t = 2$
$v = u + at$
$V\sin 10° = U\sin 40° - 19.6$
Substituting $V = \dfrac{U\cos 40°}{\cos 10°}$ into this equation:
$\dfrac{U\cos 40°}{\cos 10°} \times \sin 10° = U\sin 40° - 19.6$
$U(\cos 40° \tan 10° - \sin 40°) = -19.6$
$\Rightarrow U = 38.604... = 38.6 \text{ ms}^{-1}$ (3 s.f.)

b) Resolving vertically, taking up as positive:
$s = s$, $u = (38.604...)\sin 40° = 24.814...$,
$a = -9.8$, $t = 2$
$s = ut + \frac{1}{2}at^2$
$s = (24.814... \times 2) + (\frac{1}{2} \times -9.8 \times 2^2)$
$s = 30.0 \text{ m}$ (3 s.f.)

Q15 a) Resolving vertically, taking up as positive:
$s = s$, $u = U\sin\theta$, $v = 0$, $a = -g$
$v^2 = u^2 + 2as$
$0 = U^2\sin^2\theta - 2gs$
$\Rightarrow s = \dfrac{U^2\sin^2\theta}{2g} \text{ m}$

b) Resolving vertically, taking up as positive:
$u = U\sin\theta$, $v = 0$, $a = -g$, $t = t$
$v = u + at$
$0 = U\sin\theta - gt$
$\Rightarrow t = \dfrac{U\sin\theta}{g} \text{ s}$

Q16 a) Resolving vertically, taking down as positive:
$s = 0.02$, $u = 0$, $a = 9.8$, $t = t$
$s = ut + \frac{1}{2}at^2$
$0.02 = 4.9t^2 \Rightarrow t = 0.063... \text{ s}$
Resolving horizontally, taking right as positive:
$s = s$, $u = 15$, $a = 0$, $t = 0.063...$
$s = ut + \frac{1}{2}at^2$
$s = 15 \times 0.063... = 0.958... = 0.958 \text{ m}$ (3 s.f.)

b) Resolving horizontally, taking right as positive:
$s = 0.958...$, $u = U\cos 5°$, $a = 0$, $t = t$
$s = ut + \frac{1}{2}at^2$
$0.958... = U\cos 5° \times t \Rightarrow t = \dfrac{0.958...}{U\cos 5°}$
Resolving vertically, taking up as positive:
$s = -0.02$, $u = U\sin 5°$, $a = -9.8$, $t = \dfrac{0.958...}{U\cos 5°}$
$s = ut + \frac{1}{2}at^2$
$-0.02 = U\sin 5°\dfrac{0.958...}{U\cos 5°} - 4.9\left(\dfrac{0.958...}{U\cos 5°}\right)^2$
$4.9\left(\dfrac{0.958...}{U\cos 5°}\right)^2 = (0.958... \times \tan 5°) + 0.02$
$4.9 \times (0.958...)^2$
$\qquad = (U\cos 5°)^2 \times ((0.958...)\tan 5° + 0.02)$
$U^2 = \dfrac{4.9 \times (0.958...)^2}{(\cos 5°)^2 \times ((0.958...)\tan 5° + 0.02)}$
$U^2 = 43.666... \Rightarrow U = 6.61 \text{ ms}^{-1}$ (3 s.f.)

Q17 The coordinates (3, 1) give you the components of the projectile's displacement — when it passes through this point, its horizontal displacement is 3 m and its vertical displacement is 1 m.
Resolving horizontally, taking right as positive:
$s = 3$, $u = 3\cos\alpha$, $a = 0$, $t = t$
$s = ut + \frac{1}{2}at^2$
$3 = (3\cos\alpha) \times t \Rightarrow t = \dfrac{1}{\cos\alpha}$
Resolving vertically, taking up as positive:
$s = 1$, $u = 3\sin\alpha$, $a = -g$, $t = \dfrac{1}{\cos\alpha}$
$s = ut + \frac{1}{2}at^2$
$1 = \left(3\sin\alpha \times \dfrac{1}{\cos\alpha}\right) + \left(\dfrac{1}{2} \times -g \times \left(\dfrac{1}{\cos\alpha}\right)^2\right)$
$\Rightarrow 1 = 3\tan\alpha - \dfrac{g}{2\cos^2\alpha}$, as required

Q18 a) Resolving horizontally for particle A, taking right as positive:
$s = s$, $u = U$, $a = 0$, $t = 2$
$s = ut + \frac{1}{2}at^2 \Rightarrow s = 2U$
Resolving horizontally for particle B, taking right as positive:
$s = s$, $u = 2U\cos\theta$, $a = 0$, $t = 2$
$s = ut + \frac{1}{2}at^2 \Rightarrow s = 4U\cos\theta$
When the particles collide, their horizontal displacements will be the same:
$2U = 4U\cos\theta$
$\cos\theta = \dfrac{1}{2} \Rightarrow \theta = 60°$

b) Resolving vertically for particle A, taking down as positive:
$s = s$, $u = 0$, $a = 9.8$, $t = 2$
$s = ut + \frac{1}{2}at^2$
$s = \frac{1}{2} \times 9.8 \times 2^2 = 19.6 \text{ m}$
So, when the particles collide, A has fallen 19.6 m vertically downwards from a height of 45 m above the ground. Therefore, the particles collide at a height of 25.4 m above the ground.
Resolving vertically for particle B, taking up as positive:
$s = s$, $u = 2U\sin 60° = \sqrt{3}\,U$, $a = -9.8$, $t = 2$
$s = ut + \frac{1}{2}at^2$
$s = 2\sqrt{3}\,U + (\frac{1}{2} \times -9.8 \times 2^2) = 2\sqrt{3}\,U - 19.6$
So, when the particles collide (at a height of 25.4 m above the ground), B has travelled $(2\sqrt{3}\,U - 19.6)$ m vertically upwards from a height of 15 m above the ground. So:
$15 + (2\sqrt{3}\,U - 19.6) = 25.4$
$2\sqrt{3}\,U = 30 \Rightarrow U = \dfrac{15}{\sqrt{3}} = 8.6602...$
So, the speed of projection of A is 8.66 ms^{-1} (3 s.f.), and the speed of projection of B is 17.3 ms^{-1} (3 s.f.)

Exercise 4.1.3 — i and j vectors

Q1 a) $\mathbf{u} = (12\mathbf{i} + 16\mathbf{j})$, $\mathbf{v} = \mathbf{v}$, $\mathbf{a} = -9.8\mathbf{j}$, $t = 2$
$\mathbf{v} = \mathbf{u} + \mathbf{a}t$
$\mathbf{v} = (12\mathbf{i} + 16\mathbf{j}) - 19.6\mathbf{j}$
$\mathbf{v} = (12\mathbf{i} - 3.6\mathbf{j})$ ms^{-1}

b) When the particle reaches its maximum height, the vertical component of its velocity will be zero, and the horizontal component of its velocity will be the same as when it was projected (there is no horizontal acceleration), so its velocity will be $12\mathbf{i}$ ms^{-1}.

c) The particle follows a symmetric curved path, so when it hits the ground, the vertical component of its velocity will have the same magnitude as when it was projected, but in the opposite direction. The horizontal component of velocity remains constant, so the particle's velocity will be $(12\mathbf{i} - 16\mathbf{j})$ ms^{-1}.
You could also have answered this question by resolving horizontally and vertically and using the suvat equations to find each component rather than using the symmetry.

Q2 a) Resolving vertically, taking up as positive:
$s = s$, $u = 10$, $v = 0$, $a = -9.8$
$v^2 = u^2 + 2as$
$0 = 100 - 19.6s$
$s = 5.102...$
So the projectile reaches a maximum height of $5 + 5.102... = 10.1$ m (3 s.f.) above the ground.

b) Resolving vertically, taking up as positive:
$s = -5$, $u = 10$, $v = v_y$, $a = -9.8$
$v^2 = u^2 + 2as$
$v_y^2 = 100 + (2 \times -9.8 \times -5) = 198$
$v_y = -14.071...$ ms^{-1}
v_y is negative because the projectile is travelling downwards when it hits the ground.
Horizontally, $v_x = u_x = 17$ ms^{-1}
Using Pythagoras' theorem:
speed $= \sqrt{17^2 + 198} = 22.1$ ms^{-1} (3 s.f.)

c) Using trigonometry:
$\tan\theta = \left(\dfrac{-14.071...}{17}\right) \Rightarrow \theta = -39.615...°$
i.e. $39.6°$ (3 s.f.) below the horizontal.

Q3 a) The stone is thrown from a point 2.5 m above the ground, so when it is 6 m above the ground, it is $6 - 2.5 = 3.5$ m above its point of projection.
Resolving vertically, taking up as positive:
$s = 3.5$, $u = 9$, $a = -9.8$, $t = t$
$s = ut + \frac{1}{2}at^2$
$3.5 = 9t - 4.9t^2 \Rightarrow 4.9t^2 - 9t + 3.5 = 0$
Using the quadratic formula:
$t = \dfrac{9 \pm \sqrt{(-9)^2 - (4 \times 4.9 \times 3.5)}}{9.8}$
$\Rightarrow t = 0.559...$ or $t = 1.277...$
$1.277... - 0.559... = 0.7186...$
So the stone is at least 6 m above the ground for 0.719 s (3 s.f.)

b) Resolving vertically, taking up as positive:
$s = -2.5$, $u = 9$, $a = -9.8$, $t = t$
$s = ut + \frac{1}{2}at^2$
$-2.5 = 9t - 4.9t^2 \Rightarrow 4.9t^2 - 9t - 2.5 = 0$
Using the quadratic formula:
$t = \dfrac{9 \pm \sqrt{(-9)^2 - (4 \times 4.9 \times -2.5)}}{9.8}$
$\Rightarrow t = 2.081...$ or $t = -0.245...$
Resolving horizontally, taking right as positive:
$s = s$, $u = 6$, $a = 0$, $t = 2.081...$
$s = ut + \frac{1}{2}at^2$
$s = 6 \times 2.081... = 12.490...$ m
$20 - 12.490... = 7.509...$ m
So it falls short of the target by 7.51 m (3 s.f.)

Q4 a) $\mathbf{s} = (200\mathbf{i} - 40\mathbf{j})$, $\mathbf{u} = (a\mathbf{i} + b\mathbf{j})$, $\mathbf{a} = -9.8\mathbf{j}$, $t = 5$
$\mathbf{s} = \mathbf{u}t + \frac{1}{2}\mathbf{a}t^2$
$(200\mathbf{i} - 40\mathbf{j}) = 5(a\mathbf{i} + b\mathbf{j}) + (\frac{1}{2} \times -9.8\mathbf{j} \times 5^2)$
$5(a\mathbf{i} + b\mathbf{j}) = (200\mathbf{i} + 82.5\mathbf{j})$
$(a\mathbf{i} + b\mathbf{j}) = (40\mathbf{i} + 16.5\mathbf{j}) \Rightarrow a = 40$ and $b = 16.5$
You could also have answered this by considering the horizontal and vertical components separately, and using the suvat equations as usual.

b) The horizontal component of velocity remains constant at 40 ms^{-1}. So you only need to consider the vertical component.
$u = 16.5$, $v = v$, $a = -9.8$, $t = 5$
$v = u + at$
$v = 16.5 + (-9.8 \times 5) = -32.5$
$\Rightarrow \mathbf{v} = (40\mathbf{i} - 32.5\mathbf{j})$ ms^{-1}

Q5 a) $\mathbf{s} = (15\mathbf{i} + 6\mathbf{j})$, $\mathbf{u} = \mathbf{u}$, $\mathbf{a} = -9.8\mathbf{j}$, $t = 3$
$\mathbf{s} = \mathbf{u}t + \frac{1}{2}\mathbf{a}t^2$
$(15\mathbf{i} + 6\mathbf{j}) = 3\mathbf{u} + (\frac{1}{2} \times -9.8\mathbf{j} \times 3^2)$
$3\mathbf{u} = (15\mathbf{i} + 6\mathbf{j}) + 44.1\mathbf{j}$
$\Rightarrow \mathbf{u} = (5\mathbf{i} + 16.7\mathbf{j})$ ms^{-1}

b) $\mathbf{u} = (5\mathbf{i} + 16.7\mathbf{j})$, $\mathbf{v} = \mathbf{v}$, $\mathbf{a} = -9.8\mathbf{j}$, $t = 3$
$\mathbf{v} = \mathbf{u} + \mathbf{a}t$
$\mathbf{v} = (5\mathbf{i} + 16.7\mathbf{j}) + (-9.8\mathbf{j} \times 3)$
$\Rightarrow \mathbf{v} = (5\mathbf{i} - 12.7\mathbf{j})$ ms^{-1}

c) Velocity immediately following impact with wall is $(-2.5\mathbf{i} - 12.7\mathbf{j})$ ms^{-1}.
Resolving vertically, taking down as positive:
$s = 6$, $u = 12.7$, $a = 9.8$, $t = t$
$s = ut + \frac{1}{2}at^2$
$6 = 12.7t + 4.9t^2 \Rightarrow 4.9t^2 + 12.7t - 6 = 0$
Using the quadratic formula:
$t = \dfrac{-12.7 \pm \sqrt{12.7^2 - (4 \times 4.9 \times -6)}}{9.8}$
$\Rightarrow t = 0.4081...$ or $t = -3$
Resolving horizontally, taking left as positive:
$s = s$, $u = 2.5$, $a = 0$, $t = 0.4081...$
$s = ut + \frac{1}{2}at^2$
$s = 2.5 \times 0.4081... = 1.02$ m (3 s.f.)

d) E.g. The model could treat the ball as a three-dimensional shape with a significant diameter, instead of a particle, to better estimate the distance from the wall. The model could include other factors, such as air resistance or the spin of the ball. The model could describe the ball's motion in three dimensions rather than two, as it's unlikely to rebound perpendicular to the wall.

Q6 a) When the model submarine is moving due north, the velocity in the **i**-direction is zero.
So resolving east:
$u = -0.6$, $v = 0$, $a = 0.1$, $t = t$
$v = u + at$
$0 = -0.6 + 0.1t \Rightarrow t = 6$ s
Check that the velocity in the **j**-direction is positive at this time (otherwise the toy could be moving due south). Resolving north:
$u = 3$, $v = v$, $a = 0.5$, $t = 6$
$v = u + at$
$v = 3 + (0.5 \times 6) = 6$
So it <u>is</u> moving due north at $t = 6$ s.

b) Find the velocity when $t = 2.5$:
$\mathbf{u} = (-0.6\mathbf{i} + 3\mathbf{j})$, $\mathbf{v} = \mathbf{v}$, $\mathbf{a} = (0.1\mathbf{i} + 0.5\mathbf{j})$, $t = 2.5$
$\mathbf{v} = \mathbf{u} + \mathbf{a}t$
$\mathbf{v} = (-0.6\mathbf{i} + 3\mathbf{j}) + 2.5(0.1\mathbf{i} + 0.5\mathbf{j})$
$\mathbf{v} = -0.6\mathbf{i} + 3\mathbf{j} + 0.25\mathbf{i} + 1.25\mathbf{j} = -0.35\mathbf{i} + 4.25\mathbf{j}$
Draw a triangle to find the bearing:

$\theta = \tan^{-1}\left(\dfrac{4.25}{0.35}\right) = 85.29214...^\circ$
Bearing $= 270° + \theta = 355°$ (nearest degree)

c) Find the position when $t = 20$ s:
$\mathbf{s} = \mathbf{s}$, $\mathbf{u} = (-0.6\mathbf{i} + 3\mathbf{j})$, $\mathbf{a} = (0.1\mathbf{i} + 0.5\mathbf{j})$, $t = 20$
$\mathbf{s} = \mathbf{u}t + \dfrac{1}{2}\mathbf{a}t^2$
$\mathbf{s} = [(-0.6\mathbf{i} + 3\mathbf{j}) \times 20] + [\frac{1}{2} \times (0.1\mathbf{i} + 0.5\mathbf{j}) \times 20^2]$
$\mathbf{s} = 8\mathbf{i} + 160\mathbf{j}$
Using Pythagoras' theorem:
distance $= \sqrt{8^2 + 160^2} = 160.19... = 160$ m (3 s.f.)

d) For example:
- The model could allow for a non-uniform acceleration due to a changing resistance force.
- 3D vectors could be used to describe the variation in the submarine's depth underwater.

Q7 At $t = 0$, the particle is moving north-west:

The initial velocity, **u**, can be written as a vector $-b\mathbf{i} + b\mathbf{j}$, with a magnitude of 5 ms^{-1}.
Using Pythagoras' theorem:
speed $= \sqrt{(-b)^2 + b^2} = 5$ ms^{-1} $\Rightarrow \sqrt{2b^2} = 5$
$\Rightarrow 2b^2 = 5^2 \Rightarrow b^2 = \dfrac{5^2}{2} \Rightarrow b = \pm\dfrac{5}{\sqrt{2}} = \pm\dfrac{5\sqrt{2}}{2}$
We know we want the positive root to give a north-west direction, so initial velocity $\mathbf{u} = -\dfrac{5\sqrt{2}}{2}\mathbf{i} + \dfrac{5\sqrt{2}}{2}\mathbf{j}$
At $t = 10$, the particle is moving south, so final velocity $\mathbf{v} = -\sqrt{2}\mathbf{j}$.
$\mathbf{u} = (-\dfrac{5\sqrt{2}}{2}\mathbf{i} + \dfrac{5\sqrt{2}}{2}\mathbf{j})$, $\mathbf{v} = -\sqrt{2}\mathbf{j}$, $\mathbf{a} = (p\mathbf{i} + q\mathbf{j})$, $t = 10$
$\mathbf{v} = \mathbf{u} + \mathbf{a}t$
$-\sqrt{2}\mathbf{j} = (-\dfrac{5\sqrt{2}}{2}\mathbf{i} + \dfrac{5\sqrt{2}}{2}\mathbf{j}) + 10(p\mathbf{i} + q\mathbf{j})$
$\dfrac{5\sqrt{2}}{2}\mathbf{i} - \dfrac{7\sqrt{2}}{2}\mathbf{j} = 10p\mathbf{i} + 10q\mathbf{j}$
$\Rightarrow 10p = \dfrac{5\sqrt{2}}{2} \Rightarrow p = \dfrac{\sqrt{2}}{4}$
$10q = -\dfrac{7\sqrt{2}}{2} \Rightarrow q = -\dfrac{7\sqrt{2}}{20}$

4.2 Non-Uniform Acceleration in 2 Dimensions
Exercise 4.2.1 — Using vectors
Q1 a) (i) $\mathbf{v} = \dot{\mathbf{r}} = [(3t^2 - 3)\mathbf{i} + 2t\mathbf{j}]$ ms^{-1}
  (ii) When $t = 3$, $\mathbf{v} = (3(3)^2 - 3)\mathbf{i} + 2(3)\mathbf{j}$
    $= (24\mathbf{i} + 6\mathbf{j})$ ms^{-1}
    Using Pythagoras' theorem:
    speed $= \sqrt{24^2 + 6^2} = 24.7$ ms^{-1} (3 s.f.)
    Using trigonometry:
    $\theta = \tan^{-1}\left(\dfrac{6}{24}\right)$
      $= 14.0°$ (3 s.f.) from the positive **i**-direction.

b) (i) $\mathbf{a} = \dot{\mathbf{v}} = (6t\mathbf{i} + 2\mathbf{j})$ ms^{-2}
  (ii) When $t = 4$, $\mathbf{a} = 6(4)\mathbf{i} + 2\mathbf{j} = (24\mathbf{i} + 2\mathbf{j})$ ms^{-2}
    Using Pythagoras' theorem:
    magnitude $= \sqrt{24^2 + 2^2} = 24.1$ ms^{-2} (3 s.f.)

Q2 $\mathbf{a} = \dot{\mathbf{v}} = (8t\mathbf{i} + \mathbf{j})$ ms^{-2}
When $t = 8$, $\mathbf{a} = 8(8)\mathbf{i} + \mathbf{j} = (64\mathbf{i} + \mathbf{j})$ ms^{-2}

Q3 $\mathbf{a} = \dot{\mathbf{v}} = (t^2 + 4t - 12)\mathbf{i}$ ms^{-2}
At the maximum velocity, $\mathbf{a} = 0$, so:
$t^2 + 4t - 12 = 0 \Rightarrow (t + 6)(t - 2) = 0$
    $\Rightarrow t = -6$ and $t = 2$
$0 \le t \le 4$, so ignore the solution at $t = -6$.
When $t = 2$, $\mathbf{v} = [\frac{1}{3}(2)^3 + 2(2)^2 - 12(2)]\mathbf{i} + 14\mathbf{j}$
    $= \left(-\dfrac{40}{3}\mathbf{i} + 14\mathbf{j}\right)$ ms^{-1}

Q4 a) It's easier to work with the vectors in component form whilst integrating, so use $\mathbf{a} = 3e^{3t}\mathbf{i} + \frac{6}{\sqrt{t}}\mathbf{j}$

$\mathbf{v} = \int \mathbf{a}\, dt = \left(\int 3e^{3t}\, dt\right)\mathbf{i} + \left(\int \frac{6}{\sqrt{t}}\, dt\right)\mathbf{j}$

$= \left(\int 3e^{3t}\, dt\right)\mathbf{i} + \left(\int 6t^{-\frac{1}{2}}\, dt\right)\mathbf{j}$

$= e^{3t}\mathbf{i} + 12t^{\frac{1}{2}}\mathbf{j} + \mathbf{C}$

$= e^{3t}\mathbf{i} + 12\sqrt{t}\,\mathbf{j} + \mathbf{C}$

When $t = 0$, $\mathbf{v} = (4\mathbf{i} + 6\mathbf{j})$, so:

$4\mathbf{i} + 6\mathbf{j} = e^0\mathbf{i} + 12\sqrt{0}\,\mathbf{j} + \mathbf{C}$

$4\mathbf{i} + 6\mathbf{j} = \mathbf{i} + \mathbf{C}$

$\Rightarrow \quad \mathbf{C} = 3\mathbf{i} + 6\mathbf{j}$

So $\mathbf{v} = (e^{3t} + 3)\mathbf{i} + (6 + 12\sqrt{t}\,)\mathbf{j} = \begin{pmatrix} e^{3t} + 3 \\ 6 + 12\sqrt{t} \end{pmatrix}$ ms^{-1}

b) $\mathbf{r} = \int \mathbf{v}\, dt = \left[\int (e^{3t} + 3)\, dt\right]\mathbf{i} + \left[\int (6 + 12\sqrt{t}\,)\, dt\right]\mathbf{j}$

$= \left[\int (e^{3t} + 3)\, dt\right]\mathbf{i} + \left[\int (6 + 12t^{\frac{1}{2}})\, dt\right]\mathbf{j}$

$= \left(\frac{e^{3t}}{3} + 3t\right)\mathbf{i} + \left(6t + 8t^{\frac{3}{2}}\right)\mathbf{j} + \mathbf{D}$

When $t = 0$, $\mathbf{r} = (2\mathbf{i} - 9\mathbf{j})$, so:

$2\mathbf{i} - 9\mathbf{j} = \left(\frac{e^0}{3} + 0\right)\mathbf{i} + (0 + 0)\mathbf{j} + \mathbf{D}$

$2\mathbf{i} - 9\mathbf{j} = \frac{1}{3}\mathbf{i} + \mathbf{D} \Rightarrow \mathbf{D} = \frac{5}{3}\mathbf{i} - 9\mathbf{j}$

So $\mathbf{r} = (\frac{e^{3t}}{3} + 3t + \frac{5}{3})\mathbf{i} + (6t + 8t^{\frac{3}{2}} - 9)\mathbf{j}$

$= \begin{pmatrix} \frac{1}{3}e^{3t} + 3t + \frac{5}{3} \\ 6t + 8\sqrt{t^3} - 9 \end{pmatrix}$ m

Q5 a) $\mathbf{v} = \dot{\mathbf{r}} = [(\cos t)\mathbf{i} - (\sin t)\mathbf{j}]$ ms^{-1}

The object is moving east when the $\mathbf{j}$ component is 0, and the $\mathbf{i}$ component is positive.

$\sin t = 0$ when $t = 0, \pi, 2\pi...$

When $t = \pi$, the $\mathbf{i}$ component $\cos t = -1$, so the object is moving west, not east.

When $t = 2\pi$, $\cos t = 1$.

So the first non-zero value of t for which the object is moving east is $t = 2\pi$ seconds.

b) At $t = 2\pi$, $\mathbf{r} = (\sin 2\pi)\mathbf{i} + (\cos 2\pi)\mathbf{j} = (0\mathbf{i} + \mathbf{j})$ m.

So it is 1 m north of O.

Q6 a) $\mathbf{a} = \dot{\mathbf{v}} = [-6\mathbf{i} + (2t + 2)\mathbf{j}]$ ms^{-2}

When $t = 5$, $\mathbf{a} = (-6\mathbf{i} + 12\mathbf{j})$ ms^{-2}

b) $\mathbf{r} = \int \mathbf{v}\, dt = \left[\int (3 - 6t)\, dt\right]\mathbf{i} + \left[\int (t^2 + 2t)\, dt\right]\mathbf{j}$

$= (3t - 3t^2)\mathbf{i} + \left(\frac{1}{3}t^3 + t^2\right)\mathbf{j} + \mathbf{C}$

When $t = 2$, $\mathbf{r} = (-2\mathbf{i} + 7\mathbf{j})$, so:

$-2\mathbf{i} + 7\mathbf{j} = (6 - 12)\mathbf{i} + (\frac{8}{3} + 4)\mathbf{j} + \mathbf{C}$

$-2\mathbf{i} + 7\mathbf{j} = -6\mathbf{i} + \frac{20}{3}\mathbf{j} + \mathbf{C} \Rightarrow \mathbf{C} = 4\mathbf{i} + \frac{1}{3}\mathbf{j}$

So $\mathbf{r} = (3t - 3t^2 + 4)\mathbf{i} + (\frac{1}{3}t^3 + t^2 + \frac{1}{3})\mathbf{j}$

When the particle is directly above O:

$3t - 3t^2 + 4 = 0 \Rightarrow 3t^2 - 3t - 4 = 0$

Using the quadratic formula:

$t = \frac{3 \pm \sqrt{(-3)^2 - (4 \times 3 \times -4)}}{2 \times 3} = \frac{3 \pm \sqrt{57}}{6}$

$\Rightarrow t = 1.758...$ or $t = -0.758...$

Time must be positive, so check that $t = 1.758...$ gives a positive value for the $\mathbf{j}$ component (since the object is above, not below, O):

$\frac{1}{3}(1.758...)^3 + (1.758...)^2 + \frac{1}{3} = 5.236... > 0$,

so the particle is directly above O at 1.76 s (3 s.f.)

Q7 a) $\mathbf{v} = \int \mathbf{a}\, dt = \left[\int (2t - 1)\, dt\right]\mathbf{i} + \left[\int (t^2 + t)\, dt\right]\mathbf{j}$

$\mathbf{v} = (t^2 - t)\mathbf{i} + \left(\frac{t^3}{3} + \frac{t^2}{2}\right)\mathbf{j} + \mathbf{C}$

When $t = 3$, $\mathbf{v} = (7\mathbf{i} + 14\mathbf{j})$, so:

$7\mathbf{i} + 14\mathbf{j} = (9 - 3)\mathbf{i} + \left(\frac{27}{3} + \frac{9}{2}\right)\mathbf{j} + \mathbf{C}$

$7\mathbf{i} + 14\mathbf{j} = 6\mathbf{i} + \frac{27}{2}\mathbf{j} + \mathbf{C} \Rightarrow \mathbf{C} = \mathbf{i} + \frac{1}{2}\mathbf{j}$

So $\mathbf{v} = [(t^2 - t + 1)\mathbf{i} + \left(\frac{t^3}{3} + \frac{t^2}{2} + \frac{1}{2}\right)\mathbf{j}]$ ms^{-1}

b) When $t = 5$, $\mathbf{v} = (25 - 5 + 1)\mathbf{i} + \left(\frac{125}{3} + \frac{25}{2} + \frac{1}{2}\right)\mathbf{j}$

$\mathbf{v} = (21\mathbf{i} + \frac{164}{3}\mathbf{j})$ ms^{-1}

Using Pythagoras' theorem:

speed $= \sqrt{21^2 + \left(\frac{164}{3}\right)^2} = 58.6$ ms^{-1} (3 s.f.)

Using trigonometry:

$\tan \theta = \left(\frac{164}{3 \times 21}\right)$

$\Rightarrow \theta = 69.0°$ (3 s.f.) above the positive $\mathbf{i}$-direction.

Q8 $\mathbf{r} = \int \mathbf{v}\, dt = \left[\int (t^2 - 6t)\, dt\right]\mathbf{i} + \left[\int (4t + 5)\, dt\right]\mathbf{j}$

$= (\frac{1}{3}t^3 - 3t^2)\mathbf{i} + (2t^2 + 5t)\mathbf{j} + \mathbf{C}$

When $t = 0$, $\mathbf{r} = 0\mathbf{i} + 0\mathbf{j}$, so:

$0\mathbf{i} + 0\mathbf{j} = (\frac{1}{3}(0)^3 - 3(0)^2)\mathbf{i} + (2(0)^2 + 5(0))\mathbf{j} + \mathbf{C}$

$\Rightarrow \mathbf{C} = 0\mathbf{i} + 0\mathbf{j}$

So $\mathbf{r} = [(\frac{1}{3}t^3 - 3t^2)\mathbf{i} + (2t^2 + 5t)\mathbf{j}]$ m

Equating $\mathbf{j}$-components at position vector $(b\mathbf{i} + 12\mathbf{j})$ m:

$2t^2 + 5t = 12$

$2t^2 + 5t - 12 = 0$

$(2t - 3)(t + 4) = 0 \Rightarrow t = 1.5$ and $t = -4$

The time can't be negative, so the particle passes through the point $(b\mathbf{i} + 12\mathbf{j})$ m at time $t = 1.5$ s.

Equating $\mathbf{i}$-components and substituting $t = 1.5$:

$\frac{1}{3}t^3 - 3t^2 = b$

$\frac{1}{3}(1.5)^3 - 3(1.5)^2 = b \Rightarrow b = -5.625$

Q9 a) $\mathbf{r} = \int \mathbf{v}\, dt = \left[\int (-1)\, dt\right]\mathbf{i} + \left[\int (8t + 2)\, dt\right]\mathbf{j}$

$= (-t)\mathbf{i} + (4t^2 + 2t)\mathbf{j} + \mathbf{C}$

When $t = 1$, $\mathbf{r} = (4\mathbf{i} + 12\mathbf{j})$, so:

$4\mathbf{i} + 12\mathbf{j} = -\mathbf{i} + 6\mathbf{j} + \mathbf{C} \Rightarrow \mathbf{C} = 5\mathbf{i} + 6\mathbf{j}$

So $\mathbf{r} = [(5 - t)\mathbf{i} + (4t^2 + 2t + 6)\mathbf{j}]$ m

b) The **i** component of displacement represents the movement in the x-direction, and the **j** component represents the movement in the y-direction.

$x = 5 - t \Rightarrow t = 5 - x$ — eqn 1
$y = 4t^2 + 2t + 6$ — eqn 2

Sub eqn 1 in eqn 2:
$y = 4(5 - x)^2 + 2(5 - x) + 6$
$= 100 - 40x + 4x^2 + 10 - 2x + 6$
$= 4x^2 - 42x + 116$

Q10 a) $\mathbf{v}_A = \dot{\mathbf{r}}_A = [(3t^2 - 2t - 4)\mathbf{i} + (3t^2 - 4t + 3)\mathbf{j}]$ ms^{-1}
$(3t^2 - 2t - 4)\mathbf{i} + (3t^2 - 4t + 3)\mathbf{j} = -3\mathbf{i} + 2\mathbf{j}$
Equating **i**-components:
$3t^2 - 2t - 4 = -3$
$3t^2 - 2t - 1 = 0$
$(3t + 1)(t - 1) = 0 \Rightarrow t = -\dfrac{1}{3}$ and $t = 1$
When $t = 1$, the **j**-component of $\mathbf{v}_A$ is:
$3(1)^2 - 4(1) + 3 = 2$
So the particle's velocity is $(-3\mathbf{i} + 2\mathbf{j})$ ms^{-1} at time $t = 1$ second.

b) When the particle's direction of motion is 45° above **i**, the horizontal and vertical components of the particle's velocity will be equal.
A good way to picture this is that if the particle was moving relative to a pair of coordinate axes, it would be moving along the line $y = x$ (for positive x and y).
$3t^2 - 2t - 4 = 3t^2 - 4t + 3$
$2t = 7 \Rightarrow t = 3.5$ s
This is the value of t for which the horizontal and vertical components of velocity are equal.
You need to check that the particle is moving at 45° above **i**, not 45° below –**i** at this time.
(The components will also be equal if the particle is moving along a path 45° below –**i**.)
From part **a)**,
$\mathbf{v}_A = [(3t^2 - 2t - 4)\mathbf{i} + (3t^2 - 4t + 3)\mathbf{j}]$ ms^{-1}.
When $t = 3.5$,
$\mathbf{v}_A = [(3(3.5)^2 - 2(3.5) - 4)\mathbf{i} + (3(3.5)^2 - 4(3.5) + 3)\mathbf{j}]$
$= (25.75\mathbf{i} + 25.75\mathbf{j})$ ms^{-1}
Both components are positive, so the particle is moving along a path 45° above **i** when $t = 3.5$ s.
You don't actually need to check that both components are positive — if one is, the other one will be too.

c) $\mathbf{v}_B = \displaystyle\int \mathbf{a}_B \, dt = \left(\int 6t \, dt\right)\mathbf{i} + \left(\int 6t \, dt\right)\mathbf{j}$
$= 3t^2\mathbf{i} + 3t^2\mathbf{j} + \mathbf{C}$
When $t = 1$, $\mathbf{v}_B = (4\mathbf{i} - \mathbf{j})$, so:
$4\mathbf{i} - \mathbf{j} = 3(1)^2\mathbf{i} + 3(1)^2\mathbf{j} + \mathbf{C}$
$4\mathbf{i} - \mathbf{j} = 3\mathbf{i} + 3\mathbf{j} + \mathbf{C} \Rightarrow \mathbf{C} = \mathbf{i} - 4\mathbf{j}$
So $\mathbf{v}_B = [(3t^2 + 1)\mathbf{i} + (3t^2 - 4)\mathbf{j}]$ ms^{-1}
$\mathbf{r}_B = \displaystyle\int \mathbf{v}_B \, dt = \left[\int (3t^2 + 1) \, dt\right]\mathbf{i} + \left[\int (3t^2 - 4) \, dt\right]\mathbf{j}$
$= (t^3 + t)\mathbf{i} + (t^3 - 4t)\mathbf{j} + \mathbf{D}$
When $t = 1$, $\mathbf{r}_B = (2\mathbf{i} + 3\mathbf{j})$, so:
$2\mathbf{i} + 3\mathbf{j} = (1^3 + 1)\mathbf{i} + (1^3 - 4(1))\mathbf{j} + \mathbf{D}$
$2\mathbf{i} + 3\mathbf{j} = 2\mathbf{i} - 3\mathbf{j} + \mathbf{D} \Rightarrow \mathbf{D} = 6\mathbf{j}$
So $\mathbf{r}_B = [(t^3 + t)\mathbf{i} + (t^3 - 4t + 6)\mathbf{j}]$ m

d) $\mathbf{r}_B - \mathbf{r}_A = [(t^3 + t)\mathbf{i} + (t^3 - 4t + 6)\mathbf{j}] -$
$[(t^3 - t^2 - 4t + 3)\mathbf{i} + (t^3 - 2t^2 + 3t - 7)\mathbf{j}]$
$= [(t^2 + 5t - 3)\mathbf{i} + (2t^2 - 7t + 13)\mathbf{j}]$ m

e) When $t = 4$,
$\mathbf{r}_B - \mathbf{r}_A = (4^2 + 5(4) - 3)\mathbf{i} + (2(4)^2 - 7(4) + 13)\mathbf{j}$
$= (33\mathbf{i} + 17\mathbf{j})$ m
Using Pythagoras' theorem:
distance $= \sqrt{33^2 + 17^2} = 37.1$ m (3 s.f.)

Q11 a) $\dfrac{dy}{dt} = \dfrac{1}{t}$, and $\dfrac{dx}{dt} = -\dfrac{3}{t^4}$,
so $\dfrac{dy}{dx} = \dfrac{dy}{dt} \div \dfrac{dx}{dt} = \dfrac{1}{t} \div \dfrac{-3}{t^4} = -\dfrac{t^3}{3}$
When $t = \dfrac{1}{2}$, $\dfrac{dy}{dx} = -\dfrac{1}{3 \times 2^3} = -\dfrac{1}{24}$

b) $\mathbf{r} = x\mathbf{i} + y\mathbf{j} \Rightarrow \mathbf{v} = \dfrac{d\mathbf{r}}{dt} = \dfrac{dx}{dt}\mathbf{i} + \dfrac{dy}{dt}\mathbf{j} = -\dfrac{3}{t^4}\mathbf{i} + \dfrac{1}{t}\mathbf{j}$
$\Rightarrow \mathbf{a} = \dfrac{d\mathbf{v}}{dt} = \dfrac{d^2x}{dt^2}\mathbf{i} + \dfrac{d^2y}{dt^2}\mathbf{j} = \dfrac{12}{t^5}\mathbf{i} - \dfrac{1}{t^2}\mathbf{j}$
So when $t = \dfrac{1}{2}$,
$\mathbf{a} = \dfrac{12}{\left(\frac{1}{2}\right)^5}\mathbf{i} - \dfrac{1}{\left(\frac{1}{2}\right)^2}\mathbf{j} = 384\mathbf{i} - 4\mathbf{j}$ (as required)

Q12 Use double angle identities to change the components of **v** into expressions that are easier to integrate:
$\cos 2t \equiv 1 - 2\sin^2 t \Rightarrow 2\sin^2 t \equiv 1 - \cos 2t$
$\sin 2t \equiv 2\sin t \cos t \Rightarrow 4\sin 2t \cos 2t \equiv 2\sin 4t$
$\Rightarrow \mathbf{v} = (1 - \cos 2t)\mathbf{i} + (2\sin 4t)\mathbf{j}$
$\mathbf{r} = \displaystyle\int \mathbf{v} \, dt = \left[\int (1 - \cos 2t) \, dt\right]\mathbf{i} + \left[\int (2\sin 4t) \, dt\right]\mathbf{j}$
$= \left(t - \dfrac{1}{2}\sin 2t\right)\mathbf{i} - \left(\dfrac{1}{2}\cos 4t\right)\mathbf{j} + \mathbf{C}$
When $t = \dfrac{\pi}{4}$, $\mathbf{r} = \dfrac{\pi}{4}\mathbf{i} + \mathbf{j}$, so:
$\dfrac{\pi}{4}\mathbf{i} + \mathbf{j} = \left(\dfrac{\pi}{4} - \dfrac{1}{2}\sin\dfrac{\pi}{2}\right)\mathbf{i} - \left(\dfrac{1}{2}\cos \pi\right)\mathbf{j} + \mathbf{C}$
$\dfrac{\pi}{4}\mathbf{i} + \mathbf{j} = \left(\dfrac{\pi}{4} - \dfrac{1}{2}\right)\mathbf{i} + \dfrac{1}{2}\mathbf{j} + \mathbf{C} \Rightarrow \mathbf{C} = \dfrac{1}{2}\mathbf{i} + \dfrac{1}{2}\mathbf{j}$
$\mathbf{r} = \left(t - \dfrac{1}{2}\sin 2t + \dfrac{1}{2}\right)\mathbf{i} - \left(\dfrac{1}{2}\cos 4t + \dfrac{1}{2}\right)\mathbf{j}$
$= \dfrac{1}{2}(2t - \sin 2t + 1)\mathbf{i} - \dfrac{1}{2}(\cos 4t - 1)\mathbf{j}$
So when $t = 0$, $\mathbf{r} = \dfrac{1}{2}(0 - 0 + 1)\mathbf{i} - \dfrac{1}{2}(1 - 1)\mathbf{j} = \dfrac{1}{2}\mathbf{i}$,
so distance from the origin $= \dfrac{1}{2}$ m.

Q13 a) $\dfrac{dn}{dt} = -2$ when $n = -4 \Rightarrow k(-4) - 10 = -2$
$\Rightarrow k = -2$
$\dfrac{dn}{dt} < 0 \Rightarrow -2n - 10 < 0 \Rightarrow 2n + 10 > 0$
$\Rightarrow n + 5 > 0$ as required

b) In the **i** direction, the acceleration is a constant 0.1 ms^{-2}, so use the constant acceleration equations to find an expression for m in terms of t:
$u = 0$, $v = m$, $a = 0.1$, $t = t$
$v = u + at \implies m = 0.1t$
In the **j**-direction, form the differential equation to find n in terms of t:
$$\frac{\mathrm{d}n}{\mathrm{d}t} = kn - 10 = -2n - 10 = -2(n + 5)$$
$$\implies \int \frac{1}{n + 5}\,\mathrm{d}n = \int -2\,\mathrm{d}t$$
$\ln|n + 5| = -2t + C$
When $t = 0$, $n = 0 \implies \ln|5| = 0 + C \implies C = \ln 5$
Rearrange to give n in terms of t:
$\ln|n + 5| = -2t + \ln 5$
$\implies |n + 5| = e^{(-2t + \ln 5)}$
From part a), $n + 5 > 0$, so you can drop the modulus.
$\implies n + 5 = e^{-2t}e^{\ln 5}$
$\implies n = 5e^{-2t} - 5 = 5(e^{-2t} - 1)$
Replace both components in $\mathbf{v} = m\mathbf{i} + n\mathbf{j}$ to give:
$\mathbf{v} = \left[0.1t\mathbf{i} + 5(e^{-2t} - 1)\mathbf{j}\right]$ ms^{-1} as required.

Review Exercise — Chapter 4

Q1 Resolving vertically, taking up as positive:
$s = 0$, $u = 22\sin\alpha$, $a = -9.8$, $t = 4$
$s = ut + \frac{1}{2}at^2$
$0 = 22\sin\alpha \times 4 + \frac{1}{2} \times (-9.8) \times 4^2$
$0 = 88\sin\alpha - 78.4$
$\sin\alpha = 78.4 \div 88 = 0.890... \implies \alpha = 63.0°$ (3 s.f.)

Q2 Resolving horizontally:
$s = 60$, $u = 120$, $a = 0$, $t = t$
$s = ut + \frac{1}{2}at^2$
$60 = 120t + 0 \implies t = 0.5$ s

Resolving vertically, taking down as positive:
$s = d$, $u = 0$, $a = 9.8$, $t = 0.5$
$s = ut + \frac{1}{2}at^2$
$d = 0 + 4.9 \times 0.5^2 \implies d = 1.23$ m (3 s.f.)

Q3 a) Resolving vertically, taking down as positive:
$s = 0.3$, $u = -6.5\sin 29°$, $a = 9.8$, $t = t$
$s = ut + \frac{1}{2}at^2$
$0.3 = -(6.5\sin 29°)t + 4.9t^2$
$4.9t^2 - (6.5\sin 29°)t - 0.3 = 0$
Using the quadratic formula:
$$t = \frac{6.5\sin 29° \pm \sqrt{(-6.5\sin 29°)^2 - (4 \times 4.9 \times -0.3)}}{9.8}$$
$\implies t = 0.727...$ or $t = -0.0841...$
Time must be positive, so it lands in $t = 0.727...$ s.
Resolving horizontally:
$s = s$, $u = 6.5\cos 29°$, $a = 0$, $t = 0.727...$
$s = ut + \frac{1}{2}at^2$
$s = 6.5\cos 29° \times 0.727... + 0 = 4.13$ m (3 s.f.)

b) $v_x = u_x = 6.5\cos 29° = 5.685...$ ms^{-1}
Resolving vertically, taking down as positive:
$v = v_y$, $u = -6.5\sin 29°$, $a = 9.8$, $t = 0.727...$
$v = u + at$
$v_y = -6.5\sin 29° + 9.8 \times 0.727... = 3.976...$ ms^{-1}
Using Pythagoras' theorem:
speed $= \sqrt{5.685...^2 + 3.976...^2} = 6.94$ ms^{-1} (3 s.f.)

Q4 a) Resolving vertically, taking up as positive, for the motion up to max height:
$s = 12.5 - 1.5 = 11$, $u = u_y$, $v = 0$, $a = -9.8$
$v^2 = u^2 + 2as$
$0 = u_y^2 + 2 \times (-9.8) \times 11$
$u_y^2 = 215.6 \implies u_y = 14.683...$ ms^{-1}
$u_y = u\sin\alpha \implies 14.683... = u\sin 38°$
$\implies u = 14.683... \div \sin 38° = 23.849...$
$\implies u = 23.8$ ms^{-1} (1 d.p.)

b) Resolving vertically, taking down as positive, for the whole motion:
$s = 1.5$, $u = -14.683...$, $a = 9.8$, $t = t$
$s = ut + \frac{1}{2}at^2$
$1.5 = -14.683...t + 4.9t^2$
$4.9t^2 - 14.683...t - 1.5 = 0$
Using the quadratic formula:
$$t = \frac{14.683... \pm \sqrt{(-14.683...)^2 - (4 \times 4.9 \times -1.5)}}{9.8}$$
$\implies t = 3.095...$ or $t = -0.0988...$
Time must be positive, so it lands in $t = 3.095...$ s.
Resolving horizontally:
$s = s$, $u = 23.849...\cos 38°$, $a = 0$, $t = 3.095...$
$s = ut + \frac{1}{2}at^2$
$s = 23.849...\cos 38° \times 3.095... + 0 = 58.17...$
$s = 58$ m (to the nearest metre)

Q5 a) $\mathbf{u} = (2\mathbf{i} + 11\mathbf{j})$, $\mathbf{v} = \mathbf{v}$, $\mathbf{a} = -9.8\mathbf{j}$, $t = 0.8$
$\mathbf{v} = \mathbf{u} + \mathbf{a}t$
$\mathbf{v} = (2\mathbf{i} + 11\mathbf{j}) - 7.84\mathbf{j}$
$\mathbf{v} = (2\mathbf{i} + 3.16\mathbf{j})$ ms^{-1}

b) Resolving vertically, taking up as positive:
$s = 0$, $u = 11$, $a = -9.8$, $t = t$
$s = ut + \frac{1}{2}at^2$
$0 = 11t - 4.9t^2 \implies t(11 - 4.9t) = 0$
$\implies t = 0$ or $t = 11 \div 4.9 = 2.244...$
So the time of flight is 2.24 s (3 s.f.)

c) Resolving vertically, taking up as positive:
$s = s$, $u = 11$, $v = 0$, $a = -9.8$
$v^2 = u^2 + 2as$
$0 = 11^2 + 2 \times (-9.8) \times s$
$\implies s = 121 \div 19.6 = 6.17$ m (3 s.f.)

Q6 a) Resolving vertically, taking down as positive:
$s = 10$, $u = 4$, $a = 9.8$, $t = t$
$s = ut + \frac{1}{2}at^2$
$10 = 4t + 4.9t^2 \Rightarrow 4.9t^2 + 4t - 10 = 0$
Using the quadratic formula:
$$t = \frac{-4 \pm \sqrt{4^2 - (4 \times 4.9 \times -10)}}{9.8}$$
$\Rightarrow t = 1.077...$ or $t = -1.893...$
Time must be positive, so it lands in
$t = 1.08$ s (3 s.f.)

b) Resolving horizontally:
$s = s$, $u = 20$, $a = 0$, $t = 1.077...$
$s = ut + \frac{1}{2}at^2$
$s = 20 \times 1.077... + 0 = 21.551...$ m
It overshoots by $21.551... - 21 = 0.551$ m (3 s.f.)

c) Resolving horizontally:
$s = 21$, $u = 20$, $a = 0$, $t = t$
$s = ut + \frac{1}{2}at^2$
$21 = 20t + 0 \Rightarrow t = 1.05$ s
$v_x = u_x = 20$ ms^{-1}
Resolving vertically, taking down as positive:
$v = v_y$, $u = 4$, $a = 9.8$, $t = 1.05$
$v = u + at$
$v_y = 4 + 9.8 \times 1.05 = 14.29$ ms^{-1}
Using Pythagoras' theorem:
speed $= \sqrt{20^2 + 14.29^2} = 24.6$ ms^{-1} (3 s.f.)

Q7 a) $\mathbf{a} = \dot{\mathbf{v}} = (4\mathbf{i} + 2t\mathbf{j})$ ms^{-2}

b) $\mathbf{r} = \int \mathbf{v}\, dt = \left(\int 4t\, dt\right)\mathbf{i} + \left(\int t^2\, dt\right)\mathbf{j}$
$= 2t^2\mathbf{i} + \frac{1}{3}t^3\mathbf{j} + \mathbf{C}$
When $t = 0$, $\mathbf{r} = (0\mathbf{i} + 0\mathbf{j})$, so $\mathbf{C} = 0\mathbf{i} + 0\mathbf{j}$ and so
$\mathbf{r} = (2t^2\mathbf{i} + \frac{1}{3}t^3\mathbf{j})$ m

Q8 $\mathbf{v} = \int \mathbf{a}\, dt = \left(\int e^{0.75t}\, dt\right)\mathbf{i} + \left(\int \cos t\, dt\right)\mathbf{j}$
$\mathbf{v} = \frac{4e^{0.75t}}{3}\mathbf{i} + \sin t\, \mathbf{j} + \mathbf{C}$
When $t = 0$, $\mathbf{v} = 17\mathbf{i}$, so:
$17\mathbf{i} = \frac{4e^0}{3}\mathbf{i} + \sin 0\, \mathbf{j} + \mathbf{C}$
$17\mathbf{i} = \frac{4}{3}\mathbf{i} + 0\mathbf{j} + \mathbf{C} \Rightarrow \mathbf{C} = \frac{47}{3}\mathbf{i}$
So $\mathbf{v} = \left(\frac{4e^{0.75t} + 47}{3}\mathbf{i} + \sin t\, \mathbf{j}\right)$ ms^{-1}

Q9 a) $\mathbf{v} = \int \mathbf{a}\, dt = \left[\int -10\, dt\right]\mathbf{j}$
$\mathbf{v} = -10t\mathbf{j} + \mathbf{C}$
When $t = 0$, $\mathbf{v} = 15\mathbf{i} + 12\mathbf{j}$, so:
$15\mathbf{i} + 12\mathbf{j} = -10(0) + \mathbf{C} \Rightarrow \mathbf{C} = 15\mathbf{i} + 12\mathbf{j}$
So $\mathbf{v} = [15\mathbf{i} + (12 - 10t)\mathbf{j}]$ ms^{-1}

b) $\mathbf{r} = \int \mathbf{v}\, dt = \left[\int 15\, dt\right]\mathbf{i} + \left[\int 12 - 10t\, dt\right]\mathbf{j}$
$\mathbf{r} = 15t\mathbf{i} + (12t - 5t^2)\mathbf{j} + \mathbf{C}$
When $t = 1$, $\mathbf{r} = 15\mathbf{i} + 16\mathbf{j}$, so:
$15\mathbf{i} + 16\mathbf{j} = 15(1)\mathbf{i} + (12(1) - 5(1)^2)\mathbf{j} + \mathbf{C}$
$15\mathbf{i} + 16\mathbf{j} = 15\mathbf{i} + 7\mathbf{j} + \mathbf{C} \Rightarrow \mathbf{C} = 9\mathbf{j}$
So $\mathbf{r} = [15t\mathbf{i} + (12t - 5t^2 + 9)\mathbf{j}]$ m

c) When the particle is due east of O, the
$\mathbf{j}$-component of the position vector is 0.
So $12t - 5t^2 + 9 = 0 \Rightarrow 5t^2 - 12t - 9 = 0$
$\Rightarrow (t - 3)(5t + 3) = 0$
$\Rightarrow t = 3$ and $t = -\frac{3}{5}$
Time t must be positive, so find $\mathbf{v}$ when $t = 3$:
$\mathbf{v} = [15\mathbf{i} + (12 - 10(3))\mathbf{j}] = (15\mathbf{i} - 18\mathbf{j})$ ms^{-1}

Exam-Style Questions — Chapter 4

Q1 a) $\mathbf{u} = 7.2\mathbf{i} + 3.2\mathbf{j}$, $\mathbf{v} = 2.7\mathbf{i} + 1.2\mathbf{j}$, $t = 2$, $\mathbf{a} = \mathbf{a}$.
$\mathbf{v} = \mathbf{u} + \mathbf{a}t$
$2.7\mathbf{i} + 1.2\mathbf{j} = 7.2\mathbf{i} + 3.2\mathbf{j} + 2\mathbf{a}$
$\mathbf{a} = (-2.25\mathbf{i} - \mathbf{j})$ ms^{-2}
[3 marks available — 1 mark for correct use of
***suva**t equation, 1 mark for correct substitution,*
1 mark for correct final answer]

b) $\mathbf{s} = \mathbf{s}$, $\mathbf{u} = 7.2\mathbf{i} + 3.2\mathbf{j}$, $t = t$, $\mathbf{a} = -2.25\mathbf{i} - \mathbf{j}$
$\mathbf{s} = \mathbf{u}t + \frac{1}{2}\mathbf{a}t^2$
$\mathbf{s} = (7.2\mathbf{i} + 3.2\mathbf{j})t - \frac{1}{2}(2.25\mathbf{i} + \mathbf{j})t^2$
$\mathbf{s} = [(7.2t - 1.125t^2)\mathbf{i} + (3.2t - 0.5t^2)\mathbf{j}]$ m
[3 marks available — 1 mark for correct use of
***suva**t equation, 1 mark for correct substitution,*
1 mark for correct final answer]

c) The ball stops when:
$\mathbf{u} = 7.2\mathbf{i} + 3.2\mathbf{j}$, $\mathbf{v} = 0$, $\mathbf{a} = -2.25\mathbf{i} - \mathbf{j}$, $t = t$.
$\mathbf{v} = \mathbf{u} + \mathbf{a}t$
$0 = 7.2\mathbf{i} + 3.2\mathbf{j} - (2.25\mathbf{i} + \mathbf{j})t \Rightarrow t = 3.2$ s
From part b):
$\mathbf{s} = (7.2t - 1.125t^2)\mathbf{i} + (3.2t - 0.5t^2)\mathbf{j}$
$\mathbf{s} = (7.2 \times 3.2 - 1.125 \times 3.2^2)\mathbf{i}$
$\qquad\qquad + (3.2 \times 3.2 - 0.5 \times 3.2^2)\mathbf{j}$
$\mathbf{s} = 11.52\mathbf{i} + 5.12\mathbf{j}$
Distance $= |\mathbf{s}| = \sqrt{11.52^2 + 5.12^2} = 12.6$ m (3 s.f.)
[4 marks available — 1 mark for correct use of
***suva**t equation, 1 mark for correct value of t,*
*1 mark for using t to find **s**, 1 mark for correct*
distance s]

d) The defender and the ball must meet, so equate
their position vectors:
$(7.2t - 1.125t^2)\mathbf{i} + (3.2t - 0.5t^2)\mathbf{j}$
$\qquad\qquad\qquad = 4.05t\mathbf{i} + (xt - 1.4)\mathbf{j}$
Comparing the $\mathbf{i}$ components gives:
$7.2t - 1.125t^2 = 4.05t$
$0 = 1.125t^2 - 3.15t \Rightarrow 0 = t(1.125t - 3.15)$
$\Rightarrow t = 0$ or $t = 2.8$
Reject $t = 0$ as you're told that $t > 0$, so $t = 2.8$ s.
Comparing the $\mathbf{j}$ components and substituting t:
$3.2t - 0.5t^2 = xt - 1.4$
$\Rightarrow 3.2 \times 2.8 - 0.5 \times 2.8^2 = 2.8x - 1.4$
$\Rightarrow x = 2.3$
[4 marks available — 1 mark for equating position
vectors, 1 mark for correct method to find t,
1 mark for correct value of t, 1 mark for correct
value of x]

Q2 a) Acceleration is proportional to velocity, so:

$\dfrac{dv}{dt} = kv \Rightarrow \int \dfrac{1}{v}\, dv = k \int 1\, dt$

$\Rightarrow \ln v = kt + C \Rightarrow v = e^{kt + C} = e^{kt} \times e^{C} = Ae^{kt}$

When $t = 0$, $v = 3.6$, so $A = 3.6$
When $t = 3$, $v = 0.2$, so $0.2 = 3.6e^{3k}$

$\Rightarrow \dfrac{1}{18} = e^{3k} \Rightarrow \ln \dfrac{1}{18} = 3k$

$\Rightarrow k = -0.9634... = -0.963$ (3 s.f.)

[4 marks available — 1 mark for forming and attempting to solve differential equation, 1 mark for correct general solution in terms of A and k, 1 mark for correct value of A, 1 mark for correct value of k]

b) $s = \int v\, dt = \int 3.6e^{-0.9634...t}\, dt = -\dfrac{3.6e^{-0.9634...t}}{0.9634...} + D$

$= -3.736...e^{-0.9634...t} + D$

When $t = 0$, $s = 0 \Rightarrow 0 = -3.736... + D$
$\Rightarrow D = 3.736...$
$\Rightarrow s = -3.736...e^{-0.9634...t} + 3.736...$
$\approx 3.74(1 - e^{-0.963t})$ (giving constants to 3 s.f.)

[3 marks available — 1 mark for attempt to integrate v, 1 mark for correct general solution for s, 1 mark for correct constant of integration]

c) The formula for s found in part b) is only valid for $s < 3.6$ (i.e. until it hits the bottom of the lake). Find when $s = 3.6$:

$3.6 = 3.736...(1 - e^{-0.9634...t})$
$\Rightarrow 0.9634... = 1 - e^{-0.9634...t}$
$\Rightarrow e^{-0.9634...t} = 0.0365...$
$\Rightarrow -0.9634...t = \ln 0.0365... = -3.309...$
$\Rightarrow t = 3.434...$
So in the model, $t < 3.43$ (3 s.f.)

[2 marks available — 1 mark for stating that s < 3.6, 1 mark for correctly showing that t < 3.43 (3 s.f.)]

Q3 a) $v = (6t^2 - 3t + 2)\mathbf{i} + (4t^2 - 6)\mathbf{j}$

$\mathbf{a} = \dfrac{d\mathbf{v}}{dt} = [(12t - 3)\mathbf{i} + 8t\mathbf{j}]\ \mathrm{ms^{-2}}$

[2 marks available — 1 mark for attempt to differentiate v, 1 mark for correct answer]

b) In the third second, $\mathbf{s} = \int_{2}^{3} \mathbf{v}\, dt$

$= \int_{2}^{3} \left[(6t^2 - 3t + 2)\mathbf{i} + (4t^2 - 6)\mathbf{j}\right] dt$

$= \left[\left(2t^3 - \dfrac{3}{2}t^2 + 2t\right)\mathbf{i} + \left(\dfrac{4}{3}t^3 - 6t\right)\mathbf{j}\right]_{2}^{3}$

$= \left[\left(2(3)^3 - \dfrac{3}{2}(3)^2 + 2(3)\right)\mathbf{i} + \left(\dfrac{4}{3}(3)^3 - 6(3)\right)\mathbf{j}\right]$

$\quad - \left[\left(2(2)^3 - \dfrac{3}{2}(2)^2 + 2(2)\right)\mathbf{i} + \left(\dfrac{4}{3}(2)^3 - 6(2)\right)\mathbf{j}\right]$

$= (46.5\mathbf{i} + 18\mathbf{j}) - (14\mathbf{i} - \dfrac{4}{3}\mathbf{j})$

$= (32.5\mathbf{i} + \dfrac{58}{3}\mathbf{j})\ \mathrm{m}$

So distance travelled $= |\mathbf{s}| = \sqrt{32.5^2 + \left(\dfrac{58}{3}\right)^2}$
$= 37.8\ \mathrm{m}$ (3 s.f.)

[4 marks available — 1 mark for attempt to integrate v with correct limits, 1 mark for correct integration, 1 mark for correct s, 1 mark for correct distance travelled]

c) When parallel to $2\mathbf{i} + \mathbf{j}$, the $\mathbf{i}$ component of $\mathbf{v}$ must be double the $\mathbf{j}$ component, so:

$6t^2 - 3t + 2 = 2(4t^2 - 6)$
$\Rightarrow 0 = 2t^2 + 3t - 14 = (2t + 7)(t - 2)$
$\Rightarrow t = -3.5$ or 2, but $t > 0$, so $t = 2$
$\Rightarrow \mathbf{v} = [6(2)^2 - 3(2) + 2]\mathbf{i} + [4(2)^2 - 6]\mathbf{j}$
$\quad = (20\mathbf{i} + 10\mathbf{j})\ \mathrm{ms^{-1}}$

[4 marks available — 1 mark for deducing that the i component is double the j component, 1 mark for forming quadratic equation in t, 1 mark for correct t, 1 mark for correct v]

Q4 a) $\mathbf{s} = 7\cos t\,\mathbf{i} + 6\sin t\,\mathbf{j}$
When $t = 0$, $\mathbf{s} = 7\mathbf{i}$ m

$\mathbf{v} = \dfrac{d\mathbf{s}}{dt} = -7\sin t\,\mathbf{i} + 6\cos t\,\mathbf{j}$

When $t = 0$, $\mathbf{v} = 6\mathbf{j}\ \mathrm{ms^{-1}}$

[3 marks available — 1 mark for correct value of s, 1 mark for differentiating correctly for v, 1 mark for correct value of v]

b) $\mathbf{v} = -7\sin t\,\mathbf{i} + 6\cos t\,\mathbf{j}$

$v = |\mathbf{v}| = \sqrt{(-7\sin t)^2 + (6\cos t)^2}$

$\Rightarrow v^2 = 49\sin^2 t + 36\cos^2 t$
$\quad = 36(\sin^2 t + \cos^2 t) + 13\sin^2 t$
$\quad = 36 + 13\sin^2 t$

$0 \le \sin^2 t \le 1 \Rightarrow 0 \le 13\sin^2 t \le 13$
$\Rightarrow 36 \le 36 + 13\sin^2 t \le 49$
$\Rightarrow 36 \le v^2 \le 49 \Rightarrow 6 \le v \le 7$
(Speed is a positive scalar, so the negative values can be ignored.)

Max speed $v = 7$ occurs when $\sin t = \pm 1$, i.e. when $t = \dfrac{k\pi}{2}$, where k is an odd integer.

[4 marks available — 1 mark for finding an expression for v, 1 mark for range of sin t (or sin² t), 1 mark for showing how this leads to the range for v, 1 mark for the given expression for t or equivalent]

Q5 a) Consider the vertical movement only to the highest point:

$s = 2 - 0.5 = 1.5$, $u = u_v$, $v = 0$, $a = -9.8$
$v^2 = u^2 + 2as$
$0 = u_v^2 - 2 \times 9.8 \times 1.5$
$\Rightarrow u_v = \sqrt{29.4}\ \mathrm{ms^{-1}}$

[2 marks available — 1 mark for correct use of suvat equation, 1 mark for correct substitution]

b) Consider the vertical motion as it clears the net:

$s = 1.07 - 0.5 = 0.57$, $u_v = \sqrt{29.4}$, $a = -9.8$, $t = t$
$s = ut + \dfrac{1}{2}at^2$

$0.57 = \sqrt{29.4} \times t - \dfrac{1}{2} \times 9.8 \times t^2$

$\Rightarrow 4.9t^2 - \sqrt{29.4}\, t + 0.57 = 0$

$\Rightarrow t = \dfrac{\sqrt{29.4} \pm \sqrt{29.4 - 4 \times 4.9 \times 0.57}}{2 \times 4.9}$

$\Rightarrow t = 0.1176...$ or $0.9889...,$

The ball is on its way down when it clears the net, so we need to take the later time: $t = 0.9889...$

Now consider the horizontal motion:
$s = 12$, $u = u_h = U\cos\theta$, $a = 0$, $t = 0.9889...$
This still has U and θ, but we know that

$u_v = U\sin\theta = \sqrt{29.4} \Rightarrow U = \dfrac{\sqrt{29.4}}{\sin\theta}$

$u_h = \dfrac{\sqrt{29.4}}{\sin\theta} \times \cos\theta = \dfrac{\sqrt{29.4}}{\tan\theta}$

$s = ut + \dfrac{1}{2}at^2$

$12 = \dfrac{\sqrt{29.4}}{\tan\theta} \times 0.9889... + 0$

$\Rightarrow \tan\theta = \dfrac{\sqrt{29.4} \times 0.9889...}{12} = 0.4468...$

$\Rightarrow \theta = \tan^{-1}(0.4468...) = 24.1°$ (3 s.f.)

$\Rightarrow U = \dfrac{\sqrt{29.4}}{\sin\theta} = 13.3$ ms^{-1} (3 s.f.)

[6 marks available — 1 mark for correct use of vertical suvat equation, 1 mark for correct value of t, 1 mark for finding an expression for U in terms of θ, 1 mark for correct use of horizontal suvat equation, 1 mark for correct value of θ, 1 mark for correct value of U]

Q6 **a)** The string is 0.8 m long, so when it is taut it forms the hypotenuse of a right-angled triangle with vertical height y and horizontal length x, such that: $x^2 + y^2 = 0.8^2$

Considering the horizontal motion:
$s = x$, $u = 1.2$, $a = 0$, $t = t$
$s = ut + \dfrac{1}{2}at^2$
$\Rightarrow x = 1.2t$
Considering the vertical motion:
$s = y$, $u = 0$, $a = 9.8$, $t = t$
$s = ut + \dfrac{1}{2}at^2$
$\Rightarrow y = 4.9t^2$
Substituting into $x^2 + y^2 = 0.8^2$:
$(1.2t)^2 + (4.9t^2)^2 = 0.8^2$
$\Rightarrow 24.01t^4 + 1.44t^2 - 0.64 = 0$
$\Rightarrow t^2 = \dfrac{-1.44 \pm \sqrt{1.44^2 - 4 \times 24.01 \times (-0.64)}}{2 \times 24.01}$
$\Rightarrow t^2 = 0.1360...$ ($t^2 > 0$) $\Rightarrow t = 0.369$ s (3 s.f.)

[5 marks available — 1 mark for linking x and y to the length of the string, 1 mark for correctly using suvat equation horizontally, 1 mark for correctly using suvat equation vertically, 1 mark for forming and attempting to solve quadratic equation for t, 1 mark for correct value of t]

b) E.g. there is no account taken of the air resistance or frictional effect of the string on the yo-yo — yo-yos spin, which means that these effects will be significant.

[2 marks available — 1 mark for stating a sensible limitation of the model, 1 mark for an explanation as to why this is important in this case]

Q7 **a)** $\mathbf{a} = \dfrac{d\mathbf{v}}{dt} = (2\sin t + 2t\cos t)\mathbf{i} - 3\sin t\mathbf{j}$
When $t = \dfrac{\pi}{2}$, $\mathbf{a} = (2\mathbf{i} - 3\mathbf{j})$ cms^{-2}
*[3 marks available — 1 mark for attempt to differentiate **v**, 1 mark for correct expression for **a** in terms of t, 1 mark for correct final answer]*

b) If the ant returns to its nest, its displacement $\mathbf{s} = 0$.

$\mathbf{s} = \int \mathbf{v}\, dt = \left(\int 2t\sin t\, dt\right)\mathbf{i} + \left(\int 3\cos t\, dt\right)\mathbf{j}$
The first part needs to be done by parts:
Let $u = 2t$ so $\dfrac{du}{dt} = 2$, and $\dfrac{dv}{dt} = \sin t$
so $v = -\cos t$.

$\int 2t\sin t\, dt = -2t\cos t - \int -2\cos t\, dt$
$= -2t\cos t + 2\sin t + C_1$

$\int 3\cos t\, dt = 3\sin t + C_2$

So $\mathbf{s} = (-2t\cos t + 2\sin t + C_1)\mathbf{i} + (3\sin t + C_2)\mathbf{j}$
At time $t = 0$, $\mathbf{s} = 5\mathbf{i} - 2\mathbf{j}$:
$-2(0)\cos(0) + 2\sin(0) + C_1 = 5 \Rightarrow C_1 = 5$
$3\sin(0) + C_2 = -2 \Rightarrow C_2 = -2$.
So $\mathbf{s} = [(-2t\cos t + 2\sin t + 5)\mathbf{i} + (3\sin t - 2)\mathbf{j}]$ cm.
Can $\mathbf{s} = 0$? Looking at $\mathbf{j}$, if $3\sin t - 2 = 0$, then
$\sin t = \dfrac{2}{3} \Rightarrow t = 0.729...$ (and $\cos t = \pm\dfrac{\sqrt{5}}{3}$)

Because of the periodicity of sine,
$t = \pi - 0.729... = 2.411...$ is also a solution.
(There are no more solutions in the interval $0 \le t \le 2\pi$.)

Now, assume that we have an **i**-component of 0:
$-2 \times t \times \pm\dfrac{\sqrt{5}}{3} + 2 \times \dfrac{2}{3} + 5 = 0 \Rightarrow t = \pm4.248...$

But we've just shown that $t = 0.729...$ or $2.411...$, so our assumption is false. So the ant will not return to its nest in the given interval.

*[6 marks available — 1 mark for attempting to integrate to find **s**, 1 mark for correct method for integration by parts, 1 mark for correct **i** component of **s** including constant of integration, 1 mark for correct **j** component of **s** including constant of integration, 1 mark for using **s** = 0 for the ant returning to the nest, 1 mark for showing that when one component is 0, the other is not]*

Q8 From the information given, **j** is vertical and **i** is horizontal.

a) Consider the horizontal motion:
$s = 2p$, $u = 4p$, $a = 0$, $t = t$
$s = ut + \dfrac{1}{2}at^2$
$2p = 4pt + 0 \Rightarrow t = 0.5$ s

[2 marks available — 1 mark for correct use of suvat equation, 1 mark for correct substitution]

b) Consider the whole motion, up as positive:
$\mathbf{u} = 4p\mathbf{i} + p\mathbf{j}$, $\mathbf{v} = \mathbf{v}$, $\mathbf{a} = -9.8\mathbf{j}$, $t = 0.5$
$\mathbf{v} = \mathbf{u} + \mathbf{a}t$
$\mathbf{v} = (4p\mathbf{i} + p\mathbf{j}) - 4.9\mathbf{j} = 4p\mathbf{i} + (p - 4.9)\mathbf{j}$

Now consider the displacement.
The stick goes from $2.2\mathbf{j}$ to $(2p\mathbf{i} + 1.375\mathbf{j})$ so the change is $(2p\mathbf{i} - 0.825\mathbf{j})$ m.

$\mathbf{s} = \mathbf{u}t + \frac{1}{2}\mathbf{a}t^2$

$2p\mathbf{i} - 0.825\mathbf{j} = (4p\mathbf{i} + p\mathbf{j}) \times 0.5 + \frac{1}{2} \times (-9.8\mathbf{j}) \times 0.5^2$
$2p\mathbf{i} - 0.825\mathbf{j} = 2p\mathbf{i} + (0.5p - 1.225)\mathbf{j}$
Comparing $\mathbf{j}$ on both sides:
$-0.825 = 0.5p - 1.225 \Rightarrow p = 0.8$
So $\mathbf{v} = (4 \times 0.8)\mathbf{i} + (0.8 - 4.9)\mathbf{j} = (3.2\mathbf{i} - 4.1\mathbf{j})$ ms^{-1}

[5 marks available — 1 mark for correct use of suvat, 1 mark for finding an expression for $\mathbf{v}$ in terms of p, 1 mark for correct use of suvat equation to attempt to find p, 1 mark for correct p, 1 mark for correct $\mathbf{v}$]

c) Consider the vertical motion to reach the stream, taking up as positive:
$s = -2.2$, $u = p = 0.8$, $a = -9.8$, $t = t$
$s = ut + \frac{1}{2}at^2$
$-2.2 = 0.8t - 4.9t^2 \Rightarrow 4.9t^2 - 0.8t - 2.2 = 0$
$\Rightarrow t = \dfrac{0.8 \pm \sqrt{(-0.8)^2 - 4 \times 4.9 \times (-2.2)}}{2 \times 4.9}$
$\Rightarrow t = 0.7566... = 0.757$ s (3 s.f.) $(t > 0)$

[2 marks available — 1 mark for correct use of suvat equation, 1 mark for correct final answer]

d) Consider the horizontal motion to reach the stream: $s = s$, $u = 4p = 3.2$, $a = 0$, $t = 0.7566...$
$s = ut + \frac{1}{2}at^2$
$s = 3.2 \times 0.7566... = 2.4212...$ m away from the base of the bridge.
So to emerge from the other side, it must travel $2.4212... + 1 = 3.4212...$ m at a velocity of 1.2 ms^{-1} in the direction of the flow of water, which takes a further time of:
$t = 3.4212... \div 1.2 = 2.8510...$ s
So, the total time taken is $0.7566... + 2.8510...$
$= 3.61$ s (3 s.f.)

[4 marks available — 1 mark for correct use of suvat equation, 1 mark for finding the horizontal distance away from the bridge, 1 mark for correct use of suvat equation to find the time taken to pass under the bridge whilst in the water, 1 mark for correct total time]

Chapter 5: Dynamics

5.1 Resolving Forces

Exercise 5.1.1 — Components of forces

Q1 a) Horizontal component ($\rightarrow$) = 6.5 N
Vertical component ($\uparrow$) = 0 N

b) Horizontal component ($\rightarrow$) = 0 N
Vertical component ($\uparrow$) = 4 N

c) Horizontal component ($\rightarrow$) = 20 cos 40°
$= 15.3$ N (3 s.f.)
Vertical component ($\uparrow$) = 20 sin 40°
$= 12.9$ N (3 s.f.)

d) Horizontal component ($\rightarrow$) = 17 sin 25°
$= 7.18$ N (3 s.f.)
Vertical component ($\uparrow$) = 17 cos 25°
$= 15.4$ N (3 s.f.)

e) Horizontal component ($\rightarrow$) = -5 cos 10°
$= -4.92$ N (3 s.f.)
Vertical component ($\uparrow$) = 5 sin 10°
$= 0.868$ N (3 s.f.)

f) Horizontal component ($\rightarrow$) = 3 cos 30°
$= 2.60$ N (3 s.f.)
Vertical component ($\uparrow$) = -3 sin 30° = -1.5 N

g) Horizontal component ($\rightarrow$) = -13 sin 60°
$= -11.3$ N (3 s.f.)
Vertical component ($\uparrow$) = -13 cos 60° = -6.5 N

h) Horizontal component ($\rightarrow$) = -11 sin 45°
$= -7.78$ N (3 s.f.)
Vertical component ($\uparrow$) = -11 cos 45°
$= -7.78$ N (3 s.f.)

Q2 a) $-3.2\mathbf{i}$ N
b) $10\mathbf{j}$ N
c) $(21 \cos 45°)\mathbf{i} + (21 \sin 45°)\mathbf{j}$
$= \left(\dfrac{21}{2}\sqrt{2}\,\mathbf{i} + \dfrac{21}{2}\sqrt{2}\,\mathbf{j}\right)$ N
$= (14.8\mathbf{i} + 14.8\mathbf{j})$ N (3 s.f.)
d) $(-17 \cos 25°)\mathbf{i} + (17 \sin 25°)\mathbf{j}$
$= (-15.4\mathbf{i} + 7.18\mathbf{j})$ N (3 s.f.)
e) $(-12 \cos 55°)\mathbf{i} + (12 \sin 55°)\mathbf{j}$
$= (-6.88\mathbf{i} + 9.83\mathbf{j})$ N (3 s.f.)
f) $(-6.8 \sin 30°)\mathbf{i} + (-6.8 \cos 30°)$
$= (-3.4\mathbf{i} - 5.89\mathbf{j})$ N (3 s.f.)

Q3 a)

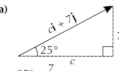

$\tan 25° = \dfrac{7}{c}$
$c = \dfrac{7}{\tan 25°} = 15.011... = 15.0$ (to 3 s.f.)

b) magnitude $= \sqrt{(15.011...)^2 + 7^2} = 16.6$ N (to 3 s.f.)

Q4

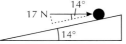

Parallel component = 17 cos 14°
= 16.49... = 16.5 N (3 s.f.)

Perpendicular component = 17 sin 14°
= 4.112... = 4.11 N (3 s.f.)

Q5

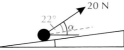

Horizontal component (→) = 65 cos 17°
= 62.2 N (3 s.f.)

Vertical component (↑) = −65 sin 17° = −19.0 N (3 s.f.)

Q6

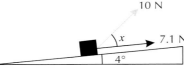

The force acts at an angle α above the horizontal.
The vertical component 20 sin α = 10
$\Rightarrow$ sin $\alpha = \frac{1}{2}$ $\Rightarrow$ α = 30°.

Then using corresponding angles, the angle
of the slope is 30° − 22° = 8°.

Q7

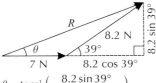

a) 10 cos x = 7.1
$x = \cos^{-1}\left(\frac{7.1}{10}\right)$ = 44.8° (to 3 s.f.)

b) 10 cos (x + 4) = 6.59 N (to 3 s.f.)

Exercise 5.1.2 — Resultant forces and equilibrium

Q1 a)

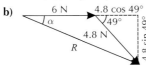

$\theta = \tan^{-1}\left(\frac{8.2\sin 39°}{7 + 8.2\cos 39°}\right)$

= $\tan^{-1}$(0.3858...) = 21.1° (3 s.f.)

$R = \sqrt{(7 + 8.2\cos 39°)^2 + (8.2\sin 39°)^2}$
= 14.3 N (3 s.f.)

b)

$\alpha = \tan^{-1}\left(\frac{4.8\sin 49°}{6 + 4.8\cos 49°}\right)$ = 21.60...°

i.e. 21.60...° below the positive horizontal,
so the direction of R is 360° − α = 338° (3 s.f.)

$R = \sqrt{(4.8\sin 49°)^2 + (6 + 4.8\cos 49°)^2}$
= 9.840... = 9.84 N (3 s.f.)

c)

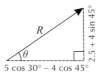

Resolving horizontally:
R(→) = 5 cos 30° − 4 cos 45°
Resolving vertically:
R(↑) = 5 sin 30° + 4 sin 45°
= 2.5 + 4 sin 45°

$\theta = \tan^{-1}\left(\frac{2.5 + 4\sin 45°}{5\cos 30° - 4\cos 45°}\right) = \tan^{-1}$(3.548...)
= 74.3° (3 s.f.)

$R = \sqrt{(2.5 + 4\sin 45°)^2 + (5\cos 30° - 4\cos 45°)^2}$
= 5.54 N (3 s.f.)

d) Resolving horizontally:
R(→) = 10 − 11 cos 75° − 12 cos 80° = 5.069... N

Resolving vertically:
R(↑) = 11 sin 75° − 12 sin 80° = −1.192... N

$R = \sqrt{(5.069...)^2 + (-1.192...)^2}$ = 5.21 N (to 3 s.f.)

$\theta = \tan^{-1}\left(\frac{-1.192...}{5.069...}\right)$ = −13.237...°

i.e. 13.237...° below the positive horizontal
So direction = 360° − 13.237...° = 347° (3 s.f.)

e) Resolving horizontally:
R(→) = 6.5 cos 69° + 10 cos 47° − 8 sin 61°
= 2.152... N

Resolving vertically:
R(↑) = 6.5 sin 69° + 8 cos 61° − 10 sin 47°
= 2.633... N

$R = \sqrt{(2.152...)^2 + (2.633...)^2}$ = 3.40 N (to 3 s.f.)

$\theta = \tan^{-1}\left(\frac{2.633...}{2.152...}\right)$ = 50.7° (to 3 s.f.)

f) Resolving horizontally:
R(→) = 3 cos 32° + 5.5 cos 67° − 9 cos 15°
= −4.000... N

Resolving vertically:
R(↑) = 3 sin 32° − 5.5 sin 67° − 9 sin 15°
= −5.802... N

$R = \sqrt{(-4.000...)^2 + (-5.802...)^2}$ = 7.05 N (to 3 s.f.)

$\theta = \tan^{-1}\left(\frac{-5.802...}{-4.000...}\right)$ = 55.41...°

i.e. 55.41...° below the negative horizontal,
so direction = 180° + 55.41...° = 235° (to 3 s.f.)

Q2 a)

b)

$$\theta = \tan^{-1}\left(\frac{16 + 18\sin 60°}{18\cos 60°}\right) = \tan^{-1}(3.509...)$$
$$= 74.1° \text{ (3 s.f.) above the positive horizontal}$$
$$R = \sqrt{(18\cos 60°)^2 + (16 + 18\sin 60°)^2}$$
$$= 32.8 \text{ N (3 s.f.)}$$

Q3 Resolving vertically (↑):
$F\cos 31° + F\cos 31° - 14 = 0$
$2F\cos 31° = 14$
$F\cos 31° = 7 \Rightarrow F = 8.17$ N (3 s.f.)

Q4 a) Resolving horizontally:
$R(\rightarrow)$: $X\cos 39° - 9.5\sin 19° = 0$
$$\Rightarrow X = \frac{9.5\sin 19°}{\cos 39°} = 3.979...$$
$$= 3.98 \text{ N (to 3 s.f.)}$$

Resolving vertically:
$R(\uparrow)$: $9.5\cos 19° + 3.979... \times \sin 39° - Y = 0$
$$\Rightarrow Y = 9.5\cos 19° + 3.979... \times \sin 39°$$
$$= 11.5 \text{ N (to 3 s.f.)}$$

b) Resolving horizontally:
$R(\rightarrow)$: $5\sin 30° - Q\sin 55° = 0$
$$\Rightarrow Q = \frac{5\sin 30°}{\sin 55°} = 3.051...$$
$$= 3.05 \text{ N (to 3 s.f.)}$$

Resolving vertically:
$R(\uparrow)$: $P - 5\cos 30° - 3.051... \times \cos 55° = 0$
$$\Rightarrow P = 5\cos 30° + 3.051... \times \cos 55°$$
$$= 6.08 \text{ N (to 3 s.f.)}$$

c) Resolving horizontally:
$R(\rightarrow)$: $A\cos 50° + 1.5 - 7\cos 30° = 0$
$$\Rightarrow A = \frac{7\cos 30° - 1.5}{\cos 50°} = 7.097...$$
$$= 7.10 \text{ N (to 3 s.f.)}$$

Resolving vertically:
$R(\uparrow)$: $7.097... \times \sin 50° - 7\sin 30° - B = 0$
$$\Rightarrow B = 7.097... \times \sin 50° - 7\sin 30°$$
$$= 1.94 \text{ N (to 3 s.f.)}$$

d) Resolving horizontally:
$R(\rightarrow)$: $X\cos 72° - 10\sin 49° = 0$
$$\Rightarrow X = \frac{10\sin 49°}{\cos 72°} = 24.42...$$
$$= 24.4 \text{ N (to 3 s.f.)}$$

Resolving vertically:
$R(\uparrow)$: $24.42... \times \sin 72° + 10\cos 49° - Y = 0$
$$\Rightarrow Y = 24.42... \times \sin 72° + 10\cos 49°$$
$$= 29.8 \text{ N (to 3 s.f.)}$$

e) Resolving horizontally:
$R(\rightarrow)$: $9.5 - 2F\cos 28° = 0$
$$\Rightarrow F = \frac{9.5}{2\cos 28°} = 5.379...$$
$$= 5.38 \text{ N (to 3 s.f.)}$$

f) Resolving horizontally:
$R(\rightarrow)$: $40\sin 30° - S\sin 75° = 0$
$$\Rightarrow S = \frac{40\sin 30°}{\sin 75°} = 20.70...$$
$$= 20.7 \text{ N (to 3 s.f.)}$$

Resolving vertically:
$R(\uparrow)$: $R - 20.70... \times \cos 75° - 40\cos 30° = 0$
$$\Rightarrow R = 20.70... \times \cos 75° + 40\cos 30°$$
$$= 40 \text{ N}$$
The magnitude of R is exactly 40 N — you can see this from the fact that the triangle of forces is isosceles.

Q5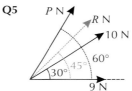

Resolving horizontally (→):
$P\cos 60° + 10\cos 30° + 9 = R\cos 45°$ ①
Resolving vertically (↑):
$P\sin 60° + 10\sin 30° = R\sin 45°$ ②
Because the resultant acts at 45°, its horizontal and vertical components are equal.
i.e. $\cos 45° = \sin 45° \Rightarrow R\cos 45° = R\sin 45°$
So, equating the left-hand sides of ① and ②:
$P\cos 60° + 10\cos 30° + 9 = P\sin 60° + 10\sin 30°$
$P\cos 60° - P\sin 60° = 10\sin 30° - 10\cos 30° - 9$
$$\Rightarrow P = \frac{10\sin 30° - 10\cos 30° - 9}{\cos 60° - \sin 60°}$$
$$= \frac{-12.6602...}{-0.36602...} = 34.6 \text{ N (3 s.f.)}$$

Q6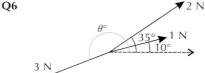

a) Resolving horizontally (→):
$1\cos 10° + 2\cos 35° + 3\cos\theta = 0$
$$\theta = \cos^{-1}\left(\frac{-\cos 10° - 2\cos 35°}{3}\right)$$
$$= \cos^{-1}(-0.874...)$$
$$= 150.970...° = 151° \text{ (to 3 s.f.)}$$
θ must lie in the range $180° \le \theta \le 360°$
$\cos\theta = \cos(360° - \theta)$, therefore
$\theta = 360° - 150.970...° = 209.029...°$
$$= 209° \text{ (to 3 s.f.)}$$

b) $R = 1 \sin 10° + 2 \sin 35° + 3 \sin (209.029...°)$
   $= -0.135$ N (to 3 s.f.)
   So, R has magnitude 0.135 N (to 3 s.f.)
   (and acts in the negative **j**-direction)

Q7 Resolving horizontally: $2P = 20 \sin \theta$ (1)
   Resolving vertically: $P = 20 \cos \theta$ (2)

   Divide (1) by (2):

   $\tan \theta = \dfrac{2P}{P} = 2$,

   $\theta = \tan^{-1}(2) = 63.43...° = 63.4°$ (to 3 s.f.)

   Substituting into (2) gives
   $P = 20 \cos \theta = 20 \cos (63.43...°) = 8.94$ N (to 3 s.f)

Exercise 5.1.3 — Harder equilibrium problems

Q1 **a)** Resolving horizontally:
   $T \cos 50° = 14$ N
   $T = \dfrac{14}{\cos 50°} = 21.78... = 21.8$ N (to 3 s.f.)
   Resolving vertically:
   $T \sin 50° = mg$
   $m = \dfrac{T \sin 50°}{g} = \dfrac{21.78... \sin 50°}{9.8}$
   $= 1.70$ kg (to 3 s.f.)

   b) Resolving horizontally:
   $T = 8 \sin 25° = 3.380... = 3.38$ N (to 3 s.f.)
   Resolving vertically:
   $mg = 8 \cos 25°$
   $m = \dfrac{8 \cos 25°}{g} = 0.740$ kg (to 3 s.f.)

   c) Resolving horizontally:
   $T \cos 25° = 9$ N
   $T = \dfrac{9}{\cos 25°} = 9.930... = 9.93$ N (to 3 s.f.)
   Resolving vertically:
   $mg = 9.930... \sin 25°$
   $m = \dfrac{9.930... \sin 25°}{g} = 0.428$ kg (to 3 s.f.)

   d) Resolving horizontally:
   $T = 7 \sin 35° = 4.015... = 4.02$ N (to 3 s.f.)
   Resolving vertically:
   $mg = 7 \cos 35°$
   $m = \dfrac{7 \cos 35°}{g} = 0.585$ kg (to 3 s.f.)

Q2 Resolving horizontally:
   $15 \sin x = 13 \sin 32°$
   $x = \sin^{-1}\left(\dfrac{13 \sin 32°}{15}\right) = 27.339...° = 27.3°$ (to 3 s.f.)
   Resolving vertically:
   $W = 13 \cos 32° + 15 \cos (27.339...°)$
   $= 24.3$ N (to 3 s.f.)

Q3 **a)**

   Resolving parallel to the plane:
   $10 \sin x = 8$
   $x = \sin^{-1}\left(\dfrac{8}{10}\right) = 53.130... = 53.1°$ (to 3 s.f.)

   b) Resolving perpendicular to the plane:
   $R = 10 \cos x = 6$ N

Q4

   a) Resolving parallel to the plane:
   $F = mg \sin 45°$
   Resolving perpendicular to the plane:
   $25 = mg \cos 45°$
   $\cos 45° = \sin 45°$, therefore $F = 25$ N

   b) Resolving perpendicular to the plane:
   $mg \cos 45° = 25$
   $m = \dfrac{25}{g \cos 45°} = \dfrac{25}{9.8 \times \cos 45°} = 3.61$ kg (to 3 s.f.)

Q5

   a) Resolving parallel to the wire:
   $mg \sin 60° = 4.2$ N
   $m = \dfrac{4.2}{9.8 \times \sin 60°} = 0.4948... = 0.495$ kg (3 s.f.)

   b) Resolving perpendicular to the wire:
   $R = 0.4948... \times g \cos 60° = 2.42$ N (3 s.f.)

Q6

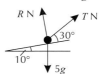

   a) Magnitude of the tension in the string $= T$
   normal reaction force $= R$
   Resolving parallel to the plane:
   $T \cos 30° = 5g \sin 10°$
   $T = \dfrac{(5 \times 9.8 \times \sin 10°)}{\cos 30°} = 9.83$ N (to 3 s.f.)

   b) Resolving perpendicular to the plane:
   $R + T \sin 30° = 5g \cos 10°$
   $R = 5g \cos 10° - T \sin 30° = 43.3$ N (to 3 s.f.)

Q7

Resolving the forces on the block parallel to the plane:

$14.7 \cos \theta = 2g \sin \theta$

$\dfrac{\sin \theta}{\cos \theta} = \dfrac{14.7}{2g} \Rightarrow \tan \theta = \dfrac{14.7}{(2 \times 9.8)} = 0.75$

Q8

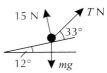

a) The string is inclined at an angle of $45° - 12° = 33°$ to the plane.
Resolving parallel to the plane:

$T \cos 33° = mg \sin 12°$,

$mg = \dfrac{T \cos 33°}{\sin 12°}$ ①

Resolving perpendicular to the plane:

$15 + T \sin 33° = mg \cos 12°$ ②

Substituting ① into ②:

$15 + T \sin 33° = \dfrac{T \cos 33°}{\sin 12°} \cos 12°$

$15 = T\left(\left(\dfrac{\cos 33°}{\sin 12°} \cos 12°\right) - \sin 33°\right)$

$T = \dfrac{15}{\left(\dfrac{\cos 33°}{\tan 12°} - \sin 33°\right)} = 4.41$ N (to 3.s.f)

b) Rearrange ① and substitute the values for T and g (= 9.8 ms^{-2}):

$m = \dfrac{T \cos 33°}{g \sin 12°} = 1.82$ kg (to 3 s.f.)

Q9

Resolving parallel to the plane:
$70 \cos 10° = mg \sin 30°$

$m = \dfrac{70 \cos 10°}{9.8 \times \sin 30°} = 14.068... = 14.1$ kg (3 s.f.)

Resolving perpendicular to the plane:
$R + 70 \sin 10° = mg \cos 30°$
$R = 14.068... \times 9.8 \times \cos 30° - 70 \sin 10°$
   $= 107.2... = 107$ N (3 s.f.)

Q10

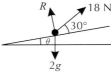

a) Resolving parallel to the plane:
$18 \cos 30° = 2g \sin \theta$

$\sin \theta = \dfrac{18 \cos 30°}{2 \times 9.8}$

$\Rightarrow \theta = \sin^{-1}\left(\dfrac{18 \cos 30°}{2 \times 9.8}\right) = 52.68...°$
$\qquad\qquad\qquad\qquad\qquad = 52.7°$ (3 s.f.)

b) Resolving perpendicular to the plane:
$R + 18 \sin 30° = 2g \cos \theta$
$R = 2 \times 9.8 \times \cos 52.68...° - 18 \sin 30°$
   $= 2.881... = 2.88$ N (3 s.f.)

Q11

The string makes an angle of $70° - 50° = 20°$ with the plane.
Resolving perpendicular to the plane:
$R + 5 \sin 20° = W \cos 50°$
$R = 4F$, so:
$4F + 5 \sin 20° = W \cos 50°$ ①
Resolving parallel to the plane:
$F + W \sin 50° = 5 \cos 20°$
$F = 5 \cos 20° - W \sin 50°$ ②
Substituting ② into ①,
$20 \cos 20° - 4W \sin 50° + 5 \sin 20° = W \cos 50°$,
$W = \dfrac{20 \cos 20° + 5 \sin 20°}{4 \sin 50° + \cos 50°} = 5.53$ N (to 3 s.f.)

5.2 Friction

Exercise 5.2.1 — Friction

Q1 The particle is on the point of slipping, so $F = \mu R$.
Resolving vertically: $R = W$, so using $F = \mu W$:

a) $F = 0.25 \times 5 = 1.25$ N

b) $F = 0.3 \times 8 = 2.4$ N

c) $F = 0.75 \times 15 = 11.25$ N

d) $F = 0 \times 6 = 0$ N

e) $F = 0.82 \times 17 = 13.94$ N

f) $F = 0.95 \times 0.5 = 0.475$ N

Q2

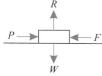

Resolving vertically: $R = W$

Resolving horizontally: $P = F$, so using $F = \mu R$, $\mu = \dfrac{P}{W}$

a) $\mu = \dfrac{5}{20} = 0.25$

b) $\mu = \dfrac{8}{15} = 0.53$ (to 2 d.p.)

c) $\mu = \dfrac{3.5}{28} = 0.125$

d) $\mu = \dfrac{6}{13} = 0.46$ (to 2 d.p.)

Q3 Resolving vertically: $R = 8g$

Find the frictional force, F:

$F \le \mu R$

$F \le 0.45 \times 8g$

$F \le 35.28$ N

The force P doesn't affect F, so it can be ignored.

Q4

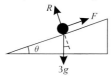

Resolving perpendicular to the slope:

$R = 3g \cos \theta$

Resolving parallel to the slope:

$F = 3g \sin \theta$

The brick is on the point of slipping so $F = \mu R = 0.7R$.

So $3g \sin \theta = 0.7R = 0.7 \times 3g \cos \theta$

$\Rightarrow \dfrac{\sin \theta}{\cos \theta} = \tan \theta = 0.7$

$\Rightarrow \theta = \tan^{-1}(0.7) = 34.99... = 35.0°$ (3 s.f.)

Q5

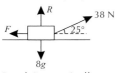

Resolving vertically:

$R + 38 \sin 25° = 8g$

$R = 8g - 38 \sin 25° = 62.34...$ N

Resolving horizontally:

$F = 38 \cos 25°$

The maximum value of μ such that the sled remains at rest occurs when $F = \mu R$.

$38 \cos 25° = \mu R = \mu \times 62.34...$

$\mu = \dfrac{38 \cos 25°}{62.34...} = 0.55$ (2 d.p.)

Q6 a)

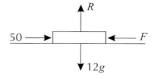

Resolving vertically: $R = 12g$

Find the frictional force, F:

$F \le \mu R$

$F \le 0.5 \times 12g$

$F \le 58.8$ N

50 N isn't big enough to overcome friction — so the particle won't move.

b) Maximum force is when $F = \mu R$, so max force is 58.8 N

Q7

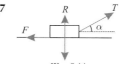

$W = 8$ N

Resolving vertically: $R + T \sin \alpha = 8$

Resolving horizontally: $T \cos \alpha = F$

T will be greatest when the object is in limiting equilibrium: $F = \mu R$

a) $\alpha = 0 \Rightarrow R = W$ and $T = F = \mu R = 8\mu$

$T = 0.61 \times 8 = 4.88$ N

b) $\alpha = 35°$

Resolving vertically: $R + T \sin 35° = 8$

$R = 8 - T \sin 35°$ ①

Resolving horizontally:

$T \cos 35° = F$

$F = \mu R \Rightarrow T \cos 35° = 0.61R$ ②

Substitute the value of R from ① into ②:

$8 - T \sin 35° = \dfrac{T \cos 35°}{0.61}$

$T \cos 35° = 0.61(8 - T \sin 35°)$

$T(\cos 35° + 0.61 \sin 35°) = 4.88$

$T = \dfrac{4.88}{\cos 35° + 0.61 \sin 35°} = 4.17$ N (to 3 s.f.)

Q8

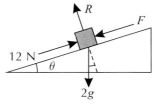

Resolving parallel to the plane:

$12 = F + 2g \sin \theta$

$F = 12 - 2g \sin \theta$

Resolving perpendicular to the plane:

$R = 2g \cos \theta$

The object is on the point of moving, so $F = \mu R$.
$$\mu = \frac{F}{R} = \frac{(12 - 2g\sin\theta)}{2g\cos\theta}$$
$\cos\theta = \frac{4}{5}$, so, drawing a right-angled triangle, the side adjacent to the angle will be 4, and the hypotenuse will be 5. Then, by Pythagoras' theorem, the opposite side will be 3.

So $\sin\theta = \frac{3}{5}$

$$\mu = \frac{\left(12 - \left(2 \times 9.8 \times \frac{3}{5}\right)\right)}{\left(2 \times 9.8 \times \frac{4}{5}\right)} = 0.02 \text{ (2 d.p.)}$$

Q9 **a)** Resolving horizontally:
$F = 4\cos 25°$
Friction is limiting, so, using $F = \mu R$:
$4\cos 25° = 0.15R$
$\Rightarrow R = 24.168... = 24.2$ N (3 s.f.)

b) Resolving vertically:
$R = mg + 4\sin 25°$
$mg = 24.168... - 4\sin 25° = 22.477...$
So $m = 22.477... \div 9.8 = 2.29$ kg (3 s.f.)

Q10 The 9 N force is only just large enough to stop the stone slipping, i.e. the motion is down the slope — so friction will act up the slope.

Resolving perpendicular to the plane:
$R + 9\sin 10° = 8g\cos 23°$
$\Rightarrow R = 8g\cos 23° - 9\sin 10° = 70.604...$ N
Resolving parallel to the plane:
$F + 9\cos 10° = 8g\sin 23°$
$F = 8g\sin 23° - 9\cos 10° = 21.770...$ N
Since the stone is on the point of slipping, $F = \mu R$:
$21.770... = \mu \times 70.604...$
$\Rightarrow \mu = 0.308... = 0.31$ (2 d.p.)

Q11

Resolving perpendicular to the plane:
$R = W\cos\alpha$ ①
Resolving parallel to the plane:
$F = W\sin\alpha$ ②
$F \leq \mu R$ when the object is at rest on the plane.
Substituting in values for F and R from ① and ②:
$W\sin\alpha \leq \mu W\cos\alpha$
$\frac{W\sin\alpha}{W\cos\alpha} \leq \mu \Rightarrow \tan\alpha \leq \mu$

Q12

Resolving parallel to the plane:
$T\cos 15° + F = 20g\sin 29°$ ①
Resolving perpendicular to the plane:
$R + T\sin 15° = 20g\cos 29°$
$R = -T\sin 15° + 20g\cos 29°$ ②
T is only just large enough to hold the sledge at rest, so the sledge is in limiting equilibrium and $F = \mu R = 0.1R$.
Substituting this and ② into ①:
$T\cos 15° + 0.1(-T\sin 15° + 20g\cos 29°) = 20g\sin 29°$
$$T = \frac{20g\sin 29° - 2g\cos 29°}{\cos 15° - 0.1\sin 15°} = \frac{77.880...}{0.9400...}$$
$$= 82.8 \text{ N (3 s.f.)}$$

Q13

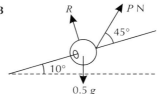

Resolving parallel to the wire:
$F + P\cos 45° = 0.5g\sin 10°$ ①
Resolving perpendicular to the wire:
$R + P\sin 45° = 0.5g\cos 10°$
Using $\sin 45° = \cos 45°$:
$R + P\cos 45° = 0.5g\cos 10°$ ②
Subtract ① from ②:
$R - F = 0.5g\cos 10° - 0.5g\sin 10°$
The bead is in limiting equilibrium so $F = \mu R = 0.25R$:
$R - 0.25R = 0.5g(\cos 10° - \sin 10°)$
$0.75R = 0.5g(\cos 10° - \sin 10°)$
$R = 5.30$ N (3 s.f.)

5.3 Newton's Laws of Motion

Exercise 5.3.1 — Newton's laws of motion

Q1 Resolving horizontally:
$F_{net} = ma$
$20 = 4a \Rightarrow a = 5$ ms^{-2}
$s = s, u = 0, a = 5, t = 2.5$
$s = ut + \frac{1}{2}at^2$
$s = 0 \times 2.5 + \frac{1}{2} \times 5 \times 2.5^2 = 15.625$ m

Q2 Resolving horizontally:
$\boldsymbol{F}_{net} = m\boldsymbol{a}$
$(4\mathbf{i} - 9\mathbf{j}) = 2\boldsymbol{a} \Rightarrow \boldsymbol{a} = (2\mathbf{i} - 4.5\mathbf{j})$ ms^{-2}
$\boldsymbol{u} = 0, \boldsymbol{v} = v, \boldsymbol{a} = (2\mathbf{i} - 4.5\mathbf{j}), t = 3$
$\boldsymbol{v} = \boldsymbol{u} + \boldsymbol{a}t$
$\boldsymbol{v} = 0 + (2\mathbf{i} - 4.5\mathbf{j}) \times 3 = (6\mathbf{i} - 13.5\mathbf{j})$ ms^{-1}

Q3 a) Resolving horizontally:
$F_{net} = ma$
$10 \cos 45° = 3a$
$a = 7.071... \div 3 = 2.357...$
$a = 2.36 \text{ ms}^{-2}$ (3 s.f.)

b) Resolving vertically:
$F_{net} = ma$
$R + 10 \sin 45° - 3g = 0$
$R = 3g - 10 \sin 45° = 22.328...$
$R = 22.3 \text{ N}$ (3 s.f.)

Q4 a) Resolving horizontally:
$F_{net} = ma$
$16 \cos 20° - 7 = (49 \div 9.8) \times a$
$a = 8.035... \div 5 = 1.607...$
$a = 1.61 \text{ ms}^{-2}$ (3 s.f.)

b) Use a constant acceleration equation.
$u = 0, v = v, a = 1.607..., t = 7$
$v = u + at$
$v = 0 + (1.607... \times 7) = 11.2 \text{ ms}^{-1}$ (3 s.f.)

c) Resolving vertically:
$R + 16 \sin 20° - 49 = 0$
$R = 49 - 16 \sin 20° = 43.527...$
$R = 43.5 \text{ N}$ (3 s.f.)

Q5 a) Resultant, $\mathbf{R} = (6\mathbf{i} - 10\mathbf{j}) + (4\mathbf{i} + 5\mathbf{j}) = (10\mathbf{i} - 5\mathbf{j}) \text{ N}$
$|\mathbf{R}| = \sqrt{10^2 + (-5)^2} = \sqrt{125} \text{ N}$
$F_{net} = ma$
$\sqrt{125} = 5a$
$a = \sqrt{125} \div 5 = 2.236... = 2.24 \text{ ms}^{-2}$ (3 s.f.)

b) $\mathbf{R}_{new} = (10\mathbf{i} - 5\mathbf{j}) + (-6\mathbf{i} + 2\mathbf{j}) = (4\mathbf{i} - 3\mathbf{j}) \text{ N}$
$|\mathbf{R}_{new}| = \sqrt{4^2 + (-3)^2} = 5 \text{ N}$
$F_{net} = ma$
$5 = 5a \Rightarrow a = 1 \text{ ms}^{-2}$
So the acceleration decreases by 1.24 ms⁻² (3 s.f.)

Q6 a) $7\mathbf{i} + \mathbf{j} = (6\mathbf{i} - 2\mathbf{j}) + (5\mathbf{i} + 5\mathbf{j}) + \mathbf{x}$
$\mathbf{x} = (7 - 6 - 5)\mathbf{i} + (1 + 2 - 5)\mathbf{j} = (-4\mathbf{i} - 2\mathbf{j}) \text{ N}$

b) $F_{net} = ma$
$7\mathbf{i} + \mathbf{j} = 10a \Rightarrow a = 0.7\mathbf{i} + 0.1\mathbf{j} \text{ ms}^{-2}$
List the variables:
$\mathbf{u} = 0, v = v, \mathbf{a} = 0.7\mathbf{i} + 0.1\mathbf{j}, t = 8$
$\mathbf{v} = \mathbf{u} + \mathbf{a}t$
$\mathbf{v} = 0 + 8(0.7\mathbf{i} + 0.1\mathbf{j}) = (5.6\mathbf{i} + 0.8\mathbf{j}) \text{ ms}^{-1}$

c) The new resultant force is
$(7\mathbf{i} + \mathbf{j}) + (-7\mathbf{i} - \mathbf{j}) = 0\mathbf{i} + 0\mathbf{j} \text{ N}$
So there is no resultant force, and hence the particle does not accelerate (i.e. it continues to move at whatever velocity it had when the fourth force began to act).

Exercise 5.3.2 — Friction and inclined planes

Q1 a) After the propelling force has stopped:
Resolving parallel to the plane ($\nearrow$):
$F_{net} = ma$
$-0.3g \sin 17° = 0.3a$
$\Rightarrow a = -g \sin 17°$
$s = s, u = 7, v = 0, a = -g \sin 17°$
$v^2 = u^2 + 2as$
$0 = 49 - 2g \sin 17° \times s$
$\Rightarrow s = \dfrac{49}{2 \times 9.8 \times \sin 17°} = 8.55 \text{ m}$ (3 s.f.)

b) Resolving perpendicular to the plane ($\nwarrow$):
$F_{net} = ma$
$R - 0.3g \cos 17° = 0$
$R = 0.3g \cos 17° = 2.81 \text{ N}$ (3 s.f.)

Q2 a) Resolving parallel to the plane ($\swarrow$):
$F_{net} = ma$
$1.5g \sin 25° = 1.5a$
$a = 9.8 \sin 25° = 4.141... = 4.14 \text{ ms}^{-2}$ (3 s.f.)

b) $u = 0, v = v, a = 4.141..., t = 3$
$v = u + at$
$v = 0 + (4.141... \times 3) = 12.4 \text{ ms}^{-1}$ (3 s.f.)

Q3 a)

b) Resolving vertically:
$R - 4g = 0$
$R = 4g = 39.2 \text{ N}$

c) Resolving horizontally:
$F_{net} = ma$
$26 - F = 4 \times 1.2$
$F = 21.2 \text{ N}$

d) The box is moving, so friction takes its maximum value, i.e. $F = \mu R$:
$21.2 = 39.2\mu \Rightarrow \mu = 0.54$ (2 d.p.)

Q4 a)

b) Resolving vertically:
$R - 7g = 0 \Rightarrow R = 7g = 68.6 \text{ N}$

c) Resolving horizontally:
$F_{net} = ma$
$P - F = 7 \times 0.8$
$P - \mu R = 5.6$
$P = 5.6 + (0.2 \times 68.6) = 19.3 \text{ N}$ (3 s.f.)

Q5 a)

b) Resolving perpendicular to the plane (↖):
$R - mg \cos 40° = 0$
$\Rightarrow R = mg \cos 40°$
Resolving parallel to the plane (↗):
$F_{net} = ma$
$70 - F - mg \sin 40° = 3.2m$
$70 - \mu R - mg \sin 40° = 3.2m$
$70 - 0.35(mg \cos 40°) - mg \sin 40° = 3.2m$
$70 = m(3.2 + 0.35g \cos 40° + g \sin 40°)$
$m = 70 \div 12.126... = 5.77$ kg (3 s.f.)

Q6 a)

b) Resolving perpendicular to the plane (↖):
$R = g \cos 50°$
Resolving parallel to the plane (↙):
$F_{net} = ma$
$g \sin 50° - F = a$
$g \sin 50° - \mu R = a$
$g \sin 50° - (0.4 \times g \cos 50°) = a$
$\Rightarrow a = 4.9875...$ ms⁻²
$s = 2, u = 0, a = 4.9875..., t = t$
$s = ut + \frac{1}{2}at^2$
$2 = \frac{1}{2}(4.9875...)t^2$
$t^2 = 0.8020... \Rightarrow t = 0.896$ s (3 s.f.)

Q7

$s = 0.5, u = 0, a = a, t = 2$
$s = ut + \frac{1}{2}at^2$
$0.5 = 0 \times 2 + \frac{1}{2} \times a \times 2^2$
$0.5 = 2a \Rightarrow a = 0.25$ ms⁻²
Resolving parallel to the plane (↙):
$F_{net} = ma$
$2g \sin 28° - F = 2 \times 0.25$
$F = 2g \sin 28° - 0.5 = 8.701...$ N
Resolving perpendicular to the plane (↖):
$R = 2g \cos 28° = 17.305...$ N
The block is moving, so friction is limiting, i.e. $F = \mu R$
so $8.701... = \mu \times 17.305...$
$\Rightarrow \mu = 0.502... = 0.50$ (2 d.p.)

Q8 Resolving perpendicular to the plane (↖):
$R = 5000 \cos 10°$
Resolving parallel to the plane (↗):
$F_{net} = ma$
$T - F - 5000 \sin 10° = (5000 \div 9.8) \times 0.35$
$T - \mu R - 5000 \sin 10° = 178.57...$
$T - (0.1 \times 5000 \cos 10°) - 5000 \sin 10° = 178.57...$
$\Rightarrow T = 1539.21... = 1540$ N (3 s.f.)

Q9

Resolving perpendicular to the plane (↖):
$R = 9g \cos 22° + 110 \sin 22° = 122.98...$
Resolving parallel to the plane (↗):
$F_{net} = ma$
$110 \cos 22° - F - 9g \sin 22° = 9 \times 1.3$
$110 \cos 22° - \mu 122.98... - 9g \sin 22° = 11.7$
$\mu 122.98... = 110 \cos 22° - 9g \sin 22° - 11.7$
$\Rightarrow \mu = 57.24... \div 122.98... = 0.47$ (2 d.p.)

Q10 You need to consider the situations where the block is on the point of sliding up the plane, and when it is on the point of sliding down the plane.
If the block is on the point of sliding up the plane, then friction acts down the plane:

Resolving perpendicular to the plane (↖):
$R = 5g \cos 35° = 40.138...$ N
The block is in limiting equilibrium, so $F = \mu R$:
$F = 0.4 \times 40.138... = 16.055...$ N
Resolving parallel to the plane (↗):
$D - F - 5g \sin 35° = 0$
$D = 16.055... + 28.105... = 44.160...$ N
If the block is on the point of sliding down the plane, then friction acts up the plane:

Resolving perpendicular to the plane (↖):
$R = 5g \cos 35° = 40.138...$ N
The block is in limiting equilibrium, so $F = \mu R$:
$F = 0.4 \times 40.138... = 16.055...$ N
Resolving parallel to the plane (↗):
$D + F - 5g \sin 35° = 0$
$D = 28.105... - 16.055... = 12.049...$ N
So the range for which the block is in equilibrium is $12.0... $ N $\leq D \leq 44.2$ N (3 s.f.)

Q11

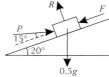

Resolving parallel to the slope ($\nearrow$):
$F_{net} = ma$
$P\cos 15° - F - 0.5g\sin 20° = 0.5 \times 0.8$
$F = P\cos 15° - 0.5g\sin 20° - 0.4$
Resolving perpendicular to the slope ($\nwarrow$):
$R = 0.5g\cos 20° + P\sin 15°$
The block is moving so friction is limiting,
i.e. $F = \mu R = 0.3R$, so
$P\cos 15° - 0.5g\sin 20° - 0.4$
$\qquad\qquad = 0.3(0.5g\cos 20° + P\sin 15°)$
$P(\cos 15° - 0.3\sin 15°)$
$\qquad\qquad = 0.5g\sin 20° + 0.4 + 0.15g\cos 20°$
$P = \dfrac{0.5g\sin 20° + 0.4 + 0.15g\cos 20°}{\cos 15° - 0.3\sin 15°} = 3.89$ N (3 s.f.)

Exercise 5.3.3 — Connected particles, pegs and pulleys

Q1 a) Resolving vertically ($\downarrow$) for B:
$F_{net} = ma$
$8g - T = 8 \times 0.5$
$\Rightarrow T = (8 \times 9.8) - 4 = 74.4$ N

b) Resolving vertically ($\uparrow$) for A:
$R - 10g = 0 \Rightarrow R = 98$ N
A is sliding, so F takes its maximum value,
i.e. $F = \mu R = 98\mu$
Resolving horizontally ($\rightarrow$) for A:
$F_{net} = ma$
$T - F = 10 \times 0.5$
$98\mu = 74.4 - 5 \Rightarrow \mu = 0.71$ (2 d.p.)

Q2 Resolve parallel to the plane ($\nearrow$) for the lower block:
$F_{net} = ma$
$20 - T - F - mg\sin\theta = ma$ ①
Resolve parallel to the plane ($\nearrow$) for the upper block:
$F_{net} = ma$
$T - F - mg\sin\theta = ma$ ②
Substituting ① into ②:
$T - F - mg\sin\theta = 20 - T - F - mg\sin\theta$
$2T = 20 \Rightarrow T = 10$ N
The thrust force acts just like a tension force, but it pushes against the blocks rather than pulling on them.

Q3 a) $s = 10$, $u = 0$, $a = a$, $t = 30$
$s = ut + \frac{1}{2}at^2$
$10 = \frac{1}{2} \times a \times 30^2 \Rightarrow a = 0.0222...$ ms^{-2}
Resolving parallel to the plane ($\nearrow$) for the car:
$F_{net} = ma$
$T - 800g\sin 25° = 800 \times 0.0222...$
$\Rightarrow T = 3331.10... = 3330$ N (3 s.f.)

b) Resolving vertically ($\uparrow$) for the truck:
$R_T = 2000g$
You're told you can assume that friction is at its maximum value, so using $F = \mu R$:
$F = 0.8 \times 2000g = 1600g$ N
Resolving horizontally ($\rightarrow$) for the truck:
$F_{net} = ma$
$W - F - T = 2000 \times 0.022...$
$W = 44.44... + 1600g + 3331.10...$
$\qquad = 19\,055.54... = 19\,100$ N (3 s.f.)

c) Resolving horizontally ($\rightarrow$) for the truck:
$F_{net} = ma$
$W - F = 2000a$
$19\,055.54... - 1600g = 2000a$
$\Rightarrow a = 1.69$ ms^{-2} (3 s.f.)

Q4 a) Resolving perpendicular to the plane ($\nwarrow$) for P:
$R = 60g\cos 50°$
Using $F = \mu R$:
$F = 0.1 \times 60g\cos 50° = 6g\cos 50°$
Resolving parallel to the plane ($\swarrow$) for P:
$F_{net} = ma$
$60g\sin 50° - F - T = 0$
$T = 60g\sin 50° - 6g\cos 50° = 412.63...$ N
Resolving vertically ($\uparrow$) for Q:
$F_{net} = ma$
$T - 20g - K = 0$
$K = 412.63... - 20g = 216.63...$
$K = 217$ N (3 s.f.)

b) Resolving vertically ($\uparrow$) for Q:
$F_{net} = ma$
$T - 20g = 20a$ ①
Resolving parallel to the plane ($\swarrow$) for P:
$60g\sin 50° - F - T = 60a$
$60g\sin 50° - 6g\cos 50° - T = 60a$ ②
Adding ① and ②:
$60g\sin 50° - 6g\cos 50° - 20g = 80a$
$\Rightarrow a = 2.707...$ ms^{-2}
$u = 0$, $v = v$, $t = 5$
$v = u + at$
$v = 0 + (2.707... \times 5) = 13.539...$
$v = 13.5$ ms^{-1} (3 s.f.)

Q5 a)

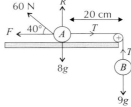

Resolving vertically ($\downarrow$) for B:
$F_{net} = ma$
$9g - T = 9 \times 0.4$
$\Rightarrow T = 84.6$ N
Resolving vertically ($\uparrow$) for A:
$R + 60\sin 40° = 8g$
$\Rightarrow R = 39.832...$ N

Resolving horizontally ($\rightarrow$) for A:
$F_{net} = ma$
$T - F - 60 \cos 40° = 8 \times 0.4$
$F = 84.6 - 60 \cos 40° - 3.2 = 35.437...$ N
$F = \mu R \Rightarrow \mu = 35.437... \div 39.832...$
$\qquad\qquad = 0.89$ (2 d.p.)

b) $s = 0.2$, $u = 0$, $v = v$, $a = 0.4$
$v^2 = u^2 + 2as$
$v^2 = 2 \times 0.4 \times 0.2 = 0.16$
$v = 0.4$ ms^{-1}

c) When A hits the pulley, A and B are both
travelling at 0.4 ms^{-1}.
$s = 0.6 - 0.2 = 0.4$, $u = 0.4$, $v = v$, $a = 9.8$
$v^2 = u^2 + 2as$
$v^2 = 0.4^2 + (2 \times 9.8 \times 0.4) = 8$
$v = 2.83$ ms^{-1} (3 s.f.)

Q6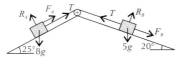

The particles are moving so friction is limiting:
$F_A = \mu R_A = \mu \times 8g \cos 25° = 71.054...\mu$
$F_B = \mu R_B = \mu \times 5g \cos 20° = 46.044...\mu$
Resolving parallel to the plane for A ($\swarrow$):
$F_{net} = ma$
$8g \sin 25° - T - \mu \times 8g \cos 25° = 8 \times 0.3$
$33.133... - T - 71.054...\mu = 2.4$
$30.733 - T = 71.054...\mu$ ①
Resolving parallel to the plane for B ($\nwarrow$):
$F_{net} = ma$
$T - 5g \sin 20° - \mu \times 5g \cos 20° = 5 \times 0.3$
$T - 16.758... - 46.044...\mu = 1.5$
$T = 18.258... + 46.044...\mu$ ②
Solving the simultaneous equations ① and ②:
$30.733... - (18.258... + 46.044...\mu) = 71.054...\mu$
$12.474... = 117.099...\mu$
$\Rightarrow \mu = 0.106... = 0.11$ (2 d.p.)

Q7 a) Treat the two blocks as one combined particle
with mass 2 kg + 3 kg = 5 kg.
Resolve the system perpendicular to the plane ($\nwarrow$):
$R = 5g \cos \alpha$
Resolve the system parallel to the plane ($\nearrow$):
$F_{net} = ma$
$48 - F - 5g \sin \alpha = 5a$
$48 - 0.4R - 5g \sin \alpha = 5a$
$48 - 0.4 \times 5g \cos \alpha - 5g \sin \alpha = 5a$

Use the fact that $\tan \alpha = \frac{3}{4}$ to find
exact values for $\sin \alpha$ and $\cos \alpha$:
$\sin \alpha = \frac{3}{5}$ and $\cos \alpha = \frac{4}{5}$.

So $48 - 0.4 \times 5g \times \frac{4}{5} - 5g \times \frac{3}{5} = 5a$
$\Rightarrow a = 0.584$ ms^{-2}

b)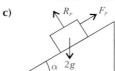

Resolving perpendicular to the plane ($\nwarrow$):
$R_P = 2g \cos \alpha = 2g \times \frac{4}{5} = 15.68$ N
Resolving parallel to the plane ($\nearrow$):
$F_{net} = ma$
$-F_P - 2g \sin \alpha = 2a$
$-0.4 \times 15.68 - 2g \times \frac{3}{5} = 2a$
$\Rightarrow a = -9.016$ ms^{-2}

Find the speed of the blocks when the string is cut:
$u = 0$, $v = v$, $a = 0.584$, $t = 3$
$v = u + at$
$v = 0 + 0.584 \times 3 = 1.752$ ms^{-1}

Now find the time taken for P to come to rest:
$u = 1.752$, $v = 0$, $a = -9.016$, $t = t$
$0 = 1.752 - 9.016t$
$\Rightarrow t = 1.752 \div 9.016 = 0.194$ seconds (3 s.f.)

c)

When P is at rest, F_P acts up the slope.
The maximum possible frictional force is
$F_P = 0.4 \times 2g \cos \alpha = 6.272$ N
The component of P's weight acting down
the slope is $2g \sin \alpha = 11.76$ N
Since 11.76 N > 6.272 N, P will not stay at rest.

Q8 a) Resolve perpendicular to the 40° plane ($\nwarrow$) for A:
$R_A = 0.2g \cos 40°$
Using $F = \mu R$:
$F_A = 0.7 \times 0.2g \cos 40° = 0.14g \cos 40°$
Resolve parallel to the 40° plane ($\nearrow$) for A:
$T - F_A - 0.2g \sin 40° = 0.2a$
$T - 0.14g \cos 40° - 0.2g \sin 40° = 0.2a$
$\Rightarrow 5T - 0.7g \cos 40° - g \sin 40° = a$ ①
Resolve perpendicular to the 20° plane ($\nearrow$) for B:
$R_B = 0.9g \cos 20°$
Using $F = \mu R$:
$F_B = 0.05 \times 0.9g \cos 20° = 0.045g \cos 20°$
Resolve parallel to the 20° plane ($\searrow$) for B:
$F_{net} = ma$
$0.9g \sin 20° - F_B - T = 0.9a$
$0.9g \sin 20° - 0.045g \cos 20° - T = 0.9a$
$\Rightarrow g \sin 20° - 0.05g \cos 20° - (1.11...)T = a$ ②
Solving the simultaneous equations ① and ②:
$5T - 0.7g \cos 40° - g \sin 40° =$
$\qquad\qquad g \sin 20° - 0.05g \cos 20° - (1.11...)T$
$\Rightarrow (6.11...)T = g \sin 20° - 0.05g \cos 20°$
$\qquad\qquad\qquad + 0.7g \cos 40° + g \sin 40°$
$\Rightarrow T = 2.363... = 2.36$ N (3 s.f.)

b) Using $\boxed{1}$ from part a):
$$a = 5T - 0.7g \cos 40° - g \sin 40°$$
$$= (5 \times 2.363...) - 0.7g \cos 40° - g \sin 40°$$
$$= 0.2648... \text{ ms}^{-2}$$

$u = 0$, $v = v$, $s = 0.35$
$v^2 = u^2 + 2as$
$v^2 = 2 \times 0.2648... \times 0.35 = 0.185...$
$\Rightarrow v = 0.431 \text{ ms}^{-1}$ (3 s.f.)

Review Exercise — Chapter 5

Q1 a)

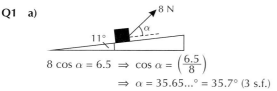

$8 \cos \alpha = 6.5 \Rightarrow \cos \alpha = \left(\dfrac{6.5}{8}\right)$
$$\Rightarrow \alpha = 35.65...° = 35.7° \text{ (3 s.f.)}$$

b) The angle between the force and the horizontal is $11° + \alpha = 46.65...°$, so the horizontal component is $8 \cos 46.65...° = 5.490... = 5.49$ N (3 s.f.)

Q2 a)

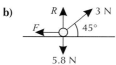

Resolving vertically:
$R = 7.2 + 10 \sin 61° = 15.946...$ N
Resolving horizontally:
$F = 10 \cos 61° = 4.848...$ N
$F = \mu R$, so $4.848... = \mu \times 15.946...$
$\Rightarrow \mu = 4.848... \div 15.946...$
$= 0.304... = 0.30$ (2 d.p.)

b)

R, F, 3 N, 45°, 5.8 N

Resolving vertically:
$R + 3 \sin 45° = 5.8$
$\Rightarrow R = 5.8 - 3 \sin 45° = 3.678...$ N
Resolving horizontally:
$F = 3 \cos 45° = 2.121...$ N
$F = \mu R$, so $2.121... = \mu \times 3.678...$
$\Rightarrow \mu = 2.121... \div 3.678... = 0.576...$
$= 0.58$ (2 d.p.)

c)

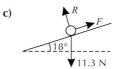

Resolving perpendicular to the plane:
$R = 11.3 \cos 18° = 10.746...$ N
Resolving horizontally:
$F = 11.3 \sin 18° = 3.491...$ N
$F = \mu R$, so $3.491... = \mu \times 10.746...$
$\Rightarrow \mu = 3.491... \div 10.746... = 0.324...$
$= 0.32$ (2 d.p.)

Q3 a)

R, 1 N, P, $2g$

Resolving horizontally ($\rightarrow$):
$F_{net} = ma$
$P - 1 = 2 \times 0.3 \Rightarrow P = 1.6$ N

b) $F = 1 = \mu R$, since friction is limiting.
Resolving vertically: $R = 2g = 19.6$ N
So $\mu = 1 \div 19.6$ N $= 0.05$ (2 d.p.)

Q4 a) $5\mathbf{i} + \mathbf{j} = (4\mathbf{i} - 7\mathbf{j}) + (6\mathbf{i} + 4\mathbf{j}) + (x\mathbf{i} + y\mathbf{j})$
$5\mathbf{i} + \mathbf{j} = (4 + 6 + x)\mathbf{i} + (-7 + 4 + y)\mathbf{j}$
$5 = 10 + x \Rightarrow x = -5$
$1 = -3 + y \Rightarrow y = 4$
So the third force is $(-5\mathbf{i} + 4\mathbf{j})$ N.

b) Resolving horizontally:
$F_{net} = ma$
$5\mathbf{i} + \mathbf{j} = 2.5\mathbf{a} \Rightarrow \mathbf{a} = 2\mathbf{i} + 0.4\mathbf{j}$
$\mathbf{s} = \mathbf{s}$, $\mathbf{u} = 0$, $\mathbf{a} = 2\mathbf{i} + 0.4\mathbf{j}$, $t = 4$
$\mathbf{s} = \mathbf{u}t + \dfrac{1}{2}\mathbf{a}t^2$
$\mathbf{s} = 0 \times 4 + \dfrac{1}{2} \times (2\mathbf{i} + 0.4\mathbf{j}) \times 4^2 = 16\mathbf{i} + 3.2\mathbf{j}$
The distance is $|\mathbf{s}| = \sqrt{16^2 + 3.2^2} = 16.3$ m (3 s.f.)
You could have solved this a different way by finding the magnitude of F_{net} first and using $F_{net} = ma$ and the suvat equation without vectors.

Q5

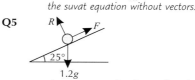

Resolving perpendicular to the plane:
$R = 1.2g \cos 25° = 10.658...$ N
Resolving parallel to the plane ($\nearrow$):
$F_{net} = ma$
$1.2g \sin 25° - F = 1.2 \times 0.3$
Friction is limiting so $F = \mu R$:
$1.2g \sin 25° - (\mu \times 10.658...) = 0.36$
$1.2g \sin 25° - 0.36 = \mu \times 10.658...$
$\Rightarrow \mu = 4.609... \div 10.658... = 0.43$ (2 d.p.)

Q6 Resolving perpendicular to the wire:
$R = 600 \cos 30°$
Resolving parallel to the wire ($\nearrow$) and using $F = \mu R$:
$600 \sin 30° - F = \dfrac{600}{g}a$
$300 - (0.5 \times 600 \cos 30°) = \dfrac{600}{g}a$
$\Rightarrow a = 40.19... \div \dfrac{600}{g} = 0.656...$ ms^{-2}
$s = 20$, $u = 0$, $v = v$, $a = 0.656...$
$v^2 = u^2 + 2as$
$v^2 = 0 + 2 \times 0.656... \times 20 = 26.25...$
$\Rightarrow v = 5.12$ ms^{-1} (3 s.f.)

Q7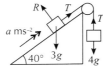

a) Resolving up the plane for the 3 kg mass:
$T - 3g \sin 40° = 3a$ ①
Resolving vertically downwards for the 4 kg mass:
$4g - T = 4a$ ②
①+②:
$4g - 3g \sin 40° = 7a$
$\Rightarrow a = 20.302... \div 7$
$= 2.900... = 2.90 \text{ ms}^{-2}$ (3 s.f.)

b) From ②, $T = 4g - 4a = 4g - 4 \times 2.900...$
$= 27.6 \text{ N}$ (3 s.f.)

c) The system is in equilibrium, so by resolving vertically on the 4 kg mass, $T = 4g$.
Resolve parallel to the plane for the 3 kg mass:
$3g \sin 40° + F = T$
$F = 4g - 3g \sin 40° = 20.3 \text{ N}$ (3 s.f.)

Exam-Style Questions — Chapter 5

Q1 a)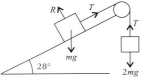

Resolving parallel to the plane ($\nearrow$)
for the m kg mass:
$F_{net} = ma$
$T - mg \sin 28° = ma$ ①
Resolving vertically ($\downarrow$) for the $2m$ kg mass:
$F_{net} = ma$
$2mg - T = 2ma \Rightarrow T = 2mg - 2ma$ ②
Substitute ② into ①:
$2mg - 2ma - mg \sin 28° = ma$
$3a = (2 - \sin 28°)g \Rightarrow a = 4.999...$
$= 5.00 \text{ ms}^{-2}$ (3 s.f.)

[3 marks available — 1 mark for correctly resolving forces on the m kg mass, 1 mark for correctly resolving forces for the 2m kg mass, 1 mark for the correct acceleration]

b)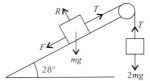

Resolving vertically ($\downarrow$) for the $2m$ kg mass:
$F_{net} = ma$
$2mg - T = 7.6m \Rightarrow T = (2g - 7.6)m = 12m$
Resolving perpendicular to the plane ($\nwarrow$)
for the m kg mass:
$R = mg \cos 28°$
Resolving parallel ($\nearrow$) to the plane
for the m kg mass:
$F_{net} = ma$
$12m - F - mg \sin 28° = 3.8m$
The block is moving so friction is limiting:
$F = \mu R = mg\mu \cos 28°$
$12m - mg\mu \cos 28° - mg \sin 28° = 3.8m$
$8.2 - g \sin 28° = g\mu \cos 28°$
$\mu = (8.2 - g \sin 28°) \div (g \cos 28°)$
$= 0.415... = 0.42$ (2 d.p.)

[3 marks available — 1 mark for calculating T, 1 mark for correct use of $F = \mu R$, 1 mark for correct value of μ]

Q2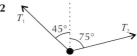

The resultant force $5\mathbf{i} + 3\mathbf{j} = T_1 + T_2 + (-3\mathbf{i} - \mathbf{j})$
$\Rightarrow T_1 + T_2 = 8\mathbf{i} + 4\mathbf{j}$
Resolving horizontally:
$-T_1 \sin 45° + T_2 \sin 75° = 8$ ① *[1 mark]*
Resolving vertically:
$T_1 \cos 45° + T_2 \cos 75° = 4$ ② *[1 mark]*
$\sin 45° = \cos 45°$, so ①+②:
$T_2 (\sin 75° + \cos 75°) = 12$ *[1 mark]*
$\Rightarrow T_2 \times \left(\dfrac{\sqrt{6} + \sqrt{2}}{4} + \dfrac{\sqrt{6} - \sqrt{2}}{4} \right) = 12$
$\Rightarrow T_2 \times \dfrac{\sqrt{6}}{2} = 12$
$\Rightarrow T_2 = 4\sqrt{6} = 9.80 \text{ N}$ (3 s.f.) *[1 mark]*
In ②: $T_1 \cos 45° + 4\sqrt{6} \cos 75° = 4$
$\Rightarrow T_1 = \dfrac{4 - 4\sqrt{6} \cos 75°}{\cos 45°} = \left(4 - 4\sqrt{6} \times \dfrac{\sqrt{6} - \sqrt{2}}{4} \right) \div \dfrac{1}{\sqrt{2}}$
$= 2(\sqrt{6} - \sqrt{2}) = 2.07 \text{ N}$ (3 s.f.) *[1 mark]*

[5 marks available in total — as above]

Q3 a)

Resolving perpendicular to the slope:

$R = mg \cos 30° = \dfrac{\sqrt{3}}{2} \times mg$

When the sled is in equilibrium: $F \le \mu R$

$\Rightarrow F \le \dfrac{1}{2\sqrt{3}} \times \dfrac{\sqrt{3}}{2} \times mg \Rightarrow F \le \dfrac{mg}{4}$

If the sled is on the point of moving up the slope, friction acts down the slope, so:

$T = F + mg \sin 30° \Rightarrow T - mg \sin 30° = F$

$\Rightarrow T - \dfrac{mg}{2} \le \dfrac{mg}{4} \Rightarrow T \le \dfrac{3}{4}mg$

If the sled is on the point of moving down the slope, friction acts up the slope, so:

$T + F = mg \sin 30° \Rightarrow mg \sin 30° - T = F$

$\Rightarrow \dfrac{mg}{2} - T \le \dfrac{mg}{4} \Rightarrow T \ge \dfrac{1}{4}mg$

So the range of values for T is: $\dfrac{1}{4}mg \le T \le \dfrac{3}{4}mg$

[4 marks available — 1 mark for resolving when the block is on the point of sliding up the plane, 1 mark for a maximum value of T, 1 mark for resolving when the block is on the point of sliding down the plane, 1 mark for a minimum value of T]

b)

The rope has been released so there is no tension. Resolving perpendicular to the plane:

$R = 3mg \cos 30° = \dfrac{\sqrt{3}}{2} \times 3mg$

$F = \mu R \Rightarrow F = \dfrac{1}{2\sqrt{3}} \times \dfrac{\sqrt{3}}{2} \times 3mg \Rightarrow F = \dfrac{3mg}{4}$

Resolving parallel to the plane ($\nearrow$):

$F_{net} = ma$

$3mg \sin 30° - F = 3ma$

$\dfrac{3mg}{2} - \dfrac{3mg}{4} = 3ma$

$a = \dfrac{1}{2}g - \dfrac{1}{4}g = \dfrac{1}{4}g$

$u = 0, v = v, a = \dfrac{1}{4}g, t = 3$

$v = u + at$

$v = 0 + \dfrac{1}{4}g \times 3 = 7.35 \text{ ms}^{-1}$

[4 marks available — 1 mark for resolving forces down the plane, 1 mark for finding the acceleration, 1 mark for using an appropriate constant acceleration equation, 1 mark for the correct velocity]

Q4 a)

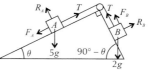

A is about to move up the slope so friction acts down the slope, and $F_A = \mu R_A$.
Resolving perpendicular ($\nwarrow$) to the slope for A:
$R_A = 5g \cos \theta$
Resolving parallel ($\nearrow$) to the slope for A:
$T = F_A + 5g \sin \theta$
$T = \mu \times 5g \cos \theta + 5g \sin \theta$
$T = g \cos \theta + 5g \sin \theta$ ①

B is about to move down the slope so friction acts up the slope, and $F_B = \mu R_B$.
Resolving perpendicular ($\nearrow$) to the slope for B:
$R_B = 2g \cos (90° - \theta)$
Resolving parallel ($\searrow$) to the slope for B:
$2g \sin (90° - \theta) = T + \mu \times 2g \cos (90° - \theta)$
$\sin (90° - \theta) = \cos \theta$ and $\cos (90° - \theta) = \sin \theta$:
$2g \cos \theta = T + 0.4g \sin \theta$ ②
Substitute ① into ②:
$2g \cos \theta = g \cos \theta + 5g \sin \theta + 0.4g \sin \theta$
$g \cos \theta = 5.4g \sin \theta$
$\dfrac{\sin \theta}{\cos \theta} = \tan \theta = \dfrac{1}{5.4} = \dfrac{5}{27}$

[5 marks available — 1 mark for resolving forces for A, 1 mark for resolving forces for B, 1 mark for using sin (90° − θ) = cos θ and cos (90° − θ) = sin θ, 1 mark for solving simultaneously, 1 mark for correct rearrangement to get the given value of tan θ]

b) From ①:

$T = g \cos \left(\tan^{-1}\left(\dfrac{5}{27}\right)\right) + 5g \sin \left(\tan^{-1}\left(\dfrac{5}{27}\right)\right)$

$= 18.558... \text{ N}$

The force P acting on the pulley is the resultant of the tensions. Tension is the same in each part of the string and they meet at right angles, so:

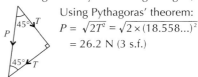

Using Pythagoras' theorem:
$P = \sqrt{2T^2} = \sqrt{2 \times (18.558...)^2}$
$= 26.2 \text{ N (3 s.f.)}$

[3 marks available — 1 mark for finding T, 1 mark for attempting to find the resultant of the tensions, 1 mark for correct force P exerted on the pulley]

Chapter 6: Moments

6.1 Moments

Exercise 6.1.1 — Moments

Q1 a) Moment = Force × Perpendicular Distance
= 3 × 2.5 = 7.5 Nm anticlockwise

b) Moment = 6 sin 30° × 4 = 12 Nm clockwise

c) Moment = 23 × 0.8 cos 18°
= 17.5 Nm (3 s.f.) clockwise

d) Moment = 5 × (7 − 3) = 20 Nm clockwise

e) Moment = 17 sin 50° × (11 − 4.5)
= 17 sin 50° × 6.5
= 84.6 Nm (3 s.f.) clockwise

f) Moment = 6.5 × (1.3 cos 20° − 0.4)
= 5.34 Nm (3 s.f.) anticlockwise
Remember to state the sense of rotation when giving the moment of a force.

Q2 Taking clockwise as positive:
(3 × 2) + (5 sin 40° × 4) = 18.9 Nm (3 s.f.) clockwise

Q3 a) Taking clockwise as positive:
(2 × 9) − (7 × 2) = 4 Nm clockwise

b) Taking clockwise as positive:
(19 × 1.5) − (14 × 2) = 0.5 Nm clockwise

c) Taking clockwise as positive:
(7 sin 30° × 3) − (15 × 1.5) = −12 Nm
i.e. 12 Nm anticlockwise

d) Taking clockwise as positive:
(10 sin 30° × 3) + (8 sin 45° × 4)
= $(15 + 16\sqrt{2})$ Nm = 37.6 Nm (3 s.f.) clockwise

e) Taking clockwise as positive:
(18 sin 25° × 13) − (24 sin 32° × 13)
= −66.4 Nm (3 s.f.), i.e. 66.4 Nm anticlockwise

f) Taking clockwise as positive:
(6 cos 15° × 10) + (2 sin 50° × 8)
− (3 sin 28° × 10) − (1 × 8)
= 48.1 Nm (3 s.f.) clockwise

Q4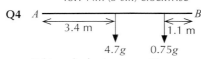
Taking clockwise as positive:
(4.7g × 3.4) + (0.75g × (6.8 − 1.1))
= 198.499 = 198 Nm (3 s.f.) clockwise

Q5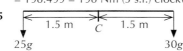
Taking clockwise as positive about the centre C:
(30g × 1.5) − (25g × 1.5) = 73.5 Nm clockwise
If you drew your diagram the other way around, your answer will be 73.5 Nm anticlockwise.

Q6 Find the sum of the moments about O, taking clockwise as positive:
(13 × 3) + (X × 1) − (21 × 3) = X − 24
For the rod to rotate clockwise, the sum of the moments must be positive:
$X − 24 > 0 \Rightarrow X > 24$

Q7 Find the sum of the moments about O, taking clockwise as positive:
4(d + 1) + (38 × 2) − (25 × 1) −
(24 cos 60° × 5) = 4d − 5
For the rod to rotate anticlockwise, the sum of the moments must be negative:
$4d − 5 < 0 \Rightarrow d < 1.25$
Also, d must be greater than or equal to zero, otherwise the 25 N force will be applied to a point which isn't on the rod, and so the rod will rotate clockwise. So: $0 \le d < 1.25$

Exercise 6.1.2 — Moments in equilibrium

Q1 a) Taking moments about A:
Moments clockwise = Moments anticlockwise
$1.5y + (2 × 8) = 16 × 5.5$
$1.5y = 72$
$y = 48$ N
Resolving vertically:
$x + 16 = y + 2$
$x = 50 − 16 = 34$ N

b) Resolving vertically:
$10 + 6 = 13 + x$
$x = 3$ N
Taking moments about C:
$10y + 2x = 6 × 5$
$10y = 30 − 6$
$y = 2.4$ m

Q2 a) Mass acts at centre of rod, i.e. 2.5 m from A, 1 m from C and 0.5 m from D.
Taking moments about the midpoint:
$0.5R_D = 49 × 1$
$R_D = 98$ N

b) Resolving vertically:
$Mg = 49 + R_D$
$M = (49 + 98) ÷ 9.8 = 15$ kg

Q3 When the rod is about to tilt about D, $T_C = 0$.
The rod is uniform, so its mass acts at its midpoint, x m from D. Taking moments about D:
$3g × 1.5 = 9g × x$
$9x = 4.5 \Rightarrow x = 0.5$
So the distance from B to the midpoint is
1.5 + 0.5 = 2 m, and so the length of the rod is
2 × 2 = 4 m

Q4 a)

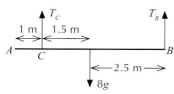

Taking moments about C:
$8g \times 1.5 = 4T_B$
$T_B = 3g = 29.4$ N
Resolving vertically:
$T_C + T_B = 8g$
$T_C = 78.4 - 29.4 = 49$ N

b) When the beam is about to tilt about C, $T_B = 0$.
Taking moments about C:
$8g \times 1.5 = 16g \times x$
$1.5 = 2x \Rightarrow x = 0.75$
So the distance of the particle from A is
$1 - 0.75 = 0.25$ m

Q5 Resolving vertically:
$4U + 11 = 20 + 15 \Rightarrow 4U = 24 \Rightarrow U = 6$ N

Taking moments about C:
$(20 \times l) + (11 \times 1) + (3U \times 3) = (15 \times 7)$
$20l + 11 + 54 = 105 \Rightarrow 20l = 40 \Rightarrow l = 2$ m

Q6

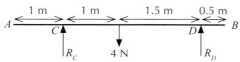

a) Taking moments about D:
$2.5 \times R_C = 4 \times 1.5$
$\Rightarrow R_C = 6 \div 2.5 = 2.4$ N

b) Taking moments about C:
$4 \times 1 = R_D \times 2.5$
$\Rightarrow R_D = 4 \div 2.5 = 1.6$ N

Q7

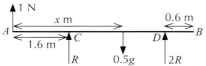

a) Resolve vertically:
$1 + R + 2R = 0.5g \Rightarrow 3R = 3.9 \Rightarrow R = 1.3$ N

So the normal reaction force at C is 1.3 N
and the normal reaction force at D is 2.6 N.

b) Taking moments about A:
$(1.3 \times 1.6) + (2.6 \times 4.2) = 0.5g \times x$
$\Rightarrow 13 = 0.5gx \Rightarrow x = 13 \div (0.5 \times 9.8)$
$= 2.65$ m (3 s.f.)

Q8

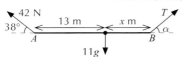

a) Taking moments about B:
$42 \sin 38° \times (13 + x) = 11g \times x$
$(11g - 42 \sin 38°)x = 13 \times 42 \sin 38°$
$81.94...x = 336.15...$
$\Rightarrow x = 336.15... \div 81.94... = 4.102...$
So the length of the rod $= 13 + 4.102...$
$\qquad\qquad = 17.1$ m (3 s.f.)

b) Resolving forces horizontally:
$42 \cos 38° = T \cos \alpha$
$\Rightarrow T = \dfrac{42 \cos 38°}{\cos \alpha}$ ①
Resolving forces vertically:
$42 \sin 38° + T \sin \alpha = 11g$ ②
Substituting ① into ②:
$42 \sin 38° + \dfrac{42 \cos 38°}{\cos \alpha} \sin \alpha = 11g$
$42 \cos 38° \tan \alpha = 11g - 42 \sin 38°$
$\Rightarrow \alpha = \tan^{-1}\left(\dfrac{11g - 42 \sin 38°}{42 \cos 38°}\right)$
$\qquad = 68.006...° = 68.0°$ (3 s.f.)

c) From part b) equation ①,
$T = \dfrac{42 \cos 38°}{\cos 68.006...°} = 88.37... = 88.4$ N (3 s.f.)

Q9 a) Taking moments about A:
$2.7mg = 20 \sin 80° \times 6$
$m = 120 \sin 80° \div (2.7 \times 9.8)$
$\qquad = 4.466... = 4.47$ kg (3 s.f.)

b) Resolving vertically:
$T \sin \alpha + 20 \sin 80° = 4.466...g$ ①
Resolving horizontally:
$T \cos \alpha = 20 \cos 80°$
$\Rightarrow T = \dfrac{20 \cos 80°}{\cos \alpha}$ ②
Substituting ② into ①:
$20 \cos 80° \tan \alpha + 20 \sin 80° = 4.466...g$
$\alpha = \tan^{-1}\left(\dfrac{(4.466... \times 9.8) - 20 \sin 80°}{20 \cos 80°}\right)$
$\qquad = 81.79... = 81.8°$ (3 s.f.)

c) $T = \dfrac{20 \cos 80°}{\cos 81.79...°} = 24.32... = 24.3$ N (3 s.f.)

Q10 a) The painter stands at the plank's COM, so the weight acting at this point is his weight plus the plank's weight, i.e. $80g + 20g = 100g$.

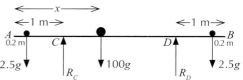

The reaction at C is 4 times the reaction at D,
i.e. $R_C = 4R_D$
Resolving vertically:
$2.5g + 100g + 2.5g = R_C + R_D$
$105g = 4R_D + R_D$
$105g = 5R_D$
$\Rightarrow R_D = 21g$ N $\Rightarrow R_C = 84g$ N
Taking moments about A:
$(2.5g \times 0.2) + (100g \times x) + (2.5g \times 3.8) = R_C + 3R_D$
$10g + 100gx = 84g + 63g$
$10g + 100gx = 147g$
$x = (147 - 10) \div (100) = 1.37$ m

b) The distance between the plank's COM and the point D is $4 - 1 - 1.37 = 1.63$ m

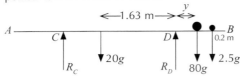

When the plank is about to tilt about D, $R_C = 0$.
Taking moments about D:
$20g \times 1.63 = (80g \times y) + (2.5g \times 0.8)$
$\Rightarrow 32.6 = 80y + 2 \Rightarrow y = 30.6 \div 80 = 0.3825$
So the distance from B is:
$1 - 0.3825 = 0.6175$ m

Q11 Taking clockwise as the positive direction:

a) Sum of moments $= (6 \times 5) - (10 \times 10)$
$= 30 - 100 = -70$ Nm
(i.e. 70 Nm anticlockwise)

b) Sum of moments $= (6 \times 0.5) + (10 \times 5) = 3 + 50$
$= 53$ Nm clockwise

c) Sum of moments $= (6 \times 2) + (10 \times 4) = 12 + 40$
$= 52$ Nm clockwise

d) Sum of moments $= (6 \times 3.5) - (10 \times 6)$
$= 21 - 60 = -39$ Nm
(i.e. 39 Nm anticlockwise)

For parts a)-d), F acts either vertically or horizontally, so you can just use x or y respectively as the perpendicular distance when taking moments. Drawing a diagram will help you to see whether it acts clockwise or anticlockwise.

e) Sum of moments $= (6 \times 2.5) + (10 \cos 30° \times 5)$
$- (10 \sin 30° \times 5)$
$= 15 + 43.301... - 25$
$= 33.3$ Nm clockwise (3 s.f.)

f) Sum of moments $= (6 \times 0.5) - (10 \sin 60° \times 1)$
$- (10 \cos 60° \times 11)$
$= 3 - 8.6602... - 55$
$= -60.7$ Nm (3 s.f.)
(i.e. 60.7 Nm anticlockwise)

Q12 a)

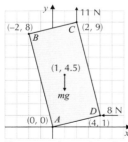

The centre of mass is at the centre of the lamina, so to find its coordinates, find the midpoint of AC (or BD).

b) Taking moments about A:
Clockwise moments = anticlockwise moments
$(mg \times 1) = (8 \times 1) + (11 \times 2)$
$\Rightarrow 9.8m = 8 + 22 = 30$
$\Rightarrow m = 30 \div 9.8 = 3.06$ kg (3 s.f.)
You don't need to split the forces into components — it's much easier to find the perpendicular distance from the line of action of the force to the pivot, since all of the forces act in either the x- or y-direction.

6.2 Reaction Forces and Friction

Exercise 6.2.1 — Reaction forces

Q1 a) Taking moments about A:
$3g \times 2 = T \times 1 \Rightarrow T = 58.8$ N

b) Resolving vertically:
$T = 3g + R \Rightarrow R = 58.8 - 29.4 = 29.4$ N

Q2 a) Taking moments about A:
$0.6g \times 0.4 = T \sin 60° \times 0.6$
$\Rightarrow T = 2.352 \div 0.519... = 4.526...$
$= 4.53$ N (3 s.f.)

b)

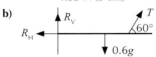

Resolving horizontally:
$R_H = T \cos 60° = (4.526...) \cos 60° = 2.263...$ N
Resolving vertically:
$R_V + T \sin 60° = 0.6g$
$\Rightarrow R_V = 0.6g - (4.526...) \sin 60° = 1.96$ N

Using Pythagoras' theorem:
$R = \sqrt{(2.263...)^2 + 1.96^2} = 2.993...$
$= 2.99$ N (3 s.f.)
Using trigonometry:
$\theta = \tan^{-1}\left(\dfrac{2.263...}{1.96}\right) = 49.106...°$ (measured anticlockwise from the upward vertical)
So direction $= 90° + 49.106...° = 139°$ (3 s.f.).

Q3 a) Taking moments about A:
$(1.5g \times 0.6) + (0.5g \times 1.2) = T \sin 20° \times 2.4$
$\Rightarrow T = 14.7 \div 0.820... = 17.908...$
$= 17.9$ N (3 s.f.)

b)

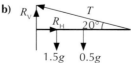

Resolving horizontally:
$R_H = T \cos 20° = (17.908...) \cos 20° = 16.828...$ N

Resolving vertically:

$R_V + T \sin 20° = 1.5g + 0.5g$

$\Rightarrow R_V = 19.6 - 6.125 = 13.475$ N

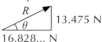

13.475 N

16.828... N

Using Pythagoras' theorem:

$R = \sqrt{(16.828...)^2 + 13.475^2} = 21.558...$

$= 21.6$ N (3 s.f.)

Using trigonometry:

$\theta = \tan^{-1}\left(\dfrac{13.475}{16.828...}\right) = 38.7°$ (3 s.f.)

Q4 a) Let the distance from A to the COM be x.

Taking moments about A:

$(1.8g \times x) + (3.5 \sin 80° \times 7) = 95 \cos 71° \times 3.5$

$\Rightarrow x = 84.123... \div 17.64 = 4.768...$

$= 4.77$ m (3 s.f.)

b)

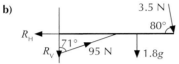

Resolving horizontally:

$R_H = 95 \sin 71° + 3.5 \cos 80° = 90.432...$ N

Resolving vertically:

$R_V + 1.8g + 3.5 \sin 80° = 95 \cos 71°$

$\Rightarrow R_V = 9.842...$ N

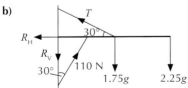

9.842... N

90.432... N

Using Pythagoras' theorem:

$R = \sqrt{(90.432...)^2 + (9.842...)^2} = 90.966...$

$= 91.0$ N (3 s.f.)

Using trigonometry:

$\theta = \tan^{-1}\left(\dfrac{90.432...}{9.842...}\right) = 83.788...°$

(measured clockwise from the downward vertical)

So direction $= 270° - 83.788...° = 186°$ (3 s.f.)

Q5 a) Taking moments about A:

$(110 \cos 30° \times 2) + (T \sin 30° \times 4)$

$\qquad\qquad = (1.75g \times 4) + (2.25g \times 8)$

$\Rightarrow T = 54.474... \div 2 = 27.237... = 27.2$ N (3 s.f.)

b)

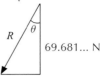

Resolving horizontally:

$R_H + (27.237...) \cos 30° = 110 \sin 30°$

$\Rightarrow R_H = 31.411...$ N

Resolving vertically:

$R_V + 1.75g + 2.25g$

$\qquad\qquad = (27.23...) \sin 30° + 110 \cos 30°$

$\Rightarrow R_V = 69.681...$ N

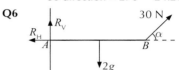

69.681... N

31.411... N

Using Pythagoras' theorem:

$R = \sqrt{(31.411...)^2 + (69.681...)^2} = 76.434...$

$= 76.4$ N (3 s.f.)

Using trigonometry:

$\theta = \tan^{-1}\left(\dfrac{31.411...}{69.681...}\right) = 24.265...°$

(measured clockwise from the downward vertical)

So direction $= 270° - 24.265° = 246°$ (3 s.f.)

Q6

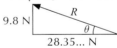

2g

a) Taking moments about A:

$2g \times 0.8 = 30 \sin \alpha \times 1.6$

$30 \sin \alpha = 9.8$

$\alpha = \sin^{-1}\left(\dfrac{9.8}{30}\right) = 19.066...° = 19.1°$ (3 s.f.)

b) Resolving horizontally:

$R_H = 30 \cos 19.066...° = 28.35...$ N

Resolving vertically:

$R_V + 30 \sin \alpha = 2g$

$\Rightarrow R_V = 2g - 9.8 = 9.8$ N

9.8 N

28.35... N

Using Pythagoras' theorem:

$|R| = \sqrt{28.35...^2 + 9.8^2} = 30$ N

$\theta = \tan^{-1}\left(\dfrac{9.8}{28.35...}\right) = 19.06...°$

This is the angle above the negative horizontal, so the direction is $180° - 19.06...° = 161°$ (3 s.f.)

Q7

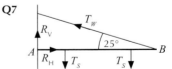

Taking moments about A:

$8 \times 0.2 + 8 \times 0.8 + 2 \times 9.8 \times 0.5 = T_W \sin 25° \times 1$

$\Rightarrow T_W \sin 25° = 17.8$ N

$\Rightarrow T_W = 42.118... = 42.1$ N (3 s.f)

Resolving horizontally:

$R_H = T_W \cos 25° = 38.172...$ N

Resolving vertically:
$R_V + T_W \sin 25° = 2g + 16$
$\Rightarrow R_V = 2g + 16 - 17.8 = 17.8$ N

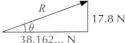
17.8 N
38.162... N

$|R| = \sqrt{38.172...^2 + 17.8^2} = 42.1$ N (3 s.f.)
$\theta = \tan^{-1}\left(\dfrac{17.8}{38.172...}\right) = 25°$

The reaction force on the rod has the same magnitude as the tension, and is the same angle above the horizontal, but faces the other way. This is because of the symmetry of the sign.

Exercise 6.2.2 — Friction

Q1 a) Taking moments about A:
$12g \times 8 = T \sin 20° \times 16$
$\Rightarrow T = 940.8 \div 5.472... = 171.919...$
$= 172$ N (3 s.f.)

b)
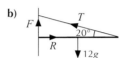

Resolving horizontally:
$R = T \cos 20° = (171.919...) \cos 20°$
$= 161.551...$ N
Resolving vertically:
$F + T \sin 20° = 12g$
$\Rightarrow F = 117.6 - (171.919...) \sin 20° = 58.800...$ N
Using $F = \mu R$:
$58.800... = \mu \times 161.551... \Rightarrow \mu = 0.36$ (2 d.p.)

Q2 a)
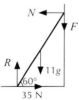

Resolving horizontally: $N = 35$ N

b) Resolving vertically: $F + 11g = R$
Taking moments about top of ladder:
$(11g \cos 60° \times 3.5) + (35 \sin 60° \times 7)$
$= R \cos 60° \times 7$
$\Rightarrow R = 400.826... \div 3.5 = 114.521...$ N
So $F = 114.521... - 11g = 6.721...$
$= 6.72$ N (3 s.f.)

c) $F = \mu N$
$6.721... = \mu \times 35 \Rightarrow \mu = 0.19$ (2 d.p.)

Q3 a)
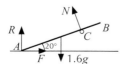

Taking moments about A:
$1.6g \cos 20° \times 0.75 = N \times 1.1$
$\Rightarrow N = 10.046... = 10.0$ N (3 s.f.)

b) Resolving vertically:
$R + (10.046...) \cos 20° = 1.6g$
$\Rightarrow R = 6.239... = 6.24$ N (3 s.f.)

c) Resolving horizontally:
$F = N \sin 20° = (10.046...) \sin 20°$
$= 3.435... = 3.44$ N (3 s.f.)

d) $F = \mu R$
$3.435... = \mu \times 6.239... \Rightarrow \mu = 0.55$ (2 d.p.)

Q4
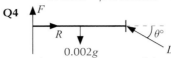

Taking moments around the point where the nail meets the wall:
$0.05 \times D \sin \theta = 0.002g \times 0.025$
$\Rightarrow D \sin \theta = 0.001g \Rightarrow D = \dfrac{0.001g}{\sin \theta}$
Resolving vertically:
$F + D \sin \theta = 0.002g$
$F = 0.002g - 0.001g = 0.001g$
Resolving horizontally:
$R = D \cos \theta$
$F = 0.7R$, so:
$0.001g = 0.7D \cos \theta \Rightarrow D = \dfrac{0.001g}{0.7 \cos \theta}$
So $\dfrac{0.001g}{\sin \theta} = \dfrac{0.001g}{0.7 \cos \theta} \Rightarrow \sin \theta = 0.7 \cos \theta$
$\Rightarrow \tan \theta = 0.7$
$\Rightarrow \theta = \tan^{-1}(0.7) = 34.99...$
$= 35.0°$ (3 s.f.)
Then $D = \dfrac{0.001g}{\sin 34.99...} = 0.01708... = 0.0171$ N (3 s.f.)

Q5
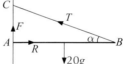

The wire is at an angle α to the horizontal such that $\tan \alpha = \dfrac{1}{2}$. Using Pythagoras,
$\sin \alpha = \dfrac{1}{\sqrt{5}}$ and $\cos \alpha = \dfrac{2}{\sqrt{5}}$.
Taking moments about A:
$20g \times 1 = T \sin \alpha \times 2$
$\Rightarrow \dfrac{1}{\sqrt{5}}T = 10g \Rightarrow T = 10g \times \sqrt{5} = 219$ N (3 s.f.)
Resolving horizontally:
$R = T \cos \alpha = 10g \times \sqrt{5} \times \dfrac{2}{\sqrt{5}} = 20g$
Resolving vertically:
$F + T \sin \alpha = 20g$
$\Rightarrow F = 20g - 10g = 10g$
The rod is on the point of slipping so $F = \mu R$:
$10g = \mu R \Rightarrow 10g = \mu \times 20g \Rightarrow \mu = 0.5$

Q6

Resolving vertically:
$R = 10g + 50g = 60g$
Resolving horizontally: $F = N$
If the ladder is on the point of slipping, then $F = \mu R$.
$\Rightarrow \mu R = N \Rightarrow N = 0.3 \times 60g = 176.4$ N
Let x be the girl's distance up the ladder from the base.
Taking moments about base of ladder:
$176.4 \sin 65° \times 6$
$\qquad = (10g \cos 65° \times 3) + (50g \cos 65° \times x)$
$\Rightarrow x = 834.986... \div 207.082... = 4.03$ m (3 s.f.)

Q7

Assuming D acts away from the wall, and
taking moments about the base of the ladder:
$80 \cos 50° \times 2 = N \sin 50° \times 4 + D \sin 50° \times 3$
$160 \cos 50° = 4N \sin 50° + 3D \sin 50°$ ①

Resolving vertically: $R = 80$ N
Resolving horizontally:
$F = N + D \Rightarrow 0.75 \times 80 = N + D$
$\qquad\qquad \Rightarrow N = 60 - D$ ②
Substituting ② into ①:
$160 \cos 50° = 4(60 - D) \sin 50° + 3D \sin 50°$
$D \sin 50° = 240 \sin 50° - 160 \cos 50°$
$D = 105.74...$ N $= 106$ N (3 s.f.) away from the wall.
If you get a negative value for D, it just means the force
is pointing in the opposite direction to your assumption.

Q8 a)

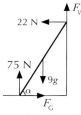

Resolving horizontally:
$F_G = 22$ N
Resolving vertically:
$75 + F_W = 9g \Rightarrow F_W = 13.2$ N
Taking moments about base of ladder:
$9g \cos \alpha \times 2.4 = (22 \sin \alpha \times 4.8)$
$\qquad\qquad\qquad\qquad + (13.2 \cos \alpha \times 4.8)$
$148.32 \cos \alpha = 105.6 \sin \alpha$
$\tan \alpha = 1.4045... \Rightarrow \alpha = 54.550...°$
$\qquad\qquad\qquad\qquad = 54.6°$ (3 s.f.)

b) $F = \mu R$
$F_W = \mu_W \times 22 \Rightarrow \mu_W = 13.2 \div 22 = 0.6$
c) $F_G = \mu_G \times 75 \Rightarrow \mu_G = 22 \div 75 = 0.29$ (2 d.p.)

Q9 a)

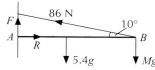

Resolving horizontally:
$R = 86 \cos 10° = 84.693...$N
Using $F = \mu R$:
$F = 0.55 \times 84.693... = 46.581...$ N
Resolving vertically:
$46.581... + 86 \sin 10° = 5.4g + Mg$
$\Rightarrow M = 8.595... \div 9.8 = 0.8770...$
$\qquad\qquad = 0.877$ kg (3 s.f.)

b) Let x be the distance of the COM from A.
Taking moments about A:
$(5.4g \times x) + (Mg \times 11) = 86 \sin 10° \times 11$
$\Rightarrow x = 69.724 \div 52.92 = 1.32$ m (3 s.f.)

Q10 If the ladder is on the point of slipping downwards:

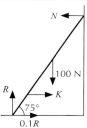

Resolving vertically: $R = 100$ N
Resolving horizontally:
$K + 0.1R = N \Rightarrow N = K + 10$
Taking moments about the base of the ladder:
$(K \sin 75° \times 1) + (100 \cos 75° \times 4) = (N \sin 75° \times 8)$
$K \sin 75° + 400 \cos 75° = 8(K + 10) \sin 75°$
$400 \cos 75° - 80 \sin 75° = 8K \sin 75° - K \sin 75°$
$400 \cos 75° - 80 \sin 75° = K(7 \sin 75°)$
$K = 26.253... \div 6.761... = 3.882...$ N

If the ladder is on the point of slipping
towards the wall:

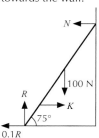

Resolving vertically:
$R = 100$ N
Resolving horizontally:
$K = N + 0.1R \Rightarrow N = K - 10$
Taking moments about the base of the ladder:
$(K \sin 75° \times 1) + (100 \cos 75° \times 4) = (N \sin 75° \times 8)$
$K \sin 75° + 400 \cos 75° = 8(K - 10) \sin 75°$
$400 \cos 75° + 80 \sin 75° = 8K \sin 75° - K \sin 75°$
$400 \cos 75° + 80 \sin 75° = K(7 \sin 75°)$
$K = 180.80... \div 6.761... = 26.73...$ N

So the possible range of values for K is
$3.882...$ N $\leq K \leq 26.73...$ N

Q11

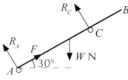

Let l be the length of the beam.
Taking moments about A:
$W \cos 30° \times 0.5l = R_C \times 0.75l$
$\Rightarrow R_C = \dfrac{\sqrt{3}}{2} W \times \dfrac{0.5l}{0.75l} = \dfrac{\sqrt{3}}{3} W$ N
Resolving perpendicular to the beam:
$R_A + R_C = W \cos 30°$
$\Rightarrow R_A = \dfrac{\sqrt{3}}{2} W - \dfrac{\sqrt{3}}{3} W = \dfrac{\sqrt{3}}{6} W$ N
Resolving parallel to the beam:
$F = W \sin 30° = \frac{1}{2} W$ N
Using $F = \mu R$:
$\frac{1}{2} W = \mu \times R_A$
$\Rightarrow \mu = \frac{1}{2} W \div \dfrac{\sqrt{3}}{6} W = \dfrac{1}{2} \times \dfrac{6}{\sqrt{3}} = \dfrac{3}{\sqrt{3}} = \sqrt{3}$
$= 1.73$ (2 d.p.)

Usually, the coefficient of friction between a body and a surface is between 0 and 1, but it can actually be any number greater than 0 — as in this case.

Q12

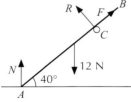

The beam is in equilibrium,
so resolving forces horizontally:
$R \sin 40° = F \cos 40°$
$F = \tan 40° \, R$

$F \leq \mu R$, so:
$\tan 40° \, R \leq \mu R$
$\tan 40° \leq \mu$
$\mu \geq \tan 40°$
So the range of possible values is $\mu \geq 0.84$ (2 d.p.)

Q13

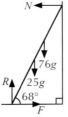

Taking moments about the base of the ladder:
$25g \cos 68° \times 4.5 + 76g \cos 68° \times 6 = N \sin 68° \times 9$
$N = \dfrac{25g \cos 68° \times 4.5 + 76g \cos 68° \times 6}{9 \sin 68°} = 250.10...$ N
Resolving vertically:
$R = 25g + 76g = 101g$ N
Resolving horizontally:
$F = N$
$F \leq \mu R$, so:
$N \leq \mu R \Rightarrow 250.10... \leq \mu \times 101g$
$\Rightarrow \mu \geq 250.10... \div 101g = 0.252...$
So the range of possible values is $\mu \geq 0.25$ (2 d.p.)

Q14

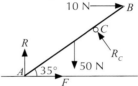

Taking moments about A:
$50 \cos 35° \times 1 + 10 \sin 35° \times 2 = R_C \times 1.4$
$\Rightarrow R_C = \dfrac{50 \cos 35° + 20 \sin 35°}{1.4} = 37.449...$ N
Resolving vertically:
$R + R_C \cos 35° = 50$
$\Rightarrow R = 50 - R_C \cos 35° = 19.323...$ N
Resolving horizontally:
$F + 10 = R_C \sin 35°$
$\Rightarrow F = R_C \sin 35° - 10 = 11.480...$ N
$F \leq \mu R$, so:
$11.480... \leq \mu \times 19.323...$
$\Rightarrow \mu \geq 11.480... \div 19.323... = 0.59$ (2 d.p.)
So the range of possible values is $\mu \geq 0.59$ (2 d.p.)

Review Exercise — Chapter 6

Q1

Taking anticlockwise as positive:
Moment $= (23 \times 12) - (1.6g \times 6)$
$\qquad = 181.92$ Nm anticlockwise

Q2 Taking moments about D:
$21 \times 10 = P \times 14 \Rightarrow P = 15$ N
Taking moments about A:
$14 \times Q = 21 \times 4 + 25 \times 14$
$14Q = 84 + 350 \Rightarrow Q = 31$ N

Q3 a) Since the rod is on the point of tilting,
the reaction force at A is 0.
Resolving vertically:
$44 = 1.5g + F \Rightarrow F = 44 - (1.5 \times 9.8) = 29.3$ N

b) Taking moments about B, where x is the
distance between points B and C:
$1.5g \times 2.5 = 29.3 \times x$
$\Rightarrow x = 36.75 \div 29.3 = 1.254...$ m
$\qquad = 1.25$ m (3 s.f.)

Q4 Let the distance from A to the centre of mass be x.
Then, taking moments about A:
$5g \cos 30° \times x = 40 \sin 30° \, b$
$5g \times \dfrac{\sqrt{3}}{2} \times x = 40 \times \dfrac{1}{2} \times b$
$\Rightarrow 5\sqrt{3}gx = 40b \Rightarrow x = \dfrac{40b}{5\sqrt{3}g} = \dfrac{8b}{\sqrt{3}g} = \dfrac{8\sqrt{3}b}{3g}$

Q5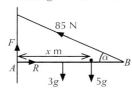

a)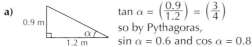
$\tan \alpha = \left(\dfrac{0.9}{1.2}\right) = \left(\dfrac{3}{4}\right)$
so by Pythagoras,
$\sin \alpha = 0.6$ and $\cos \alpha = 0.8$

Taking moments about A:
$3g \times 0.6 + 5g \times x = 85 \sin \alpha \times 1.2$
$17.64 + 49x = 85 \times 0.6 \times 1.2$
$\Rightarrow x = (61.2 - 17.64) \div 49$
$\qquad = 0.8889... = 0.889$ m (3 s.f.)

b) Resolving horizontally:
$R = 85 \cos \alpha = 85 \times 0.8 = 68$ N
Resolving vertically:
$3g + 5g = 85 \sin \alpha + F$
$F = 3g + 5g - 51 = 27.4$ N
$F \le \mu R$, so $27.4 \le \mu \times 68$
$\Rightarrow \mu \ge 0.402... \Rightarrow \mu \ge 0.4$ (2 d.p.)

Q6 a)

Let the length of the ladder be x m. Then
taking moments about the base of the ladder:
$20g \cos 60° \times \dfrac{1}{2}x = N \sin 60° \times x$
$\Rightarrow N = (10gx \cos 60°) \div (x \sin 60°) = \dfrac{98}{\sqrt{3}}$ N
Resolving vertically:
$R = 20g = 196$ N
Resolving horizontally:
$F = N = \dfrac{98}{\sqrt{3}}$ N
The ladder is on the point of slipping, so:
$F = \mu R \Rightarrow \dfrac{98}{\sqrt{3}} = \mu \times 196$
$\Rightarrow \mu = \dfrac{98}{\sqrt{3}} \div 196 = \dfrac{\sqrt{3}}{6}$ as required.

b)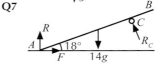

Taking moments about the base of the ladder:
$20g \cos 60° \times \dfrac{1}{2}x + 60g \cos 60° \times \dfrac{3}{4}x$
$\qquad\qquad = N \times x \sin 60°$
$Nx \sin 60° = 55gx \cos 60° \Rightarrow N = \dfrac{55g}{\sqrt{3}}$
Resolving vertically: $R = 20g + 60g = 80g$
Resolving horizontally: $P + F = N$
The ladder is in limiting equilibrium so $F = \mu R$:
$P + \dfrac{\sqrt{3}}{6} \times 80g = \dfrac{55g}{\sqrt{3}} \Rightarrow P + \dfrac{40\sqrt{3}g}{3} = \dfrac{55g}{\sqrt{3}}$
$P = \dfrac{55g}{\sqrt{3}} - \dfrac{40\sqrt{3}g}{3} = 84.87... = 84.9$ N (3 s.f.)

Q7

Taking moments about A:
$14g \cos 18° \times 7.5 = R_C \times 13$
$\Rightarrow R_C = 75.279...$ N
Resolving vertically:
$R + R_C \cos 18° = 14g$
$\Rightarrow R = 14g - R_C \cos 18° = 65.604...$ N
Resolving horizontally:
$F = R_C \sin 18° = 23.262...$
The beam is on the point of slipping, so $F = \mu R$:
$\mu \times 65.604... = 23.262...$
$\mu = 23.262... \div 65.604... = 0.354... = 0.35$ (2 d.p.)

Exam-Style Questions — Chapter 6

Q1 Taking moments about A:

$26 \sin \alpha \times 0.03 = 2g \cos \alpha \times \dfrac{0.05}{2}$ [1 mark]

$\Rightarrow 0.78 \sin \alpha = 0.05g \cos \alpha$ [1 mark]

$\dfrac{\sin \alpha}{\cos \alpha} = \tan \alpha$ [1 mark], so $\tan \alpha = \dfrac{5}{78}g$

$\Rightarrow \alpha = \tan^{-1}\left(\dfrac{5 \times 9.8}{78}\right) = 32.13...°$
$= 32.1°$ (3 s.f.) [1 mark]

[4 marks available — as above]

Q2

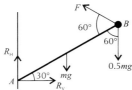

a) Let the length of the plank be $2l$, and take moments about A:

$mg \cos 30° \times l + 0.5 \, mg \cos 30° \times 2l$
$= F \sin 60° \times 2l$

$2mgl \cos 30° = 2lF \sin 60° \Rightarrow F = mg$

[2 marks available — 1 mark for taking moments about A, 1 mark for correct value of F]

b) Resolving vertically:

$R_H + mg \sin 30° = 1.5 \, mg \Rightarrow R_H = mg$

Resolving horizontally:

$R_V = mg \cos 30° = \dfrac{\sqrt{3}}{2} \, mg$

Using Pythagoras' theorem:

$|R| = mg\sqrt{1^2 + \left(\dfrac{\sqrt{3}}{2}\right)^2} = \dfrac{\sqrt{7}}{2} mg$

$\theta = \tan^{-1}\left(\dfrac{2}{\sqrt{3}}\right) = 49.1°$ (3 s.f.)

[6 marks available — 1 mark for resolving vertically, 1 mark for resolving horizontally, 1 mark for using Pythagoras, 1 mark for correct R, 1 mark for using the inverse tan function, 1 mark for correct angle]

Q3 **a)**

Resolving horizontally:
$F_1 = N \Rightarrow 3\mu R = N$

Resolving vertically:
$R + F_2 = 4mg$
$\Rightarrow R + 2\mu N = 4mg$
$\Rightarrow R + 2\mu(3\mu R) = 4mg$
$\Rightarrow R(1 + 6\mu^2) = 4mg$
$\Rightarrow mg = \dfrac{R}{4}(1 + 6\mu^2)$

[3 marks available — 1 mark for resolving horizontally, 1 mark for resolving vertically, 1 mark for substituting and rearranging to get the required equation]

b) Taking moments around the base of the ladder:

$3mg \cos 45° \times \dfrac{2}{3}l + mg \cos 45° \times l$
$= N \sin 45° \times 2l + F_2 \cos 45° \times 2l$

$3mg \cos 45° = 2N(\sin 45° + 2\mu \cos 45°)$

$\Rightarrow 3mg \cos 45° = 2(3\mu R)(\sin 45° + 2\mu \cos 45°)$

$\Rightarrow mg = 2\mu R(\tan 45° + 2\mu)$

Use the result from part a) to eliminate mg:

$\Rightarrow \dfrac{R}{4}(1 + 6\mu^2) = 2\mu R(\tan 45° + 2\mu)$

$\Rightarrow 1 + 6\mu^2 = 8\mu(1 + 2\mu)$

$\Rightarrow 1 + 6\mu^2 = 8\mu + 16\mu^2$

$\Rightarrow 10\mu^2 + 8\mu - 1 = 0$

Using the quadratic formula:

$\mu = \dfrac{-8 \pm \sqrt{8^2 - 4 \times 10 \times -1}}{2 \times 10} = 0.1099...$ or $-0.909...$

So $\mu = 0.11$ (2 d.p.)
(ignore the negative result as $\mu > 0$)

[4 marks available — 1 mark for taking moments about the base of the ladder, 1 mark for substituting the result from part a), 1 mark for using the quadratic formula, 1 mark for the correct value of μ]

Practice Paper

Q1 a) Input the x and y values into the correct statistical function on your calculator: $r = -0.936$ (3 s.f.)
[1 mark for correct answer]

b) r is close to -1 so there is a strong negative correlation between distance from the road and density of air pollution particles. The greater the distance from the road the lower the density of air pollution particles — and vice versa.
[2 marks available — 1 mark for identifying strong negative correlation, 1 mark for relating to context of question]

c) The test statistic is $r = -0.936$.
This is a one-tailed test, so the hypotheses are H_0: $\rho = 0$ and H_1: $\rho < 0$.
Test for significance with $\alpha = 0.01$ and sample size 8. Using the critical values table, the critical value is $r \leq -0.7887$.
$-0.936 < -0.7887$, so there is sufficient evidence at the 1% level of significance to reject H_0 in favour of the alternative hypothesis that there is a negative correlation between distance from the road and density of air pollution particles.
[3 marks available — 1 mark for correct hypotheses, 1 mark for correct critical value, 1 mark for correct conclusion]

Q2 a) Let X be the number of natterjack toads in the sample, then $X \sim B(80, 0.1)$.
So use a normal approximation $Y \sim N(\mu, \sigma^2)$ with $\mu = np = 80 \times 0.1 = 8$ and $\sigma^2 = np(1 - p) = 80 \times 0.1 \times 0.9 = 7.2$
So approximate X with $Y \sim N(8, 7.2)$.
Using a continuity correction you're looking for $P(5 < X < 10) \approx P(5.5 < Y < 9.5) = 0.5362$ (4 d.p.)
[3 marks available — 1 mark for correct normal approximation, 1 mark for continuity correction, 1 mark for correct answer]

b) E.g. n is large and although p is not close to 0.5, $np = 8 > 5$ and $n(1 - p) = 72 > 5$.
[1 mark for correct explanation]

Q3 a) $P(A' \cap B') = P(B') - P(A \cap B')$
$= (1 - P(B)) - P(A \cap B')$
$= (1 - 0.18) - 0.2952$
$= 0.5248$
[2 marks available — 1 mark for correct working, 1 mark for correct answer]

b) If A and B are independent then
$P(A \cap B) = P(A) \times P(B)$.
$P(A \cap B) = P(A) - P(A \cap B') = 0.36 - 0.2952$
$= 0.0648$
$P(A) \times P(B) = 0.36 \times 0.18 = 0.0648$,
so A and B are independent.
[2 marks available — 1 mark for finding $P(A \cap B)$, 1 mark for using $P(A \cap B) = P(A) \times P(B)$]

c) Use the product law to find $P(A \cap C')$:
$P(A \cap C') = P(A) \times P(C'|A) = 0.36 \times 0.25 = 0.09$
Use the product law again to find $P(A' \cap C')$:
$P(A' \cap C') = P(A') \times P(C'|A')$
$= (1 - 0.36) \times 0.5 = 0.32$
Add these probabilities:
$P(C') = P(A \cap C') + P(A' \cap C')$
$= 0.09 + 0.32 = 0.41$
So $P(C) = 1 - P(C') = 0.59$
[3 marks available — 1 mark for correctly using the product law twice, 1 mark for correct method for finding $P(C')$, 1 mark for correct answer]

Q4 a) Take logs of both sides of the equation $P = ab^t$ to get $\log P = \log a + t \log b$
Comparing this to the equation
$\log P = 7.17 - 0.45t$:
intercept $= \log a = 7.17$
$\Rightarrow a = 10^{7.17} = 14\,791\,083.88$
$= 14\,800\,000$ (3 s.f.)
gradient $= \log b = -0.45$
$\Rightarrow b = 10^{-0.45} = 0.3548\ldots = 0.355$ (3 s.f.)
[3 marks available — 1 mark for equation for $\log P$ in terms of t, 1 mark for value of a, 1 mark for value of b]

b) The number of bacterial cells was recorded for two hours (i.e. 120 minutes), so the range of values suitable for estimating P is $0 \leq t \leq 120$.
[1 mark for correct answer]

Q5 a) Let X be the height of a palm tree, then $X \sim N(\mu, \sigma^2)$.
$P(X < 4.5) = 0.5793 \Rightarrow P\left(Z < \dfrac{4.5 - \mu}{\sigma}\right) = 0.5793$
$\Phi(z) = 0.5793$ for $z = 0.20\ldots$
$\Rightarrow \dfrac{4.5 - \mu}{\sigma} = 0.20\ldots \Rightarrow 4.5 - \mu = 0.20\ldots\sigma$ ①
$P(X > 5.5) = 0.0626 \Rightarrow P\left(Z > \dfrac{5.5 - \mu}{\sigma}\right) = 0.0626$
$P\left(Z \leq \dfrac{5.5 - \mu}{\sigma}\right) = 1 - P\left(Z > \dfrac{5.5 - \mu}{\sigma}\right) = 0.9374$
$\Phi(z) = 0.9374$ for $z = 1.53\ldots$
$\Rightarrow \dfrac{5.5 - \mu}{\sigma} = 1.53\ldots \Rightarrow 5.5 - \mu = 1.53\ldots\sigma$ ②
Subtracting equation ① from ② gives:
$5.5 - 4.5 - \mu - (-\mu) = 1.53\ldots\sigma - 0.20\ldots\sigma$
$\Rightarrow 1 = 1.33\ldots\sigma \Rightarrow \sigma = 0.75\ldots$
Putting $\sigma = 0.75\ldots$ into equation ① gives:
$\mu = 4.5 - 0.20\ldots \times 0.75\ldots = 4.34\ldots$
So $\mu = 4.35$ m (2 d.p.) and $\sigma = 0.75$ m (2 d.p.).
[4 marks available — 1 mark for finding correct z-values, 1 mark for setting up simultaneous equations from probabilities, 1 mark for correctly solving for σ, 1 mark for correctly solving for μ]

b) Let X be the height of a palm tree on the second island. Let the mean height of the palm trees on the second island be μ.

The significance level is $\alpha = 0.05$ and this is a two-tailed test.

Then H_0: $\mu = 4.35$ and H_1: $\mu \neq 4.35$.

Let $\overline{X}$ be the sample mean of the palm tree heights on the second island.

Then under H_0, $X \sim N(4.35, 0.75^2)$,

so $\overline{X} \sim N\left(4.35, \dfrac{0.75^2}{15}\right) = N(4.35, 0.0375)$.

So under H_0, $Z = \dfrac{\overline{X} - 4.35}{\sqrt{0.0375}} \sim N(0, 1)$.

$\bar{x} = 4.7$, so $z = \dfrac{4.7 - 4.35}{\sqrt{0.0375}} = 1.8074$ (4 d.p.)

This is a two-tailed test, so the critical region will be split. You want to find critical values, $\pm z$, such that $P(Z > z) = \dfrac{\alpha}{2} = 0.025$.

The percentage points table gives a critical value of 1.9600. The other critical value will be –1.9600.

So the critical region is $Z < -1.9600$ or $Z > 1.9600$. Since $z = 1.8074 < 1.9600$, the result does not lie in the critical region and is not significant. There is insufficient evidence at the 5% significance level to reject H_0 in favour of the alternative hypothesis that the mean height of the palm trees on the two islands is different.
You could have worked out the p-value instead — i.e. $P(Z \geq 1.8074)$.

[5 marks available — 1 mark for correct hypotheses, 1 mark for identifying test is two-tailed, 1 mark for correct expression for Z in terms of $\overline{X}$ (allow errors carried forward from part a)), 1 mark for correct z-value, 1 mark for correct conclusion]

Q6 a)

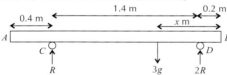

Resolving vertically:
$R + 2R = 3g \Rightarrow R = g$ N

Taking moments about D:
$R \times 1.4 = 3g \times (x - 0.2)$
$\Rightarrow 1.4g = 3gx - 0.6g$
$\Rightarrow 2g = 3gx \Rightarrow x = \dfrac{2}{3}$ m

[4 marks available — 1 mark for resolving vertically, 1 mark for finding the reaction force, 1 mark for taking moments, 1 mark for the correct distance x]

b)

Resolving vertically:
$R_C + R_D = 3g + mg$

The rod is on the point of turning about C, so the reaction force at D is 0 $\Rightarrow R_C = (3 + m)g$

To find m, take moments about C:
$3g \times (\tfrac{4}{3} - 0.4) = mg \times (0.4 - 0.15)$
$\Rightarrow 4g - 1.2g = 0.25mg$
$\Rightarrow 2.8 = 0.25m \Rightarrow m = 11.2$

So $R_C = (3 + 11.2)g = 139$ N (3 s.f.)

[5 marks available — 1 mark for using the fact that the reaction force at D is 0, 1 mark for resolving vertically, 1 mark for taking moments, 1 mark for finding m, 1 mark for the correct reaction force at C]
You could have taken moments about a different point, but that would have required solving trickier simultaneous equations in m and R_C

Q7 a) Resolving vertically ($\uparrow$):
$s = 0$, $u = 12$, $a = -g$, $t = t$
Remember, s is displacement — the ball starts and ends its motion at the same vertical height, so the vertical displacement is 0.
$s = ut + \dfrac{1}{2}at^2$
$0 = 12t + \dfrac{1}{2} \times -g \times t^2$
$\Rightarrow t(12 - 4.9t) = 0$
$\Rightarrow t = 0$ s and $t = 2.448...$ s

So the ball spends 2.45 s (3 s.f.) at a height greater than its initial point of projection.

[3 marks available — 1 mark for using the vertical component of velocity, 1 mark for an appropriate constant acceleration equation, 1 mark for the correct value of t]

b) Find when the ball reaches the wall:
Resolving horizontally ($\rightarrow$):
$s = 9$, $u = 5$, $a = 0$, $t = t$
$s = ut + \dfrac{1}{2}at^2$
$9 = 5t + \dfrac{1}{2} \times 0 \times t^2 \Rightarrow t = 9 \div 5 = 1.8$ s
So the ball will reach the wall in 1.8 s.

Find the vertical distance above the ball's projection point as it clears the wall.

Resolving vertically ($\uparrow$):

$s = s$, $u = 12$, $a = -9.8$, $t = 1.8$

$s = ut + \frac{1}{2}at^2$

$s = 12 \times 1.8 + \frac{1}{2} \times -9.8 \times 1.8^2 = 5.724$ m

The top of the wall is 5.724 m above the point of projection, so $x = 6.5 - 5.724 = 0.776$ m.

[4 marks available — 1 mark for resolving horizontally to find t, 1 mark for an appropriate constant acceleration equation, 1 mark for the height of the wall above the point of projection, 1 mark for the correct value of x]

Q8 **a** $= (12t\mathbf{i} - 2\mathbf{j})$ ms^{-2}

$\mathbf{v} = \int \mathbf{a}\, dt = \left[\int 12t\, dt\right]\mathbf{i} + \left[\int -2\, dt\right]\mathbf{j}$

$= (6t^2)\mathbf{i} + (-2t)\mathbf{j} + \mathbf{C}_1$

When $t = 0$, $\mathbf{v} = -\mathbf{i}$ $\Rightarrow$ $-\mathbf{i} = (6(0)^2)\mathbf{i} + (-2(0))\mathbf{j} + \mathbf{C}_1$

$\Rightarrow \mathbf{C}_1 = -\mathbf{i}$

So $\mathbf{v} = [(6t^2 - 1)\mathbf{i} - 2t\mathbf{j}]$ ms^{-1}

$\mathbf{r} = \int \mathbf{v}\, dt = \left[\int (6t^2 - 1)\, dt\right]\mathbf{i} + \left[\int -2t\, dt\right]\mathbf{j}$

$= (2t^3 - t)\mathbf{i} + (-t^2)\mathbf{j} + \mathbf{C}_2$

When $t = 1$, $\mathbf{r} = (\mathbf{i} + 3\mathbf{j})$:

$\Rightarrow \mathbf{i} + 3\mathbf{j} = (2(1)^3 - 1)\mathbf{i} + (-(1)^2)\mathbf{j} + \mathbf{C}_2$

$\Rightarrow \mathbf{i} + 3\mathbf{j} = \mathbf{i} - \mathbf{j} + \mathbf{C}_2 \Rightarrow \mathbf{C}_2 = 4\mathbf{j}$

So $\mathbf{r} = (2t^3 - t)\mathbf{i} + (4 - t^2)\mathbf{j}$ m

*[4 marks available — 1 mark for integrating **a**, 1 mark for finding the constant of integration for **v**, 1 mark for integrating **v**, 1 mark for correct final answer]*

Q9 **a)** Using a right-angled triangle and Pythagoras:

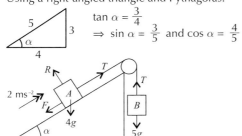

$\tan \alpha = \frac{3}{4}$

$\Rightarrow \sin \alpha = \frac{3}{5}$ and $\cos \alpha = \frac{4}{5}$

Resolving vertically ($\downarrow$) for B:

$F_{net} = ma$

$5g - T = 5 \times 2$

$T = 5g - 10 = 39$ N

Resolving perpendicular to the plane ($\nwarrow$) for A:

$R = 4g \cos \alpha = 4g \times \frac{4}{5} = \frac{16}{5}g$

Resolving parallel to the plane ($\nearrow$) for A:

$F_{net} = ma$

$T - 4g \sin \alpha - F = 4 \times 2$

$39 - 4g \times \frac{3}{5} - F = 8$

$F = \mu R$, so:

$39 - 4g \times \frac{3}{5} - \mu \times \frac{16}{5}g = 8$

$\frac{16}{5}g\mu = 31 - \frac{12}{5}g$

$\Rightarrow \mu = (31 - \frac{12}{5}g) \div \frac{16}{5}g = 0.2385...$

$= 0.24$ (2 d.p.)

[5 marks available — 1 mark for resolving vertically for B, 1 mark for finding the reaction force, 1 mark for resolving forces parallel to the plane for A, 1 mark for using F = μR, 1 mark for the correct value of μ]

b) For the motion before the string is cut:

$u = 0$, $v = v$, $a = 2$, $t = 2$

$v = u + at$

$v = 0 + 2 \times 2 = 4$ ms^{-1}

For the motion after the string is cut:

Resolving parallel to the plane ($\nearrow$) for A:

$F_{net} = ma$

$-4g \sin \alpha - F = 4a$

$-\frac{12}{5}g - 0.2385... \times \frac{16}{5}g = 4a$

$\Rightarrow a = -7.75$ ms^{-2}

Find the distance up the slope that A travels after the string is cut:

$s = s$, $u = 4$, $v = 0$, $a = -7.75$

$v^2 = u^2 + 2as$

$0^2 = 4^2 + 2 \times -7.75 \times s$

$\Rightarrow s = 16 \div 15.5 = 1.032...$ m

The particle travels 1.032... m < 1.2 m in the subsequent motion before coming to rest, so it does not hit the pulley, as required.

[5 marks available — 1 mark for finding the velocity immediately before the string is cut, 1 mark for resolving forces to find acceleration after the string is cut, 1 mark for correct acceleration, 1 mark for finding the distance travelled by Particle A before it comes to rest, 1 mark for showing that A does not hit the pulley]

Statistical Tables

Percentage points of the normal distribution

The z-values in the table are those which a random variable
$Z \sim N(0, 1)$ exceeds with probability p, i.e. $P(Z > z) = 1 - \Phi(z) = p$.

p	z	p	z
0.5000	0.0000	0.0500	1.6449
0.4000	0.2533	0.0250	1.9600
0.3000	0.5244	0.0100	2.3263
0.2000	0.8416	0.0050	2.5758
0.1500	1.0364	0.0010	3.0902
0.1000	1.2816	0.0005	3.2905

Critical values for the Product Moment Correlation Coefficient, r

The r-values in the table are the minimum values of the Product Moment Correlation Coefficient for which a one-tailed hypothesis test at the given significance level on a data set of size n is statistically significant.

n	0.10	0.05	0.025	0.01	0.005
3	0.9511	0.9877	0.9969	0.9995	0.9999
4	0.8000	0.9000	0.9500	0.9800	0.9900
5	0.6870	0.8054	0.8783	0.9343	0.9587
6	0.6084	0.7293	0.8114	0.8822	0.9172
7	0.5509	0.6694	0.7545	0.8329	0.8745
8	0.5067	0.6215	0.7067	0.7887	0.8343
9	0.4716	0.5822	0.6664	0.7498	0.7977
10	0.4428	0.5494	0.6319	0.7155	0.7646
11	0.4187	0.5214	0.6021	0.6851	0.7348
12	0.3981	0.4973	0.5760	0.6581	0.7079
13	0.3802	0.4762	0.5529	0.6339	0.6835
14	0.3646	0.4575	0.5324	0.6120	0.6614
15	0.3507	0.4409	0.5140	0.5923	0.6411
16	0.3383	0.4259	0.4973	0.5742	0.6226
17	0.3271	0.4124	0.4821	0.5577	0.6055
18	0.3170	0.4000	0.4683	0.5425	0.5897
19	0.3077	0.3887	0.4555	0.5285	0.5751
20	0.2992	0.3783	0.4438	0.5155	0.5614

Formulas

These are the formulas you'll be given in the exam, but make sure you know exactly **when you need them** and **how to use them**.

Trigonometric Identities

$$\sin (A \pm B) \equiv \sin A \cos B \pm \cos A \sin B$$

$$\cos (A \pm B) \equiv \cos A \cos B \mp \sin A \sin B$$

$$\tan (A \pm B) \equiv \frac{\tan A \pm \tan B}{1 \mp \tan A \tan B} \quad (A \pm B \neq (k + \tfrac{1}{2})\pi)$$

$$\sin A + \sin B = 2 \sin \frac{A+B}{2} \cos \frac{A-B}{2}$$

$$\sin A - \sin B = 2 \cos \frac{A+B}{2} \sin \frac{A-B}{2}$$

$$\cos A + \cos B = 2 \cos \frac{A+B}{2} \cos \frac{A-B}{2}$$

$$\cos A - \cos B = -2 \sin \frac{A+B}{2} \sin \frac{A-B}{2}$$

Small Angle Approximations

$$\sin \theta \approx \theta \qquad \cos \theta \approx 1 - \frac{1}{2}\theta^2 \qquad \tan \theta \approx \theta \qquad \text{where } \theta \text{ is measured in radians}$$

Probability

$$P(A') = 1 - P(A)$$

$$P(A \cup B) = P(A) + P(B) - P(A \cap B)$$

$$P(A \cap B) = P(A)P(B|A)$$

$$P(A|B) = \frac{P(B|A)P(A)}{P(B|A)P(A) + P(B|A')P(A')}$$

For independent events A and B:

$$P(B|A) = P(B), \quad P(A|B) = P(A),$$

$$P(A \cap B) = P(A)P(B)$$

Kinematics

For motion in a straight line with constant acceleration:

$$v = u + at$$

$$s = ut + \frac{1}{2}at^2$$

$$s = \frac{1}{2}(u + v)t$$

$$s = vt - \frac{1}{2}at^2$$

$$v^2 = u^2 + 2as$$

The Binomial Distribution

If $X \sim B(n, p)$, then $P(X = x) = \binom{n}{x}p^x(1-p)^{n-x}$

Mean of $X = np$ Variance of $X = np(1 - p)$

Hypothesis Test for the Mean of a Normal Distribution

If $X \sim N(\mu, \sigma^2)$, then $\dfrac{\overline{X} - \mu}{\sigma/\sqrt{n}} \sim N(0, 1)$

Glossary

Acceleration
The rate of change of an object's **velocity** with respect to time.

Addition law
A formula linking the probability of the **union** and the probability of the **intersection** of events A and B.

Alternative hypothesis
The statement that you will accept instead if you decide to reject the **null hypothesis** in a **hypothesis test**. It gives a range of values for the **parameter** and is usually written H_1.

Assumption
A simplification of a real-life situation used in a **model**.

Beam
A long, **thin**, straight, **rigid** body.

Binomial distribution B(n, p)
A discrete probability distribution which models the number of successes x in n independent trials when the probability of success in each trial is p.

Coding
Transforming all the readings in a data set to make the numbers easier to work with.

Coefficient of friction
A number greater than or equal to zero which measures the effect of **friction** between an object and a surface.

Component
The effect of a **vector** in a given direction.

Conditional probability
A probability is conditional if it depends on whether or not another event happens.

Continuity correction
A correction made in order to approximate a discrete distribution with a continuous distribution.

Correlation
A linear relationship between two variables showing that they change together to some extent. (A correlation does not necessarily mean a causal relationship.)

Critical region
The set of all values of the **test statistic** that would cause you to reject the **null hypothesis**.

Critical value
The value of the **test statistic** at the edge of the **critical region**.

Displacement
A **vector** measurement of an object's distance from a particular point.

Equilibrium
A state where there is no **resultant force** or **moment** acting on a body, hence the body is at **rest** (or moving with constant **velocity**).

Explanatory variable
In an experiment, the variable you can control, or the one that you think is affecting the other.

Extrapolation
Predicting a value of y corresponding to a value of x outside the range for which you have data.

Force
An influence which can change the motion of a body (i.e. cause an **acceleration**).

Friction
A frictional force is a resistive **force** due to **roughness** between a body and surface. It always acts against motion, or likely motion.

g
Acceleration due to gravity. g is usually assumed to be 9.8 ms^{-2}.

Hypothesis
A statement or claim that you want to test.

Hypothesis test
A method of testing a **hypothesis** using observed sample data.

i unit vector
The standard horizontal **unit vector** (i.e. along the x-axis).

Independent events
If the probability of an event B happening doesn't depend on whether or not an event A happens, events A and B are independent.

Inextensible
Describes a body which can't be stretched (usually a **string**).

Interpolation
Predicting a value of y corresponding to a value of x within the range for which you have data.

Intersection (of events A and B)
The set of outcomes corresponding to both event A and event B happening.

j unit vector
The standard vertical **unit vector** (i.e. along the y-axis).

k unit vector
The standard **unit vector** used in 3D to represent movement along the z-axis.

Kinematics
The study of the motion of objects.

Lamina
A flat two-dimensional body whose thickness can be ignored.

Light
Describes a body which is modelled as having no mass.

Limiting equilibrium
Describes a body which is at **rest** in **equilibrium**, but is on the point of moving.

Linear regression
A method for finding the equation of a line of best fit on a scatter diagram.

Magnitude
The size of a **vector**.

Model
A mathematical approximation of a real-life situation, in which certain **assumptions** are made about the situation.

Moment
The turning effect a **force** has about a pivot point.

Mutually exclusive
Events are mutually exclusive (or just 'exclusive') if they have no outcomes in common, and so can't happen at the same time.

Non-uniform
Describes a body whose mass is unevenly distributed throughout the body.

Normal distribution
A 'bell-shaped' continuous probability distribution where the further from the mean a value is, the less likely it is to occur.

Normal reaction
The reaction **force** from a surface acting on an object. It acts perpendicular to the surface.

Null hypothesis
A statement which gives a specific value to the **parameter** in a **hypothesis test**. Usually written H_0.

One-tailed test
A **hypothesis test** is 'one-tailed' if the **alternative hypothesis** is specific about whether the **parameter** is greater or less than the value specified by the **null hypothesis**. E.g. it says $p < a$ or $p > a$ for a parameter p and constant a.

Parameter (hypothesis testing)
A quantity that describes a characteristic of a population.

Particle
A body whose mass is considered to act at a single point, so its dimensions don't matter.

Peg
A fixed support which a body can hang from or rest on.

Plane
A flat surface.

Product law
A formula used to work out the probability of two events both happening.

Product moment correlation coefficient
A measure of the strength of the **correlation** between two variables.

Projectile
A body projected into the air that moves only under the influence of gravity.

Pulley
A wheel, usually modelled as fixed and **smooth**, over which a **string** passes.

Regression line
A line of best fit found using **linear regression**.

Resolving
Splitting a **vector** up into **components**.

Response variable
In an experiment, the variable you think is being affected.

Rest
Describes a body which is not moving. Often used to describe the initial state of a body.

Resultant force/vector
The single **force/vector** which has the same effect as two or more forces/vectors added together.

Rigid
Describes a body which does not bend.

Rod
A long, **thin**, straight, **rigid** body.

Rough
Describes a surface for which a **frictional force** will oppose the motion of a body in contact with the surface.

Sense
The direction of a rotation (clockwise or anticlockwise).

Significance level (α)
Determines how unlikely the observed value of the **test statistic** needs to be (under H_0) before rejecting the **null hypothesis** in a **hypothesis test**.

Significant result
The observed value of a **test statistic** is significant if, under H_0, it has a probability lower than the **significance level**.

Smooth
Describes a surface for which there is no **friction** between the surface and a body in contact with it.

Standard normal variable, Z
A random variable that follows a **normal distribution** with mean 0 and variance 1.

Static
Describes a body which is not moving. Often used to describe a body in **equilibrium**.

Statistic
A quantity that is calculated using only known observations from a sample.

String
A **thin** body, usually modelled as being **light** and **inextensible**.

Taut
Describes a **string** or **wire** which is experiencing a **tension force** and is tight and straight.

Tension
The **force** in a taut **wire** or **string**.

Test statistic
A **statistic** calculated from sample data which is used to decide whether or not to reject the **null hypothesis** in a **hypothesis test**.

Thin
Describes a body which is modelled as having no thickness.

Thrust
The **force** in a compressed **rod**.

Trajectory
The path followed by a **projectile**.

Two-tailed test
A **hypothesis test** is 'two-tailed' if the **alternative hypothesis** specifies only that the **parameter** doesn't equal the value specified by the **null hypothesis**. E.g. it says $p \neq a$ for a parameter p and constant a.

Uniform
Describes a body whose mass is evenly spread throughout the body.

Union (of events A and B)
The set of outcomes corresponding to either event A or event B (or both) happening.

Unit vector
A **vector** of **magnitude** one unit.

Vector
A quantity which has both a **magnitude** and a direction.

Velocity
The rate of change of an object's **displacement** with respect to time.

Weight
The **force** due to a body's mass and the effect of gravity: $W = mg$.

Wire
A **thin** body often modelled as being **light**. It can be bent to form a shape.

Index